For information on obtaining wines described in this book,

call **(800) 321-4300**

THE WINEWRIGHTS REGISTER

& MARKETPLACE FOR SMALL CALIFORNIA WINERIES

FOURTH EDITION

Published by The Winewrights Register
175 Cascade Court
Rohnert Park, California 94928
(707) 584-8590

Written and Edited by Bruce Cass

Photography by Richard Gillette (RG), Craig Lovell (CL) and Bob LeRoy (RL)
with contributions by
Ray Baltar (RB), Bruce Shippee (BS), Kim Frazier (KF),
Jeff Reinking (JR) and Chris Springman (CS).

Illustrations by Michael Brewer (MB), Ric Wheeler (RW) and Ron Slyh (RS).

Cover designed by Michael Brewer and photographed by Richard Gillette.
Book design and typography by Communication Graphics.
Printed in the United States by Paragraphics.

ISBN # 0-9619304-1-1

REFACE

In the Middle Ages, social position was indicated by the amount one was able to consume. The limits of that distinction were reached by the Renaissance Popes. Since the seventeenth century, the measure of one's civility has moved toward gustatory discrimination, or taste. Brillat-Savarin put it succinctly, "Animals feed, men eat, and gentlemen dine."

The importance of taste, as separate from appetite, has created a niche for artisan wineries because they have options unavailable to factories operating on economies of scale. Often little wineries get grapes from single vineyards with vines over 50 years old. Distinctively flavored wines are the result. We coined the term "winewright" to suggest strenuous, hands-on labor common among tiny producers. They take satisfaction from the physical effort of winemaking. They also recognize aesthetic benefits conferred on their wines by close supervision. Some craftsmen turn modern technology to their purposes. Others opt for traditional methods. But they all leave a personal imprint on every bottle they make.

The story behind these wines is an important part of the product. The vineyards are not vast tracts owned by absentee syndicates for tax purposes. These vines are gnarled expressions of the struggle that ties weather, science, dirt and ethics together with human beings. The wines are not corporate investments made by executive consultants either. These wines are labors of love, vigorously pursued through many years.

Most wine today is a commodity made by expensive machinery. The creative part of the process is applied when an advertising agency is hired to fluff up the marketing materials. Wines in this book are different. They represent a more personal art form. It requires panache and muscular strength as well as attention to detail. It takes years to understand the tools and generations to produce the best results. No school can teach artistic talent to top winemakers. There aren't even absolute standards against which to compare performance. This art concerns smell and taste, the most subtle and primordial of human senses. A passion for wine should start with how people made it for their families and friends before Big Business entered the picture. "In water we see our own reflection, but in wine we sense the soul of another."

Winewrights is a membership organization dedicated to wine as an artistic and educational medium. Our purpose is to use the best products from California's smallest vintners to illustrate this craft. We update the Register regularly, hold lecture/tastings in major cities, publish an evaluative newsletter, offer telephone advisory service and provide a convenient mechanism for members to acquire wines. If you would like to join Winewrights, please call (800) 321-4300 or write Constance A. Brunson, c/o Winewrights, 175 Cascade Court, Rohnert Park, California 94928.

TABLE OF CONTENTS

INTRODUCTION

There are 400 micro-wineries in California. Their names are not well known. When told of Winewrights special interest in small wineries, many consumers remark, "Oh, like Jordan and Chalone." At that point it is helpful to define what we mean by "small."

One or two people, doing a large amount of hard physical labor, can produce around 7,000 cases of handcrafted wine a year. That volume of wine can support a family, or two if it is top quality wine sold relatively direct to consumers. With bigger equipment and some part-time help, a micro-winery can produce up to 10-12,000 cases in a year. Expansion beyond that point requires full-time help in at least two of three areas: the vineyard, the winery or sales. To pay for full-time help (i.e. supporting additional families), the winery must expand to 20,000 css/yr. The category between 10,000 css/yr and 20,000 css/yr doesn't exist in a way that makes financial sense.

Selling more than 20,000 css/yr requires a winery to PUSH their product through a "three tiered distribution system" which has been traditional in the U.S. since Prohibition. The winery sells to a distributor (tier, or transaction, one), who sells to a retail store or restaurant (tier two), who sells to the consumer (tier three). The multiplier effect of this system spreads the wine widely. If, however, demand is high and only 20,000 cases were made, availability may be thin in any single location. For example, there are 20,000 cases of Beaulieu Vineyards Georges deLatour ("BV Private Reserve") Cabernet Sauvignon made every year. Big wineries hire marketing professionals to manage this "demand tension." The idea is to release the wine to any single location at a rate slightly less than that which would satisfy demand. Whenever supply increases beyond existing demand, new markets (i.e. tier one) are opened to spread the supply more widely and maintain its thin availability. Lunch with certain wine writers can also spur demand.

Jordan and Chalone are examples of this phenomenon. They both make excellent wine, but they are not micro-wineries. Jordan is a 60,000 case winery owned by one of the ten wealthiest men in California. Tom Jordan does **not** spend 14 hour days lifting lug boxes of grapes into a crusher at the winery. Chalone is a publically owned corporation; a boutique conglomerate which includes Edna Valley Vyds, Carmenet and Acacia. None of these wineries are small today, although Chalone was until the early '70s. On occasion it may be hard to get their wines, but the reason has a lot to do with the large number of consumers who know about them, and very little to do with the volume produced. Chalone and Jordan make wine on a magnitude of volume 5 to 50 times greater than the wineries in this book.

Micro-vintners do not manage "demand tension." They don't have time. Most of them are reluctant to engage the "three tiered distribution system" for the same reason. It takes a lot of money and effort to get distributors set up to handle a brand. It isn't worth it to either party unless hundreds of cases can be made available. Micro-vintners know their limited quantities will get lost in the system unless tremendous publicity creates sufficient consumer PULL to make the brand important.

The three separate transactions of the traditional distribution system are also quite expensive. Big wineries can use economies of scale to produce wine for half the per bottle cost incurred by micro-vintners. That advantage is eliminated, however, in moving each bottle to the consumer. Small wineries can sell their limited volume to consumers in one transaction. Therefore, each bottle is twice as expensive to make, and a third as expensive to market. Overall, wine from tiny producers is likely to be a bargain. The trick for consumers is learning how to locate wine from small producers without the convenience of having it delivered to one's local grocery store. That is the function that Winewrights is designed to perform.

Naturally, some wineries evolve from year to year as their circumstances change. They may grow in response to demand. Sometimes that demand develops through word of mouth publicity. More often, a well read wine writer or national magazine takes a shine to them, thus increasing their customer base ten-fold overnight. Such exposure can put a lot of pressure on winemakers who would rather be pruning vines than talking on the telephone. A common reaction is to expand enough to turn marketing chores over to third party professionals. Ownership changes also occur frequently in the California wine business. Struggling wine craftsmen and well-heeled absentee investors usually find their mutual interests are best served in a winery producing 20-30,000 css/yr.

Growth does not necessarily mean diminished quality. Some expanding wineries improve their product through superior equipment and additional expert help. It doesn't matter whether wineries grow for financial reasons or to satisfy their ambitions. The wines change. As often as not this change is an improvement. A more noticeable difference occurs in the marketing structure. The wines become more widely available and the drumbeat of publicity picks up. At Winewrights we think this transition is marvelous. It is like watching people from your hometown make names for themselves in the big city. Every year several wineries move out of Winewrights purview. Either we raise them to icon status (Dunn Vyds) because demand has reached manic proportions, or we watch them graduate to national distribution when their size exceeds our somewhat arbitrary definition. We still endorse them and report on their progress in our newsletter. In most instances we will also procure their wines for members who ask. These "emeritus" wineries are replaced in the *REGISTER* by vintners who are not as well known. In each new edition of the book, 25% of the wineries change to provide a fresh perspective.

WINEWRIGHTS EMERITUS WINERIES:

Dunn Vyds
Congress Springs
Morgan/St. Vrain
Hidden Cellars
Johnson-Turnbull
Leeward
Martin Brothers
Cronin
ZD
Sycamore Creek
Mastantuono
Calafia
Ahern
Las Montanas
Yverdon

Bonny Doon
Kalin
Karly
Amador Foothill
Quivira
Williams & Selyem
La Jota
Piconi
Tudal
S. Anderson
Long
Mountain House
Pepperwood Springs
Soleterra

ABOUT THE AUTHOR

Bruce Cass graduated from Stanford University in 1969. He had lived in Palo Alto most of his life, and he took a job with a national home wine-making supplier hoping to stay in northern California. The company failed, but Bruce was hooked. He began teaching wine appreciation classes on the Stanford campus in 1972, then wrote The Wine Educators Handbook for Wine Institute and helped found the Society of Wine Educators. "I spent three nights a week for fifteen years being grilled by students," Bruce says. "Emboldened by our 'laboratory' sessions, they questioned every half-baked opinion I tried to sneak past them."

In 1979 Bruce expanded his wine appreciation seminars to include college campuses all over the U.S. and Australia. Many prestigious retailers and restaurateurs attended. Bruce was hired to do consulting work for 35 of these businesses when they discovered the quality of the little-known wines he was using to illustrate points from his lecture. Bruce has been a principal of Winewrights since 1985. He is a judge at the American Wine Competition in New York and the California State Fair.

RB

THE WINERY STORIES

ADELAIDA

John Munch was born in Costa Rica. His father is an American civil engineer who went on a two week mapping expedition to Mexico and ended up staying 38 years in Central America as a general manager for the United Fruit Company. After living in a number of small villages primarily involved with banana production, John's parents brought him back to the United States to enter 9th grade. He went to a series of schools around the Bay Area and then, in his early twenties, he left on a three week European vacation. "It must be genetic," he says. "I stayed five years."

John met his wife Andre while he was working in a para-legal capacity for an international investment company in Geneva. Her family is from the French Alps. John brought Andre to the United States when his Swiss employers offered

to send him through law school. Once back in the academic traces though, John's interest in language blossomed. He ended up taking a Masters degree in Old English Poetry at San Francisco State. But the financial realities of a scholarly existence forced him to take part-time work renovating Victorian houses. By the mid-'70s he had become a licensed contractor.

"Up to this point," John comments, "my wine attention had all been directed to one side of the cork." However, Andre was speaking with French friends about export of California wines. Eventually this discussion evolved into a desire on the part of European interests to purchase California vineyard land. Given John's technical disposition, he was designated to gather viticultural data and take a few classes at U.C. Davis. In the process of this research, he and Andre visited Cambria on the San Luis Obispo coast. They were thoroughly smitten by the area. They were also quite surprised, upon analysis of many grape samples, to learn that Paso Robles offered what they wanted. "For sparkling wine, grapes are picked between 17° and 19°Brix," explains John. "Grapes from cool, Region 1 coastal areas have too much acid at that sugar level."

200 acres of raw land were purchased near the Estrella River in 1982 by Swiss investors, but planting ground to a halt when the U.S. dollar started to hike upwards. Interest resumed in 1986 and a 10,000 sq. ft. winery was completed the following year. John currently manages 8,000 cases of sparkling wine inventory (under the Tonio Conti label) which won a Sweepstakes award at the Grand National Wine Competition in Snowbird, Utah. Investors in this project, who call themselves Chat Botte, are now trying to figure out their marketing and future capitalization strategy.

Meanwhile, the Munchs have purchased 10

acres for themselves on Paso Robles westside. They have bonded their home there to make still wines under the Adelaida label. One thousand Syrah vines have been planted on their own roots with close spacing on a steep hillside. Conditions are harsh. Chunks of carbonate rock give the soil an alkalinity which holds back vine vigor. No fertilizer is used. Grapes must be picked and hauled out by hand. The first harvest, in 1988, yielded 50 cases. Eventually the Munchs hope to produce 250 cases from their Estate vineyard.

Most of the grapes for the Adelaida wines are purchased. John is emphatic about using grapes from different sources to gain complexity. "My experience indicates that blends are superior to the best element in the lot," he says. "Twenty years ago there were 400 acres in Paso Robles. Now we're pushing 10,000." John likes Chardonnay from the Carver and McBride vineyards in part because of the limestone in their soils. He gets Cabernet from 18-year-old vines at Jones Ranch in the north part of the county, and also from the Colina Poca Vyd owned by the Kluckler family just north of Paso Robles. John thinks 2,500 cases a year each of Chardonnay and Cabernet would be just about right for his Adelaida label.

John is willing to incur the expense of many small fermenters in order to get complexity for his blends. "We believe identical grapes picked at the same time and fermented with the same yeast will produce noticeably different wines if they are fermented in separate batches," he explains.

1985

Adelaida

CHARDONNAY

PRODUCED & BOTTLED BY ADELAIDA CELLARS, PASO ROBLES, CA • ALC. 12.6% BY VOL

PASO ROBLES

lidbury

1985 Chardonnay — 2,520 cases — 750 ml

Grapes from 6 different vyds. Whole clusters in press w/o SO$_2$. Settle overnight, barrel frmt w/ Epernay 2 yeast. 6 mo on lees. SO$_2$ only after removal from lees. French oak, plus fire coopered American which has been air dried 2 yrs and split, not sawn. 25% new oak. Sterile filtered, then btld at 12.9 alc, .79 acid, 3.4 pH, 0.3% rs.

1985 Cabernet Sauvignon — 1,300 cases — 750 ml

5% Syrah to open up the nose. Picked at 24°Brix, 3.2 pH. Frmt with Epernay 2 in 4' high open topped 6-ton frmtrs. M-L induced during alc frmt, inoculum chosen for convenience of culture build up. Lightly punched, off skins at 5°-8°Brix. "Fruit is more desirable than tannin given modern bottling technology." 18 mos in French and air dried, fire bent A&K oak. DE filtration and cold stabilized. Btld at 13.5 alc, .7 acid, 3.3 pH.

1982 Blanc de Blanc Sparkling — 1,784 cases — 750 ml

All Chardonnay from various vyds fermented in separate small batches for complexity. 2 yrs en tirage, 0.4% rs, Sibel corks.

How much control can you exert over grapes you buy?

"The growers we deal with are very proud of their vineyards. They want to see top wines made. Logically, small wineries are the ones most likely to fulfill their ambitions. If I have a suggestion, they will certainly consider it. Take leaf removal in Chardonnay as an example. It costs them about $100 an acre to go through and open the vines up to more sunlight. That amounts to $25 or $35 a ton. When grape prices are going up hundreds of dollars per ton each year, the growers I buy from are not inclined to niggle where quality is concerned. Neither am I.

"The difference in the grapes is important too. Without leaf removal the fruit is shaded. In that situation the proportion of malic acid to the Total Acid was always very high. We never wanted to induce malo-lactic fermentation before because it would cause a massive pH shift. When that happens, you usually have to add tartaric acid back after the end of fermentation. I think you can tell when acid has been added after fermentation because the finish of the wine has a distinct acid bite. Now with leaf removal, the Chardonnay grapes come in with low pH and a reduced proportion of malic acid. We are considering doing some malo-lactic fermentations in part of the wine because we're confident the pH won't shift dramatically.

"We ask the growers to do leaf removal right at cluster set. The result is more of a golden color in the grapes and less of a citrus flavor. I'm not saying they all jump at the prospect of doing extra work, but they are quite interested in good results. So far we've always been able to accommodate each other."

John Munch

RB

ADLER FELS

David Coleman grew up on the East Coast. He attended MIT, the Parsons School of Design and, later, the Architecture School at UCLA. "I never graduated from anything," he says with a shrug. A stint of "conscripted federal service" left him at Fort Ord in 1968, and he moved on to a graphics job in Santa Rosa. His 1973 redesign of Chateau St. Jean's label made winery owners gasp. It cost five times more than normal labels of that period. But the winery enjoyed a sales boom, and the label received rave reviews. Over the next five years, David went on to design more than 40 winery labels.

He married Ayn Ryan, whose mother's family started Chateau St. Jean, and in 1978 the Colemans began building a house on a promontory overlooking Sonoma Valley from the north. In 1981 they launched a winery in the garage. They expanded continuously until 1986, with David doing the construction "on the side." The winery now occupies 7,000 sq. ft. in three stories built on a 26-foot-wide ridge. David thinks he is done. "I ran out of room," he says. The name Adler Fels is German for Eagle Rock, a landmark rising behind the house.

Much of the winery equipment has been redesigned by David including adjustable head stainless steel tanks. They buy grapes from seven vineyards, and volume varies according to what the vineyards produce. David needed the ability to make his tanks smaller, "or else I'd be bubbling nitrogen through the wines to fill head spaces," he points out. "That is no way to treat fine wine. Do you realize that the world's biggest consumer of nitrogen gas is the sewage industry? They use it to remove color, odor and taste in water treatment plants." He feels the design of the adjustable head tank was simply a need waiting for a winemaker to come along who knew how the bombay doors on a B-52 worked. They run their bottling line twice, once to bottle and cork and then again to label. "I hate being held up by something cosmetic like a label," points out California's most hyperactive label designer.

Coleman is not exactly a disciple of traditional French winemaking thought either. He seeks "naturalness" and aroma in the white wines for which Adler Fels is best known. "We want to find good grapes and then not screw them up. Malo-lactic fermentation has no place in white wines," opines the ebullient Coleman. "The French need it because their weather is so damn bad. The only thing to like about French winemaking is the language. I mean you are always reading about somebody putting something in the wine over there and then going to jail for it." He chuckles as he gets his teeth into the issue. "Take Champagne for example. Our Melange a Deux is probably the only sparkling wine in the world that is all grapes. When the French add the dosage, it is 20% sugar, water and brandy. Remember that next time you pay for one of those famous labels."

Adler Fels' Gewürztraminer has won wide recognition since the '85 vintage. Coleman considers it a difficult wine to make and sell, but also one of the most distinctive wines in California. "The tight little balled up clusters are so horribly susceptible to rot," he says. "Cool climate means later ripening, often with fog and the constant threat of rain. Once you do get it in the winery, it won't start fermenting, nor stop fermenting, and it is filled with stuff that won't filter."

1986 Chardonnay	480 cases	
Nelson Vyd	750 ml	

2.5 acre vyd near Glen Ellen in Sonoma Vly. 11-yr-old vines on a SE facing hillside. Irrigated, 3 t/a, picked early Sept at 23.2°Brix, 40 hr skin soak. Old Platten press, 24 hr cold settle, 30 day frmt with Champagne yeast at 48°F in stnls. 2 wks on lees, aged in 60 gal Center of France Burgundy barrels, new to 5 yrs old, with light to medium toast. No M-L, bentonite fining, no sterile filter. Btld July '87 at 13.3 alc, .84 acid, 0.1% rs.

1987 Fumé Blanc	3,800 cases	
	750 ml	

Blend of grapes from 8 acre, dry farmed Salzgeber/Chan Vyd on Westside Rd in Dry Creek Vly and the higher elevation Tudor Ranch Vyd on Sonoma Mtn Rd in Sonoma Vly. 23°Brix at harvest, 10 ppm SO₂ at crusher, 24 hr skin soak, frmtd with Champagne yeast at 50°F in stnls. Aged 2 mos in 1 to 3-yr-old 60 gal Center of France barrels. Bentonite fined, sterile filtered. Btld Feb '88, 0.25% rs, .78 acid, 12.9 alc. 48 medals from 8 competitions since 1982.

1983 Pinot Noir	420 cases	
	750 ml	

Picked at 23.8°Brix from 52-yr-old vines. No stems, frmtd 26 days at 60°F, on skins an additional 45 days. 1 yr in 101-yr-old 1,000 gal oval for M-L, 1 yr in 6-yr-old 60 gal Seguin-Moreau Nevers barrels. No fining. Btld July '86 at 13.8 alc.

1988 Gewürztraminer	750 cases	
Salzgeber/Chan Vyd	750 ml	

Picked at 22.6°Brix. 24 hr skin soak, Champagne yeast, 48°F frmt. Sterile filtered, btld Nov '88 at 1.4% rs, .72 acid, 11.8 alc.

Is there a class consciousness among wineries?

"Yes, and it has become extreme the last few years. On one hand you have people like Richardson and ourselves who start a winery in their garage, and then struggle to survive for ten years with nary a kind word from B of A. Increasingly the competition is people who don't have to generate any income out of their winery. They have millions coming in from some other source which they choose to piss away on some manufactured wine fantasy.

"Visiting these places astounds me. Some guy, with the misfortune to be born of multi-billionaire parents, shows you around a winery with every possible amenity. Then he takes you over to the hotel half of the place saying poor mom and dad had to actually camp out in this 2,500 sq. ft. condo for two years while they waited for the money to accumulate to build the main house. Making money *while* you start a winery? What planet is this kid from? Then he allows that response to their free hospitality has been so overwhelming mom and dad have had to build another home in Carmel to escape. If you sheepishly inquire why they bother with wine-making, he'll say 'Mom and Dad **really** like wine.'

"I just can't see how this misrepresentation of the wine biz does anybody any good. None of these owners actually make wine. If they couldn't hire somebody to create the product for them, they would be out of business. It's a lie; a shallow ambience which has more to do with Silicon Valley than with agriculture. It has a negative effect on the marketplace. These guys publicize their wine at $20 a bottle, but 80% of it goes off at $6.99 in the discount stores. Consumers start thinking everything is done with mirrors. We need to show people there is value in a tired, dirty family sitting around a modest dinner table being cheered by the product of their labor. Touring four-star restaurants is not the best thing a trip to Beaune has to offer.

"There you go, Bruce. That ought to prevent any sales this year."

David Fredrick Coleman

AHLGREN VINEYARD

Val Ahlgren started making mead, elderberry wine and beer as a hobby while attending U.C. Berkeley for her Masters degree in Rhetoric. By 1972 she and Dexter, her civil engineer husband, had converted their garage into a mini-winery and were buying Zinfandel grapes in prodigious quantities. In 1973 they made their first Cabernet Sauvignon and began building a house in Boulder Creek. California State Architect Sym Van Der Ryn is a friend from Inverness. He designed their house specifically to allow two people to do the construction. The Ahlgrens spent six months milling all the lumber from redwood cut on the property. They searched out recycled doors and windows, then made openings to fit. The maple floor was reclaimed from an abandoned high school gymnasium. The house is heated by a passive solar panel and a wood stove.

In 1976 the Ahlgrens bonded an area under the house and began commercial wine operations. The winery is still "dinky," only 22 x 60 feet, and they have to lease space in San Jose for case goods. They do their own bottling, but in two steps, bringing the cased bottles back for labels and capsules as they sell them. They have very little stainless steel other than a 520-gallon bottling tank. Most of the winery space is taken up by their hundred or so 60-gallon oak barrels (a mix of U.S. and French). Ahlgren Cabernets are generally not fined nor filtered. "They do throw some sediment with age," Dexter explains, "but our customers understand. I think I can tell when a wine has been filtered; the wine seems to lose something."

Ahlgren has also made highly regarded Chardonnays from Ventana Vineyards since 1976. They like the fact that Doug Meador makes wine himself. "We talk in the spring about tonnage," explains Dexter. Once Doug starts picking, I talk to him daily to see what numbers are being produced. Finally, I want to taste the berries. I'm not sure tasting berries tells me a whole lot more than the numbers do, but it gives me a sense of how the parts will fit together."

The Ahlgrens have three basket presses and need them all, because pressing is the slowest part of their winemaking operation. There is a stemmer-crusher for red grapes, but whites go through a roller crusher which bursts berries without removing stems. Free-run white juice goes immediately to barrels for fermentation. Then white skins are bucketed into the press where stems are necessary to provide channels for the juice to escape. Each press is tightened down once, then loosened while the "cake is tossed" to break up cavities and finally tightened down again to finish pressing. The Ahlgren's don't worry about over-pressing in their ratchet-type equipment powered by the strength of human muscles. "We rarely get more than 135 gallons per ton," they say. "You have to stop before the ratchet bar breaks your arm." Their whole operation is designed to handle 5 tons of grapes in a day because that is how much Dexter's truck can carry in one trip. Two and a half tons will fill all three presses one time.

In 1986, Val and Dexter fenced ten acres and planted 110R rootstock on their Boulder Creek property. It is a new, phyloxera resistant rootstock which U.C. Davis predicts will do well in heavy soils and low moisture conditions. Lack of water is always an issue in the Santa Cruz mountains. It does not arrive in a pipe maintained by the city. There is also a continuous pruning operation conducted by local deer. "The buck stops here," Dexter says with resignation. For two years there have been individual deer who take up residence in Ahlgren's young vineyard, eating press cake and "entertaining friends in the vegetable garden." The Ahlgrens would never shoot these intruders, although they do make sporadic attempts to shoo them out the gate. The Ahlgrens enjoy all aspects of living in the mountains, and obviously their intention is to make the winery compatible with the environment instead of vice versa.

For several years Val and Dexter's grown children have helped out in the winery. In 1988 these offspring all had children of their own or commitments elsewhere. Dexter and Val hired 25-year-old Jennifer Reed, a graduate of U.C. Davis, to work 4 days a week with them. Jennifer had previously worked at Stags Leap Wine Cellars and continues to put in one day a week at David Bruce Winery. "She's a big help with the physical labor, and she does lab tests a lot better than I do," Dexter reports.

Winemaker's Comments
Rich, aromatic fruity bouquet with suggestions of pineapple and butterscotch. Well-structured, complex flavors, long finish. Firm acid/fruit balance. Barrel fermented. Bottled July 1987

AHLGREN
VINEYARD

1986 CHARDONNAY
Monterey County, Ventana Vineyards
Alcohol 13.8% by volume

PRODUCED AND BOTTLED BY AHLGREN VINEYARD BW 4764
BOULDER CREEK, SANTA CRUZ MOUNTAINS, CA 95006   CONTAINS SULFITES

1984 Cabernet Sauvignon York Creek Vyd, Napa

300 cases
750 ml

16-yr-old vines in Fritz Maytag's main vyd on Spring Mt west of St Helena. Picked at 23.5°Brix, .85 acid, 3.5 pH. Frmtd dry in 300-gal open redwood tanks for 10 days at 90°F with Pasteur Champagne yeast. M-L during alc frmt, 4 mo to complete. Punch down 3x/day, settled 2 days. Aged in 50 gal Kentucky Blue Grass barrels. Btld July '86.

1987 Chardonnay Ventana Vyd

600 cases
750 ml

16-yr-old vines in flat part of Salinas Valley near the river south of Soledad. 50 ppm SO_2 at crusher, no skin soak, basket press, settled overnight, racked immediately in 60-gal Sirugue barrels from new to 7 yrs old. Frmtd 2 wks at 70°F with Pasteur Champagne yeast. M-L 34, 4 mo to complete, 4 mo on lees. Bentonite fining, sterile filter, btld Aug '87 at 13.5 alc, .83 acid, 3.4 pH.

1984 Cabernet Sauvignon Bates Ranch

500 cases
750 ml

600 to 1,000 ft vyd with SE aspect on Santa Clara side of Santa Cruz Mtns, red soil and 14 yr old dry farmed vines. Transported in 30# lugs. Frmtd dry in 300-gal open redwood tanks for 10 days at 90°F with Pasteur Champagne yeast. Induced M-L during alc frmt. Punched down 3x/day. Aged in Kentucky Blue Grass barrels.

1986 Semillon St. Charles Vyd

180 cases
750 ml

Grapes from 50-yr-old Jesuit-owned vyd farmed by Dan Gehrs from Congress Springs. Located on the Santa Clara side of Bear Creek Rd with a SE slope and heavy clay soil. 1.5 t/a at 22.5°Brix. Barrel frmtd in American oak. Off the lees quickly, SO_2 after fermentation, no M-L, sterile filtered. 3.3 pH.

Are you getting more local area grapes?

"Val and I were very active in getting the Santa Cruz Mtns viticultural appellation approved and are quite enthusiastic about using local grapes. But much of the land is quite steep, and vineyard acreage would have to increase five-fold to satisfy the wineries currently operating here.

"1984 will be our last York Creek Cabernet. We like the wine, but in years with short crops they choose to service their biggest customers first. Being a small customer, of course we would rather see a pro rata arrangement similar to the way Bates Ranch divides up their crop. In '85 we made Cabernet from the Beauregard Ranch near Felton. Then in '86 we returned to George Besson's vyd in the Hecker Pass. We last made Cabernet from Besson in 1978. That wine is now selling for $50 a bottle in a Santa Cruz restaurant. I wish I had a few cases left. I honestly can't remember why I stopped buying those grapes. The vineyard slopes a bit to the north and has one section with severe virus which never ripens past 20°Brix. It is right next to the Grenache vyd Randall Grahm uses for his Bonny Doon wines. I'm getting Cabernet from a healthy section which ripens completely, and I'm excited about it.

"As of 1988 we are also ending our Chardonnay relationship with big vineyards in Santa Barbara County in favor of a 1.5 acre plot on Cox Road about 5 miles southwest of Corralitos in the Santa Cruz Mtns. It is owned by a retired couple named Buerge. They love to garden and take wonderful care of the grapes. The vyd is about 600' elevation and not irrigated. We got 3.5 tons from it this year at 23.3°Brix, 3.2 pH and .97 acid."

Dexter Ahlgren

Jennifer   CL

CL

AMIZETTA

Spencer Clark and his wife Amizetta spent their childhood near Houston, and married in their teens. Amizetta is a sixth generation Texan whose Spanish-origin name goes back to her great-great-grandmother on her father's side. Spencer was a rock-n-roll guitarist, singer and songwriter. He began playing in his garage in Junior High School, then formed a four-man band to perform in clubs all over Texas, Louisiana and Oklahoma. But travel and late hours started to become oppressive to Spencer after their first son was born in 1976. Amizetta had grown up on a ranch, and the rat race of metropolitan life lost its appeal as Houston boomed. They decided to move to the country to raise their children. Then Spencer's sister married Napa Valley vintner Charles Shaw.

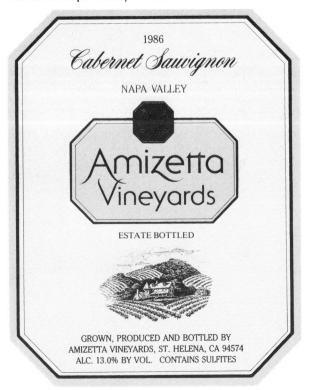

The Clarks came to visit and fell in love with the place. A taste for the gentlemanly pursuit of agriculture bloomed in Spencer's mind. In 1979 the Clarks bought 40 acres of raw land from the Shaws high in the mountains northeast of Napa's Hennessey Reservoir. Amizetta says her relatives still call "to see if we've fallen in the ocean."

As soon as they arrived, the Clarks planted 10 acres of Sauvignon Blanc while Spencer enrolled in the Enology and Viticulture program at U.C. Davis. He worked at Shaw and his neighbor, Buehler Winery, while his own grapes matured. "The University's Viticulture program was wonderful," Spencer reports, "but for winemaking it is hard to beat the hands-on experience you get working in a winery." Clark's land is extremely steep and rocky with a southern exposure. The elevation averages 900 feet with a vertical drop of 200 feet from top to bottom. Frost is never a problem. They do get fog cover some mornings, but pop out above it quickly.

There is very little water available to Amizetta Vineyard. In many places, terracing required a 5-10 foot height differential between vines, and the rows could not follow parallel lines. "It looks like it was laid out by a tractor driver on drugs," says Spencer. In 1982 they planted an additional 10 acres of Cabernet Sauvignon. Their estimate of 20 total acres is based on the number of vines in the ground. In actuality the vineyard almost fully occupies their 40 acres because the slope is so severe. Views of the lake and nearby Napa Valley are, however, spectacular.

The Clarks built their winery in 1984 with advice from consultant Justin Meyer. The Cabernet Sauvignon vineyard began producing in 1985. The results of that first Cabernet vintage prompted Spencer to make a financial decision. He liked the Sauvignon Blanc he was making from his vineyard, but found it hard to get recognition with that varietal in a crowded market. His

Cabernet showed the promise of much more attention. After the '86 harvest he began grafting the Sauvignon Blanc to Cabernet Sauvignon. They got a 97% take on the grafts. This success convinced Spencer to complete the job the following year. He added 15% Merlot and 5% Cabernet Franc as well. Picking is arduous. 9 men average 6 tons per day. In many places they must kneel to get at the grapes. Small containers slide down the hills on the ground to avoid runaway gondolas.

The 2,700 sq. ft. winery building includes a barrel room, offices and case storage in addition to the winemaking area. Fermentations are done in 2-3,000 gallon stainless steel with the goal of producing "accessible," restaurant-styled wines. Their Bordeaux field blend stays on the skins 5-7 days and is pumped over. Grapes are picked at 22.5° to 23.5°Brix. They have never added acid. The wine is racked 3 times before going into barrels. It stays in oak 2 years. The Clarks bottle by hand using a 6-spout filler and a manual corker. They can do 350 cases a day, but have to bring bottles back later for labels and capsules.

The Clarks now have 4 children: Spencer Jr. is 12, Perry is 6, Edward is 5 and Amizetta is 2. Young Spencer is able to help out on the bottling line and even worked on the crusher in 1988. Elder Spencer's demeanor when asked about the subject of child labor can only be described as wistful.

1985 Cabernet Sauvignon Estate	1,800 cases 750 ml

Picked mid-Sept at 23°Brix. Frmtd in stnls, 7 days on skins, pumped over. Inoculated with M-L 34 after alc frmt. Racked 3x before aging 2 yrs in 60-gal Nevers and 25% American oak. Filtered.

1987 Sauvignon Blanc Estate	1,300 cases 750 ml

Picked late August at 22°Brix. Settled, frmtd in stnls at 60°F, no M-L.

How did you decide to graft over your Sauvignon Blanc?

"I do all the marketing. Justin Meyer gives me some leads and I go call on them. I started in Texas and then expanded to Los Angeles. Sauvignon Blanc from our vineyard is kind of controversial. I think it is delicate, and flinty with refreshing marjoram-like overtones. (Agreed! - Ed.) A lot of restaurants, however, seem to prefer softer, fruitier, more melon-like examples.

"Our Cabernet cuttings come from a highly pedigreed vineyard with a reputation for mint in the nose. When I took barrel samples of my '85 Cabernet around, the reaction was extremely enthusiastic. People commented on the fruit and the style. I pre-sold hundreds of cases. I also got twice as much money for the Cabernet as for the Sauvignon Blanc. I probably don't have to point out that Cabernet is *not* twice as much work to produce.

"The financial part of the decision was clear. We originally planned to graft a third of the Sauvignon Blanc each year, but our Cabernet ripens very early. It is difficult to get the Sauvignon Blanc out of the tanks in time to make room for the Cabernet. It is also hard to get pickers to come for a small crop and then return a couple weeks later. So we grafted the remaining two-thirds of the Sauvignon Blanc over after the '87 harvest."

Spencer Clark

RG

AU BON CLIMAT

Clendenen-Tolmach Vintners embodies the bootstrap approach to artistic winemaking. In the beginning they picked the grapes themselves, did all the winery work and had a two-man bottling line. Clendenen was the salesman; Tolmach was the book keeper. Since 1985, critical acclaim has eased cash-flow problems and changed marketing issues, but Jim and Adam still make the wines by hand.

Jim Clendenen was born in Akron, Ohio. He grew up expecting to be a lawyer. That is what self-confident people who talk fast usually become. But Jim turned 21 in Europe while taking a year off from UC Santa Barbara. He returned home to finish school, then began working at Zaca Mesa Winery where he met Adam. Jim quit in 1981 to go to Australia. "I had a job set up with Tyrell's in the Hunter Valley," he says, "but Murray took one look at the hair down my back and sent me packing. I walked across the street and got a job at a winery there." He also

worked the crush in the cooler Golburn Valley Melbourne, then went to Europe for the fall. His third harvest of 1981 was spent at Domaine Duc de Magenta in Chassagne-Montrachet.

Adam Tolmach's public personality is as reticent as Clendenen's is demonstrative. Adam was raised in Oxnard and attended UC Davis. His father is a pediatrician; his mother a politician. In 1981 Adam planted 5.5 acres of Sauvignon Blanc, Semillon and Syrah on family property 8 miles from the coast up the Ventura River. Today he makes about a thousand cases from these grapes, with his wife Helen, under the name "Ojai Vineyard." Harvest is a busy season because the Ojai grapes ripen about the same time as the Au Bon Climat Pinot Noir and Chardonnay. Adam usually ends up sending instructions to Helen over the phone.

Clendenen-Tolmach Vintners opened in a 1,000 sq. ft. dairy shed at Los Alamos Vineyards in 1982. When that property was sold to Franzia in 1988, Jim and Adam decided to join Bob Lindquist (Qupé Winery and Jim's partner for the Vita Nova label) in a new facility at Bien Nacido

Vyds 100 yards over the San Luis Obispo County line in Santa Maria. This location is important because Santa Barbara County puts severe restrictions on where wineries can obtain grapes. Unfortunately, the building was not completed in time for the '88 crush. As a result, these three winemakers and their four micro-winery labels have become short-term tenents in five different buildings. "The pressure is incredible," Jim says. "I love making wine, but I hate looking for a place to do it."

Clendenen and Tolmach pick grapes in several stages over a month long period. They don't use a crusher, preferring to put their Chardonnay into the press as whole berries on the stems. The Pinot Noir is fermented as 100% whole berries which have been trodden with sterilized boots. The barrel-fermented Chardonnay is started with only 25 gallons of must per barrel, then gradually topped up and cooled with an additional 5 gallons per barrel of fresh must at 50°F each time they pick a new batch of grapes. They have a gallon of French oak capacity for each gallon of wine they make, giving them more barrels than a lot of wineries 7 or 8 times their 5,000 case/year size.

Au Bon Climat has pioneered experimentation with grapes picked at low sugars from very cool vineyards. They prefer not to work with Chardonnay grapes that have started to turn translucent, the point that most winemakers think ripeness has occurred. "We think those ripe, fruity smells are fine in wines meant to be drunk at age two," says Clendenen. "For long aging, we would rather get the grapes a little earlier and build up the flavors through barrel fermentation in new oak, forced malo-lactic and time on the lees. That way the fruit of the wine develops slowly as a classic bouquet."

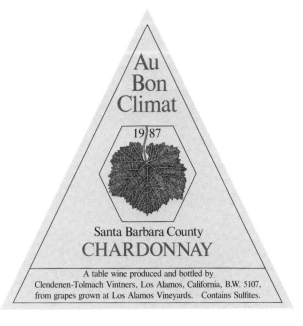

1987 Chardonnay   2,880 cases
Los Alamos Vineyard   750 ml

Sandy, well drained soil on a slope 10 mi from the ocean through the San Antonio Creek mountain break. Shy bearing part of the vineyard grafted onto Merlot rootstock. Last vintage from this vyd. Picked over 3 wk period in mid Sept between 22° and 23.8°Brix. No SO_2, no skin soak, pressed whole clusters, chilled must then stirred up solids before starting frmt in Francois Freres Troncais 60 gal barrels with heavy toast, 25% new through 3 yrs old. Champagne yeast, inoculate with MCW for M-L only as the alc frmt slows down. On lees 7 mos, fined, cold stabilized, gently filtered. Btld June '88 at 13.3 alc, 3.25 pH. '87 Chardonnay Reserve (850 cases) is picked at 21.8°Brix, 3.1 pH, frmtd in new wood and not filtered.

1987 Pinot Noir   220 cases
Rancho Vinedo   750 ml

Picked 24°Brix, all stems out, 14 day maceration (w/o stems cap falls sooner and heat maintainence is less). Neutral oak only 10 months, no filtration.

1987 Pinot Noir   200 cases
Benedict Vyd   750 ml

1 t/a, dry-farm, picked at 23°Brix, 3.2 pH with very little malic acid content. 50% stems retained, clusters very small and tight, stems don't swell. Boot crushed in 1 ton bins. 14 days on skins frmtg with Assmanhausen yeast at 88°F, punched down 2x/day, MCW for M-L. Aged in Francois Freres Troncais 60 gal barrels, 35% new. Filtered.

Is your "condominium" winery project coming together?

"I should have called off this vintage and gone to work in France. Normally crush is the happiest period of the year for me. But overcoming real estate obstacles is giving me sleepless nights at a time when I expect to be in a state of crush euphoria. Adam and Bob and I are friends. This situation is really testing our comraderie because it requires us to divide things up. If we can get into the Bien Nacido location next year, the opposite situation will apply and we can cooperate to help each other out more. Bob is probably the calmest one these days even though he has to work the hardest. He has been moving around each year and is more used to it than I am. Right now Adam and I are crushing at Los Alamos, but Franzia wants us out by January 1. We have wine at the old CBS record building and at Byron. My key ring weighs five pounds.

"My whole attitude about owning grapes is changing. You need economic clout to get fine fruit any more. When we talk to growers, the price starts to change based on what our wines have sold for in the past. From '82 to '85 a lot of wineries kicked the growers. The shoe has changed feet today. Adam and I never asked for better terms when the growers were struggling, but big wineries drove hard bargains. Now Santa Barbara Chardonnay grapes are commanding a 20% premium over North Coast prices. Very few growers even care where their grapes end up. The only advantage they see to having their grapes used by Au Bon Climat would be if we agree to pay a higher price. Forget what we put into the winemaking process.

"Dale Hampton, Bob Woods (Rancho Vinedo) and Bob Miller (Bien Nacido) are exceptions to these broad generalizations, and that makes a big difference in my attitude. Linquist, Adam and I are now seeking contracts with growers. A lot of our relationships in the different labels are based on who is legally responsible for a particular grape contract. It makes sense. We can apply different winemaking philosophies to the different labels, but the real foundation will probably end up being the grape souces."

Jim Clendenen

Adam & Helen Tolmach   RL

Jim Clendenen   RL

BABCOCK

A great deal has been learned about cool viticultural regions along California's coast since they began to be planted in the early '70s. 1981 convinced a great many insiders that Central Coast Chardonnay might be the best California could produce. During the last five years Chardonnay has boomed in the marketplace and cool coastal vineyards have appreciated at the same pace.

Babcock Vineyard is just about the coolest one in Santa Barbara County. It is in the Santa Rita Valley near Lompoc and north of the Santa Rosa Valley which contains the Santa Ynez River. Babcock is 10 miles from the ocean on a bench 50 feet above the valley floor. The soil of the vineyard is light colored, shallow and sandy, with very little organic matter. It drains well and

seems to be potassium deficient because the pH of grapes grown there is astonishingly low. Nothing impedes the maritime influence. Fog and wind are common, but frost is not. "I think our location on the bench is an important quality consideration," says winemaker Brian Babcock. "In the valley floor the soil is quite deep. Vines grown there produce bigger crops, but have trouble ripening in our cold climate." When Babcock Vineyard was young, the wind caused some damage. Ten years later the vines are big enough to withstand the conditions. They are planted in rows parallel to the direction the wind blows, and broken canes rarely occur beyond the first vine. "We think conditions out here yield spectacular fruit," Brian reports. "We buy 10 tons of Chardonnay from Rancho Dos Mundos half a mile south and west of us, and also get Gewurztraminer from Rancho San Antonio which lies between us and Vandenberg Air Force Base. There are lots of good vineyard sites on the benches in our vicinity."

Brian is not your most obvious candidate to become a grower/winemaker in an excitingly experimental viticultural area. His family is from Nebraska. They moved to Long Beach when Brian was a child. Brian's father is a dentist who also owns Walt's Wharf, a restaurant in Seal Beach. In 1977 Brian's parents were looking for an acre or two near Solvang as a weekend home. They didn't like

anything the realtor showed them. When they explained their Nebraska heritage and the interest they had in making land productive, the realtor suggested they look at this 110 acre parcel out toward the coast. "The price is attractive," he said. Two years later the Babcocks were planting Chardonnay, White Riesling and Sauvignon Blanc grapes.

Brian, at this point, was graduating from high school in Huntington Beach. "I was indifferent to the wine game," he explains. "Football and girls figured rather more prominently in my plans." Brian attended Occidental College and thought he might like to pursue an advanced business degree. But in 1982 Au Bon Climat winery purchased some of Babcock's Chardonnay grapes. Flabbergasted by the ripe fruit and low pH, Clendenen and Tolmach designated the wine a Reserve bottling. They sold it all in a matter of weeks for $20 a bottle. Brian Babcock decided to forego business school in favor of an Enology education at U.C. Davis.

In 1984 the Babcocks built a barn on their property with a bedroom and a kitchen. The winery has subsequently been annexed to that structure, and a 4,500 sq. ft. freestanding warehouse has been added.

Although unusual for Gewürztraminer, primary and malolactic fermentations were conducted in the barrels. While maintaining its focus on spiciness, the wine is also rich, round and complex. Production is limited, and for those who cherish a dry style of Gewürztraminer, the wine is a treasure.

Bryan Babcock

BABCOCK VINEYARDS
5175 HIGHWAY 246
LOMPOC, CALIFORNIA
93436

CONTAINS SULFITES

Babcock
V I N E Y A R D S

1 9 8 7
Estate Grown
(Dry, Barrel Fermented)
GEWÜRZTRAMINER

PRODUCED AND BOTTLED BY BABCOCK VINEYARDS
BW 5194 LOMPOC, CALIFORNIA   ALCOHOL 13.7% BY VOLUME

1987 Chardonnay	400 cases
Estate Reserve	750 ml

Frmt started in stnls with Prise de Mousse, then transfered cold to tight-grained French barrels, 60% of which are new. 14 mos on lees, sterile filter.

1987 Dry Gewurztraminer	112 cases
Rancho San Antonio	750 ml

1986 Sauvignon Blanc	1,400 cases
Estate	750 ml

Picked at 23.5°Brix, 3.07 pH. Frmtd in Limousin oak barrels, 10% of which are new.

1987 LH J. Riesling	45 cases
Estate	375 ml

10% rs.

How do you work with your Chardonnay grapes?

"I call it expansion and integration. My fruit may come in anywhere from 22°-23.5°Brix, but it's always around 3.05 pH. I try to expand it with all the winemaking tools at my disposal. I ferment with a lot of solids. I stay on the lees 9-14 months. I try to build my malo-lactic culture up to a vigorous volume before adding it. I barrel ferment and age in 25-60% new oak with medium to heavy toast. If the fermentation stops on me, leaving 0.3% residual sugar, that's okay. I wouldn't intentionally leave residual sugar though. I'd rather build up the succulence and mouth feel with alcohol, oak and lees instead.

"The corollary to all these expansion techniques is integrating them together. They should balance the acid, the fruit and each other. Nothing should be left hanging outside the flavor profile of the wine."

Does a single guy get lonely in Lompoc?

"(pause) Yes. Of course, I say that because I'm here now. The reality is that it's great to have a mix. I love to go to the city and sell wine. It's tranquil here, but in the back of my mind I know I'll be going to the city. I enjoy the deals and the noise, and girls. After a couple of days though, I know I'll be stuck in a traffic jam thinking about how I want to come back here. At the vineyard I can feel like I'm accomplishing something when I work hard. I can also be alone with my thoughts, and I enjoy that. . .for a while."

Brian Babcock

BAY CELLARS

Born in Brooklyn and raised in North Hollywood, Richard Rotblatt absorbed the healthy attitudes about wine which are typical of the Jewish community. Kosher wine was regularly served at the Friday meal in his home, and with guests on Saturday before or after Temple. At the time Richard thought nothing of the grape syrup character exhibited by most of the wines that came his way.

In 1963 Rotblatt enrolled at U.C. Berkeley to study Math and Architecture. Those were lively times in Berserkly. By 1968 Richard was living in a communal house for very little rent, and drinking good wine with his income from structural engineering work in the power plant industry. He and his friends had started with '59 Sauternes. They gradually worked their way through red Bordeaux to Beaulieu Vineyards, then Mayacamas and the occasional Martin Ray.

Could a batch of homemade wine be far behind? Not in Berkeley 1971.

Richard had always enjoyed activities that mixed art and technology. He was involved in a glass blowing workshop at the University where he met a man who had been making wine at home for 15 years. Richard was fascinated with the intensity of the wine's style compared to standard commercial products. He became a habitue of Wine and the People, Berkeley's seminal home wine and beer making shop. "Having my hopes dashed by continuous rains in '72 and '73 convinced me that 90% of good winemaking is selection of grapes," says Rotblatt. "I see the winemaker as a stylist and caretaker."

Wanting a winery had gotten into his blood. It wasn't just the activity or the community of people involved. Richard had a vision of the type of wines he would make. His was a drive for artistic expression. Unfortunately, his "real job" was growing in leaps and bounds. The engineering company for which he worked was involved in the nuclear field. They grew from 40 employees in '72 to 700 employees in '76. Working 60 hours per week and being paid well as a project manager made the cost of unpaid winemaking time seem quite large.

By 1982 he couldn't stand it any longer. Little wineries had been opening up right and left. Some were achieving a lot of recognition. Richard needed a place. Veedercrest Winery had just gone bankrupt in the old

Shell Development facility in Emeryville, and Richard went over to check it out. The rent was nominal and the temperature situation was great, so he took out a bond and moved in. Jorg Rupf, of St. George Spirits, was already there distilling eau-de-vie. Rosenblum Cellars moved in as well shortly thereafter. This improbable "fermenting ghetto" stayed 5 years and created a substantial cult following.

Rotblatt moved in 1987 when Cetus bought the building. He was not unhappy to leave. "Those underground research labs were very hard to keep clean," he reports. "I'd been looking for another place since '85, but 2,000 sq. ft. with a yard and floor drains is not easy to come by." He moved into a building on Fourth Street in Berkeley just south of the area being rehabilitated with a plethora of trendy restaurants. "It's a great location," he says. "We've got 3,200 sq. ft. and plenty of space for a weekend tasting room." With friends Mike McKinney and John Reynolds helping out, can an increase from 1,500 cases/year be far behind?

This 1983 Pinot Noir is a rich and complex wine produced from single-vineyard grapes grown in the Bay-cooled Carneros district. It is a riper version of our fine 1982 Pinot Noir from the same vineyard.

The wine has strong varietal character, with intense aromas of ripe cherry, plum, and roasted coffee bean. Concentrated flavors of cherry fruit and sweet, toasty oak fill the mouth and unfold in layers across the palate. A velvety texture and good acidity enhance the long finish of the wine.

Only about 240 cases of this wine were bottled in early 1985.

Bay Cellars specializes in Pinot Noir, Chardonnay, and Bordeaux-style wines made in the French manner.

Advance notice of new releases is available by writing the winery at 1675 Tacoma Avenue Berkeley, California 94707.

| 1983 Cabernet Sauvignon | 400 cases |
| State Lane Vyd | 750 ml |

Cabernet Sauvignon from Napa vyd 3 miles north of Stag's Leap. 8% Merlot and 3% Cabernet Franc. 10-16 days on the skins. Seguin-Moreau barrels "for cedary flavor."

| 1984 Merlot | 200 cases |
| Narsai David Vyd | 750 ml |

Napa Vly Merlot with 15% Cabernet Sauvignon from Kitty Hawk Vyd on Mt. Veeder and 6% Cabernet Franc.

| 1985 Chardonnay | 400 cases |
| | 750 ml |

65% of the grapes from Carneros District, 35% from Soscol road near city of Napa. Partial barrel frmt, 18 mos on lees, full m-l.

| 1985 Pinot Noir | 45 cases |
| Bethel Heights | 750 ml |

Oregon grapes macerated with skins for a long time at 40°F, punched 3x/day. Frmtn with Prise de Mousse yeast allowed to peak around 80°F.

Tell me about your early home winemaking experience.

"I was so taken with the idea in spring, 1971 that I rushed out and bought a book by some English author. I plunged right in. Chapter One was a wine made from parsnips, bananas and white grape juice concentrate. I thought it smelled a little strange while it was fermenting, but Peter (Brehm, founder of Wine and the People) didn't have much experience with parsnip wine so I ignored his advice to pour down the drain. By the time I got to the chapter on Defective Wines, however, I had convinced myself that this wine had an ominous haze which accounted for my friend's poor reaction to it. I mean I had nothing against parsnips personally.

"That fall my household on Hearst Street decided to get serious. We bought half a ton of Zinfandel and fermented it in the living room, which cost us a few roommates. We aged it in a small American oak barrel. Lo and behold, the wine was pretty good. We thought it was extraordinary, but we were young.

"For the next ten years I hung out with a circle of home winemakers who met at least once a week in various tasting groups. Many of them (Channing Rudd, Denis Kelly) have gone on to some prominence in the wine industry or local restaurant scene (Bay Wolf, Mama's). There was tremendous competition among us to see who could make the best wine. I became infatuated with Burgundies from the middle '60s, and spent a lot of my disposable income making Pinot Noirs. The '73 from Winery Lake Vyd, made in conjunction with Peter, received a significant amount of acclaim and that just whet my appetite. By 1980 the social evolution in Berkeley, my age, my job, and the financial evolution of Wine and the People had all combined to change my perspective. A commercial winery was the next logical step."

Richard Rotblatt

CL

BELLEROSE VINEYARD

Softspoken Charles Richard (pronounced rish-ARD) is a virtuoso of the classical guitar, having played and taught professionally for many years. He has written a book named *Classical Guitar Repertory from the Renaissance to the Present* and holds a Master's Degree in Music and Esthetics. Today he blends this training in the arts, with science and manual labor to pursue an agricultural expression.

Originally from Pennsylvania, Charles was raised in the hotel and restaurant business. Fine food and wine were taken seriously when he was a child. His Italian-born father was the owner and master-chef of a Mount Pocono country inn named Villa Charles. Bellerose Vineyard is the culmination of a interest in quality red wines from the Medoc region of France that Charles Richard has carried his entire life. He and his wife Nancy belonged to San Francisco's Vintner's Club for many years. There they enjoyed the opportunity to taste great vintages, quiz visiting luminaries and read everything they could find about Bordeaux. They became convinced that the key to the complexity and depth of the classified growths lay in the right mix of red grapes.

First they became home winemakers with an experimental vineyard in Mendocino County. Then, in 1978, they acquired their 70 acre Dry Creek Valley estate. It is located near the mouth of the valley, where Dry Creek runs into the Russian River. The property includes 6 different soil types ranging from bottomland along the river, to benchland and hillsides as it runs up into the mountains on the west. The place had originally been settled right after the Civil War. It functioned as a typical North Coast ranch raising walnuts and fruit trees, drying prunes and growing vegetables near the river. The first winery on the property was built in 1887 by a retired Army Captain named Everett A. Wise. It burned down in 1937 and no wine was made commercially until the Richards took over. They have renovated a stone chai for barrel storage and Charles would like to carve some caves out of the hill behind it. The "art" of farming is still practiced as the Richards use two Belgian draft horses, named Rowdy and Curly, to cultivate or move loads around the terraced vineyards.

Some very large Douglas Fir trees on the Bellerose property testify to a marine intrusion which reaches all the way from Tomales Bay. It is a cool location compared with most of Dry Creek Valley. To the Richards, it seemed like an ideal place to test their chateau concept for blending the "big five" red grape varieties of Bordeaux. Malbec is the first to ripen. It has deep color with luscious fruit and a lot of spice in the nose. Cabernet Franc comes in next because they have it on a hillside above the winery. It has a definite blackberry component in nose. Petite Verdot is like black ink; besides color, even a tiny percentage contributes body and tannin. Merlot adds a cherry nose and earthy flavor. It also serves to soften the cuvee as a counterbalance to the Cabernet Sauvignon. Their Cabernet Sauvignon is the basis for the blend. It shows different characteristics in different vintages, and is the last grape to ripen. Its usual contribution is a green olive note, and some backbone for the structure of the wine. So far the blend has ranged from 70% Cabernet Sauvignon in '80 to 89% in '85.

Bellerose produces around 4,000 cases each year. The Richards carefully guard the integrity of their product. Their goal is complexity and elegance, as opposed to a more opulent style typically found in California. They "declassified" the '81 to $5 generic status when it failed to meet their expectations. They also sell wine, which is not chosen for the blend, to negociants. They currently have 35 bearing acres. 20 acres are Cabernet Sauvignon planted in the mid '60s. 5 acres are Merlot planted at the same time. 5 more acres of Merlot are being planted. There are five acres of Sauvignon Blanc and Sémillon used for a Graves-style blend. The remainder is divided among Malbec, Cabernet Franc and Petite Verdot.

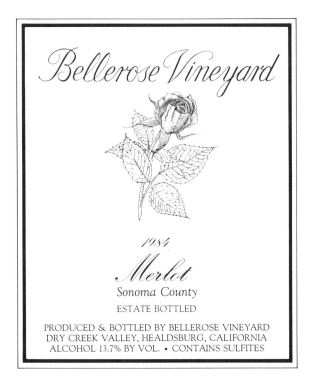

Bellerose Vineyard

1984

Merlot

Sonoma County

ESTATE BOTTLED

PRODUCED & BOTTLED BY BELLEROSE VINEYARD
DRY CREEK VALLEY, HEALDSBURG, CALIFORNIA
ALCOHOL 13.7% BY VOL. • CONTAINS SULFITES

1985 Cuvee Bellerose	2,800 cases
Estate	750 ml

89% Cab Sauv, 5% Cab Franc, 14% Merlot, 2% Petite Verdot and Malbec. Aged in Nevers oak. Btld Sept '87.13.2 alc, 3.4 pH, .70 acid.

1985 Merlot	900 cases
Estate	750 ml

88% Merlot,6% Cab Franc, 6% Cab Sauv. Btld Dec '86. 13.7 alc, 3.3 pH, .73 acid.

1986 Sauvignon Blanc	1,300 cases
Estate	750 ml

76% Sauv Blanc, 24% Semillon. Barrel frmtd to 80°F, then left sur lie for 5 mo. No m-l, aged in Nevers oak.12.4 alc, 3.1 pH, .88 acid.

Do you enter your wine in competitions?

"No. I have served as a judge. We were required to evaluate several hundred wines over three days. Therefore, each wine gets a minimal amount of each judge's attention. In those conditions the starting point is always negative. You begin by looking for faults. Of course, there is no opportunity to try the wine with food; a situation which I consider contrary to wine's natural ambience. Then there is the matter of palate fatigue. Even the most dedicated judge suffers by the end of the day.

"It is all too easy to be influenced by soft, 'pretty' wines. And that is probably the role that competitions serve. They help promote wines which Alexis Lichine once refered to as 'regionally excellent.' Many winemakers can achieve success by styling their wines for these competitions, and that means making the wine approachable at an early age. But my opinion is that great wines typically do not show well when young. They develop over a period of years. Wine judgings can not possibly evaluate this significant aspect of a world class wine.

"Lastly, one must consider Americans infatuation with Gold medals to the degree that Bronze medals become a badge of disgrace. I think the meaningful competition is the judgement of the marketplace. Connoisseurs and wine writers will evaluate a wine in much different circumstances than a county Fair judging. They will watch the wine as the years pass. They will taste it several times with food, and they will have a sense of the winery's track record."

Charles Richard

KF

J. CAREY CELLARS

La Cuesta Vineyard is a shale hilltop northeast of the Danish community in Solvang. The first grapes were planted in 1973. The vineyard is primarily Cabernet Sauvignon with a small amount of Merlot. The nutritive value of the soil is meager, and the drainage is very pronounced. As a result, the vines struggle. Water stress naturally reduces the canopy. There is no need to hedge the vines, nor to open them up for more sunlight. Even at the peak of the season, you can look through vines 5 rows deep in La Cuesta Vineyard. Crop sizes are always small and the water stress promotes early ripening. Even at low sugar levels the Merlot has cherry notes to the nose, and there is rarely any need to mute the herbaceous smell commonly found in cool climate Cabernet Sauvignon.

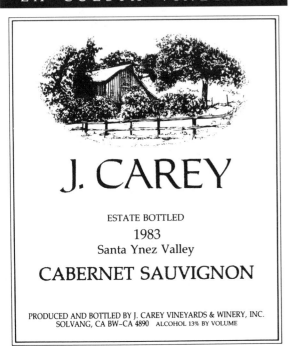

For ten years, La Cuesta was owned by the Carey family. Drs. Jim and Joe are, respectively, a plastic surgeon and a heart surgeon. They insulated a dairy barn on Alamo Pintado Road below the vineyard and made 5,000 cases of wine a year. They also had vineyards in a gravel draw named Adobe Canyon and on a sandy slope surrounding the winery. There were 42 acres in total. Winemaking conditions were fairly primitive. The crusher, for instance, was a 1950's Amos which required grapes to be put in with a pitchfork.

The reputation of La Cuesta accelerated at Christmas 1986 when J. Carey Cellars was purchased by Firestone Vineyards. Normally real estate transactions where physicians cash out of investments just prior to a change in the tax laws would not cause much notice. However, Kate Firestone has gone out of her way to explain that La Cuesta Vineyard was the key to the deal. Her husband Brooks went so far as to say that La Cuesta was the best vineyard in Santa Ynez Valley.

Kate Firestone was born in India and danced as a soloist with the Royal Ballet in London. Now she has taken on J. Carey Cellars as her personal project. "If money were the issue, nobody would be in the wine business," Brooks says. "It is an expression, a labor of love. Kate is making this project her own brand of madness." She has overseen a renovation of the winery with a new crusher and an expanded crush pad. Case inventory has been moved to Firestone's air-conditioned warehouse, which in turn increased the barrel space at J. Carey. During 1988 a television show, called *Aaron's Way* starring Merlin Olsen as a modern day Amish farmer, was filmed on the property. They made use of the 1920's farm house that serves as a tasting room, but the only permanent construction they left behind was an arbor which Kate now uses

for visitors' picnics. La Cuesta Vineyard is receiving attention in the form of replacements for missing vines. The technique is called "mother vining." It involves rooting a shoot in the ground from the vine growing next to the missing space. This method means that acreage and the mix of vines will not change, but production will eventually increase because there will be more plants. Kate says they are also attacking a severe gopher problem with a band of wild cats which now call La Cuesta home.

In 1988 Kate hired Ken Barthman as winemaker for J. Carey. A 30-year-old Chico State graduate, Barthman had previously worked at Ch. St. Jean and Far Niente. "We went to a winery-specific headhunter," Kate explains, "because we wanted someone who had made small amounts of wine with no compromises." Ken's Chardonnay experience may open up a whole new era for J. Carey. He is getting grapes from at least three different vineyard locations and ripenesses to create a "layered" style. He also brings with him a sophisticated yeast program.

1987 Sauvignon Blanc   1,200 cases
750 ml

No skin soak, 35 ppm SO_2 at crusher, frmtd at 65°F in stnls. Aged 6 mos French oak barrels, 15% new. Sterile filtered. Btld May '88 at 12.4 alc, .88 acid, 3.27 pH. Also 400 cases of '87 Semillon from Buttonwood Vyd located across Alamo Pintado Road from the winery.

1983 Cabernet Sauvignon   900 cases
La Cuesta Vyd (reserve)   750 ml

Picked mid Oct at 20.8-23°Brix, 3.15-3.45 pH, .69-.58 acid. 50 ppm SO_2 at crusher. Frmtd with Pasteur Red yeast at 80°F, on skins 7 days to 1°Brix. M-L complete by Dec, 4 rackings, aged 19 mos in Demptos Chateau barrels 1 & 2-yrs-old. No fining, medium pad filter, btld May '85 at 13 alc, .6 acid, 3.55 pH. Also '85 (regular) Cabernet Sauvignon and 560 cases of '86 La Cuesta Merlot.

Are small wineries better than big ones?

"I get to see both sides. Making wine on a limited scale lets you style for a narrow segment of the market. That is great fun. La Cuesta Vyd provides ideal fruit for that type of program. Small wineries can also charge higher prices because their wines are so rare. That helps the image of the region. We can have a spontaneous, low-key approach in the tasting room at J. Carey, and you could never do that in a big place which handles bus loads of people at a time. Bicycle tours are our biggest groups at J. Carey.

"But I sympathize with micro-vintners who don't have the benefits a big place can provide. I would go nuts without clerical help on government paperwork, for instance. Most small wineries must be swimming in it. Another clear advantage is the way we can bottle the J. Carey wines on a sophisticated bottling line at Firestone. BATF won't let us use the phrase 'Estate Bottled' on the label, but I'd rather protect the condition of the wines. We get similar benefits in areas like air-conditioned case storage and transportation to store or restaurant accounts.

"I'm adament about maintaining the small winery nature of J. Carey. That is why we kept the name. But I think I can dovetail the best aspects of both sides in a positive way. When I took over, there were a lot of loose ends to the marketing program. We've drawn those in, and not replaced them. We are only active in 6 states. We started writing a newsletter as a response to conversations I had with visitors at the winery. We're not awash with people, and I've had plenty of opportunity to chat with folks."

Kate Firestone

La Cuestra Vyd   RL

Kate Firestone   RL

CASA NUESTRA VINEYARDS

Gene Kirkham's father grew up on a farm, then spent his adult years being a lawyer in San Francisco. Gene finds himself drawn to reverse that process. When he was 10, in 1956, his parents bought a weekend house in Napa. "They decided I was maladjusted in the expensive private boys school, so they parked me in the Napa public school system," he says. Harvard, Boalt Law School, a 1968 marriage announcement in *Ramparts* magazine because the San Francisco newspapers were on strike, C.O. status providing legal services to impoverished Indians, and a Fulbright Scholarship in New Zealand followed. But daughter Freda was born in 1973, and Gene decided he had best get a real job. He went to work for a law firm in San Francisco and spent his weekends "writing away for color brochures of islands for sale in British Columbia."

One bleak January day, Gene and his wife Cody went to see an old farm south of Calistoga and just west of the Silverado Trail. It was called Casa Nuestra (our house). The realtor apologized for the condition of the property and volunteered that he hadn't received a serious offer on it in about a year. The Kirkhams were charmed, and not entirely ignorant about the potential for "up-valley" real estate. They bought a house, a small shed and 8 acres of grapes on the Napa River the next day. Gene went to work part-time for a law firm in St. Helena and sold his grapes to Gallo through the Napa Co-op. By 1979 he had made partner. At the law firm, that is. The Gallos were not quite so magnanimous. He kept feeling, however, that he would "rather be in overalls than fighting with some judge."

He decided to become Napa's smallest winery. It took him a year to get bonded because the County kept insisting that "wineries needed parking for 30 cars." There were 15 year old Chenin Blanc vines on the property along with Grey Riesling. Gene budded the Grey Riesling over to Chenin Blanc, told Gallo the bad news and installed a jacketed stainless steel fermenter in his 20' x 40' shed. Today he makes about 1,000 cases per year in a dry, fragrant style. Most of the wine is sold through a homespun newsletter and delivered by Gene. "I went to college planning to become T.S. Eliot," says one of Napa Valley's best educated truck drivers. "The winery was supposed to create enough leisure to pursue a life of art. It hasn't quite happened yet."

Gene admits Napa Chenin Blanc is often treated as a "cash flow" wine. "Make it quick, sweeten it up and out the door," he intones sarcastically. "We, on the other hand, take pains to conserve the grape's flowery, fruity components." Hand picked clusters are brought directly to the winery from vines surrounding it. The Kirkham's

son Martin gets a day off from school to act as "bicycle walkie-talkie" between vineyard and crusher. Fermentation temperatures are kept cool. Kirkham believes that wood fermentation or aging overpowers Chenin Blanc's delicate flavors.

Gene and Cody feel Chenin Blanc is under-appreciated as a varietal in California. Pointing out that it is the basis for Vouvray, Gene adds, "It ages well for a white. Some of the Loire wines improve for years. Ours from the early '80s are beautiful, complex, lovely to drink right now." Their '83 took the only Gold Medal in its class at the 1985 San Francisco Expo and was rated Wine of the Year by *Bon Appetit* magazine. The '85 disappeared shortly after 15 cases were purchased by the White House.

Casa Nuestra also makes a few hundred cases of Cabernet Franc. It comes from 4 acres of grapes that were field grafted in '81 by their neighbor. The vines are on alluvial soil and relatively vigorous. At one point the grapes went to Duckhorn. Gene bought the vineyard in '86. That vintage of the wine has a flowery/minty nose and light structure, but Gene can't complain about the reception it received. John Movius, the Chief Judge at several national wine competitions, called it "the best Cabernet Franc yet made in California." Gene says he doesn't want to produce a wine that needs 4 years in the cellar. He is thinking about adding 10-20% Cabernet Sauvignon, but plans to do blending trials every year before deciding.

| 1986 Chenin Blanc | 600 cases |
| Estate Vyd | 750 ml |

Picked 1 Sept from flat vyd near Napa River south of Calistoga at 22.4°Brix. No skin soak. Frmtd 4 wks at 57°F in stnls with Pasteur Champagne yeast. No sweet reserve. Sterile filtered. Btld Jan '87 at less than 0.1% rs.

| 1987 Chenin Blanc | 400 cases |
| Estate Vyd | 750 ml |

Picked 7 Sept 22.8°Brix. Sweet reserve. Sterile filtered. Btld Jan '88 at 0.7% rs.

| 1986 Dorado | 170 cases |
| Estate | 375 ml |

Late harvest Chenin Blanc from older, ungrafted vines with well developed canopy. 5" rain in mid-Sept aided botrytis formation. Picked three separate times as botrytis developed. Grapes chilled to 40°F. Had to be pressed and forked over several times in old basket press. Inoculated with huge, vigorously frmtg starter of Pasteur Champagne yeast. Frmt around 55°F, then chilled and bentonited to pull yeast down. 1.0 acid, 14 alc, 8% rs.

| 1986 Cabernet Franc | 400 cases |
| Estate | 750 ml |

Do you charge for tasting?

"That is a new phenomenon in Napa. It may be an adroit marketing move, and it may be a financial necessity. It eliminates the casual traffic of people who have no intention to buy wine. Same thing with wineries who do not welcome people on bicycles because they obviously aren't going to carry away case purchases. Lastly, I think charging for tastes is a subtle psychological move to indicate that the wine must be good if you have to pay to taste it.

"Having pointed out all the reasons why it is done, the answer to your question is no, we do not charge for tasting. Gene, the Happy Farmer, does not see himself as a sophisticated marketing analyst. He grows the grapes, makes the wine and meets the customers. Our strength is sincerity; not glitz. Many wineries in Napa take french names. We maintain the spanish name of our property and choose spanish names for our proprietary labels because we think they accurately reflect the history of this place. We want to be friendly and accessible. I'm proud of the personal attention we give visitors. And it seems to work. Almost everybody who comes here buys wine. We have picnic tables and a hammock because we view the visit as an experience in the country; not just a commercial transaction. We're a bonafide mom-n-pop operation as opposed to Bartles and James. We appreciate your support, but we won't turn you away if you're not prepared to buy wine.

"So far we haven't had any problems with this attitude. We get very few drunks. We usually serve 5 wines, but the total volume is rarely more than a couple of ounces. Water is always available too. It is well water, and people even comment on how good it tastes."

Cody Kirkham

RG

CHATEAU CHEVRE WINERY

A retired cargo airline pilot, a production enologist and a goat farm seem an unlikely combination, but somehow they all came together to form Chateau Chevre. Gerry Hazen was looking for something to do after retiring, Bob Mueller was beginning his career as an enologist at Mondavi Winery, and the old goat farm was right in the middle of an old lake bed in southern Napa Valley.

Gerry bought the land in 1973. There had been 150 goats on 21 acres. There was an old hay barn and one building, about 150 feet long, which included the goat run. Looking at six foot weeds and assorted debris lying around the property, Gerry decided to bulldoze everything. "The place made Tobacco Road look like the Ritz," he says. No matter how hard he tried, however, he couldn't budge the building where they had milked the goats and processed the

milk. The walls were about a foot thick and made of solid concrete. So Gerry planted his grapes around it.

After a few years of growing Merlot, he decided to start making wine himself and brought in enologist Bob Mueller as a partner. They put the winemaking operation in the only structure left standing, the old goat barn. It was a logical choice. The heavy walls were ideal insulation, plus it had drainage, cement floors, everything they needed. Chateau Chevre, French for goat, was a natural name.

The winery specializes in Merlot. Cabernet Franc and Cabernet Sauvignon have been planted more recently, along with Sauvignon Blanc, on Gerry's property and in Bob Mueller's vineyard next door. Gerry's interest in Merlot dates back to his flying days when he had a chance to taste wines all over the world. Chateau Petrus, the great Merlot of Pomerol, was a particular favorite. It remains a model for Chateau Chevre because both wineries grow their grapes in heavy clay soil. "Merlot in this cool southern end of the Napa Valley has more intense fruit and depth than grapes grown farther north in the warmer "Cabernet Country" near Rutherford," says Gerry. "We have a pronounced advantage in warm or dry years."

Chateau Chevre makes a total of 2,700 cases/year in 8 open-top 220-gallon stainless steel fermenters and 2 larger jacketed tanks. They use a Zambelli crusher-stemmer and a wooden basket press. Wines are aged exclusively in French oak with 25% of the barrels replaced each year.

Between them Bob and Gerry own 6 acres of Cabernet Franc and 3.5 acres of Cabernet Sauvignon in addition to their 9 acres of Merlot. They have great opportunities for Bordeaux-style blending. They have been gradually increasing the percentage of Cabernet Franc in their Merlot

since '83. They have also done a few cases of varietal Cabernet Franc with 10-25% Merlot. Gerry thinks varietally labeled Cabernet Franc needs a healthy jolt of Merlot to round out its middle. It has a spicy tobacco nose, but it seems flat without help. They are still deciding whether or not to do the Cabernet Franc every year as a separate wine. The '85 Cabernet Franc is a fine wine, but they don't know whether that is because it has 22% Merlot, or because '85 was such an exceptional vintage.

In '86 they will have to go with a real mixture because Gerry's Merlot crop got wiped out by a freak frost on May 5th and 6th. He thinks he may have been the only guy in Napa Valley who got burned. His wind machine failed. He has replaced it now, but the '86 crop amounted to less than 7 tons of Merlot. "We're going to try a blend with 55% Cabernet Franc, 35% Cabernet Sauvignon and 10% Merlot," Gerry says. "Maybe we'll call it Nubian Reserve."

1985

Chateau Chevre

NAPA VALLEY

SAUVIGNON BLANC

ESTATE BOTTLED

GROWN, PRODUCED & BOTTLED BY CHATEAU CHEVRE INC.
ALCOHOL 12% BY VOLUME • CONTAINS SULFITES·BW 4933

1987 Sauvignon Blanc   480 cases
Estate Vyd   750 ml

From cordon pruned, 6-yr-old vines on west side of vly floor. Hand-picked end of Aug. Aged in 60 gal French oak. Light filtration, btld July '88 at 12.7 alc.

1986 ChevReserve   1,100 cases
Estate   750 ml

55% Cabernet Franc, 35% Cabernet Sauvignon, 10% Merlot.

1986 Merlot Reserve   100 cases
Estate   750 ml

16-yr-old vines, cordon-trained, AxR rootstock, clay/loam soil 60" deep, no irrigation, 4 t/a. Frmtd in open 220 gal stnls at 84°F with Champagne yeast, 50% left on the skins 30 days. 22 mos in 60 gal French oak. Btld Aug '88.

1986 Cabernet Franc   180 cases
Estate   750 ml

80% Cabernet Franc, 10% Merlot, 10% Cabernet Sauvignon.

Have you always planned on Bordeaux blends?

"It has evolved with a good deal of luck, both good and bad. Fifteen years ago the Merlot vineyard at my house was put in for me by the former owners of Franciscan. I had a 25 year contract for them to take care of the vines and buy the grapes. They ran into financial difficulties and never did fulfill their end of the management contract. At the time I was pretty upset, but today I'm delighted with how it worked out.

"Then in '86 my Merlot was largely wiped out by frost. That spurred us to increase our blending experiments. We've found that a little Cabernet Franc clearly boosts the nose of Merlot. Cabernet Franc also has more of deep purple color compared to the ruby red tone of Merlot. They look good together. By itself, the Cabernet Franc is a little flat tasting. It starts fine and ends well, but seems to miss something in between. A small amount of Merlot in the Cabernet Franc contributes roundness to the middle.

"These taste factors are only part of the equation though. Our Cabernet Franc vineyard is 4 miles south of here in the middle of the valley on Big Ranch road. This year ('88) we have a full crop on the Cabernet Franc, but a severe shatter problem on Cabernet Sauvignon and Merlot. It looks like we may have lost 50% of the crop here at the house. It had to do with cold weather and wind right at flowering. I've never used the second crop, but a lot of people in the valley are out picking their second crop right now. It is tempting when the shatter is so bad in your first crop. Now that we have begun getting such good results from the blends, we feel that we have a lot of options.

"In the future there may be even more choices. My partner has a venture of his own in the Carneros District which involves 50 south facing acres. He has planted 15 of them to Cabernet Sauvignon and will probably put in 10 or more acres of Merlot. Those cool climate grapes will be different than any we have handled so far. It is experimental, but exciting. I'd like to say everything has been pre-planned, but fortune plays a big role."

Gerry Hazen

RG

CHOUINARD

George Chouinard (pronounced "shin HARD") was on his construction engineering firm's fast track. That included the chance to manage their Paris office. So George and Carolyn moved in 1974 with their two teenage sons to the old farming community of Chavenay. Rick and Damian attended the American School while George commuted by train to the city. The whole family was struck by the enthusiasm and dedication of the small winemaking family operations in the nearby Champagne District. "There may be more creativity in the California industry," Carolyn says, "but the French appreciation for tradition is so admirable. We saw both sides. The younger, more cosmopolitan people helped us learn the language, but the town we lived in had a timeless quality."

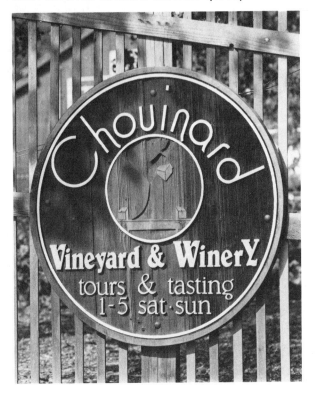

Upon return to the U.S. in 1976, George was offered the presidency of his company's international operations unit. It was an important career move. He would be directing 8-900 people from headquarters in Chicago. Then his wife handed him a letter she had written him. In it she explained how emotionally distracted she became everytime they talked about another move. She wanted a home. George considered how supportive his family had always been of his career. He considered the activities in his life that pleased him the most. Then he quit his job and started looking for property in Northern California.

The Chouinards bought 110 acres along a creek bed tributary to the Palomares Canyon. Their property is in the hills which separate San Francisco Bay from Livermore Valley. At 800 feet elevation they get some fog and are quite a bit cooler than Pleasanton, 8 miles to the east. Twenty years ago this area was known for Queen Anne cherries, but urbanization is surrounding it on all sides. The Chouinards have planted 3 acres of terraced vines in the fertile loam of an old corral, and they plan to put in another 4 acres soon. Cabernet Sauvignon, Chardonnay and Sauvignon Blanc make up their vineyard. The remaining property is quite steep and heavily forested. The Chouinards would like to get more grapes from the area, so they are encouraging their neighbors with more easily plantable property to consider small vineyards. They offer free consulting on how to plant, prune and spray. "We don't do the work for them though," says Damian. "We've had a couple of takers. And we will buy the grapes."

Damian first attended Humboldt State in the Wildlife Management program, returning home to help his parent's home winemaking efforts. By 1985, however, he had assessed the job prospects in forestry and decided to switch to the

Viticulture and Enology program at Fresno State. His parents built a 2,200 sq. ft. winery on their property and bonded it the same year. They made 200 cases in '85 and 400 in '86. Damian graduated in June of 1987. Production jumped to 2,200 cases that year and doubled to nearly 5,000 in '88. As a carpenter and electrician, Rick is extremely useful around the fledgling winery. Harvesting of the Estate vineyard is done by friends in exchange for wine. Damian rents a 6-ton flatbed truck to pick up purchased grapes from Bacigalupi Vineyard in Alexander Valley and 3 vineyards in the Salinas Valley. George handles marketing and runs the tasting room on weekends. He is currently trying to crush Granny Smith apples from a friend's charmingly named Hog Canyon Orchard near Paso Robles. Damian wants to try making a 7% residual sugar dessert wine using a modified applejack technique. He will partially freeze the juice and pour the concentrated liquid off the ice prior to fermentation.

Carolyn does PR as well as government compliance, which is any winery's most dreaded task. Chouinard's location lends itself well to publicity. Palomares Canyon is extremely scenic. At one time it was also the last leg of the transcontinental railroad journey. A non-profit group of retired railroad employees is in the process of restoring a 3-mile stretch of track between Sunol and Niles on which they hope to run a 1930's Skunk train, steam locomotives and historic dining cars complete with the last of the famous railway chefs. The terminus town of Niles was once a movie capital where westerns and Charlie Chaplin films were made.

1987 Chardonnay 300 cases each
San Bernabe and Zabala Vyds 750 ml

Two separate wines and styles. San Bernabe Vyd is near King City. Those grapes are picked at 23°Brix, .75 acid and 3.3 pH. They are acid adjusted, not given any SO₂, and cold frmtd in stnls with Steinberg yeast. At 7°Brix they are transfered to medium toast, shaved, Nevers barrels. Partial M-L, sterile filter. The second wine is made from Zabala Vyd grapes grown in Arroyo Seco. They are picked at 21.5°Brix with .9 acid and 3.1 pH. Barrel frmtd in neutral wood with Prise de Mousse yeast. 45 ppm SO₂ at the crusher, no M-L, but on the stirred gross lees for 6 mos. Sterile filter.

1988 Gewürztraminer 200 cases
Ventana Vyd 750 ml

No skin soak, free run juice only, cold frmtd with Prise de Mousse yeast to .7% rs. Btld Nov 88. '87 won a Silver medal at Orange County.

1986 Cabernet Sauvignon 300 cases
Bacigalupi Vyd 750 ml

Alexander Valley grapes picked at 23.5°Brix. Frmt in open tank under 70°F with Montrachet yeast to retain fruit and big style. Transfer to refrigerated tanks if necessary to maintain temperature. Punch 3x/day, on skins 12 days to dryness. Inoculated for M-L at warmest point. Aged 12 mos in small Limousin oak and 1,000-gal American oak uprights.

Tell me about the class program at Fresno.

"It is very practical; all the equipment is there. You have to make wine, and you do it in tanks, not carboys. The core course is a production class where everyone makes 3-400 gallons each of 3-4 wines. It is really valuable when there are only 15-20 people in the class because there is so much work to do. When there are 40 people in the class, you don't get as much out of it. In a year long course you go through every point of production. It's a tough 3 units. You have to be at school 3 weeks early in the fall and do a lot of work on weekends. There is 4 hours of lecture a week plus time in the cellar.

"Our four Viticulture classes were kind of separate from the Enology sections. They included plant physiology and soils as well as identifying grape varieties visually and by taste. All the Enology majors take minors in Chemistry. We had classes in wine analysis and micro-biology as well as the practical courses and independent production projects. There were five levels of organoleptic instruction: components; defects; varietals and styles; specific oils and essences; and finally a weekend seminar duplicating the awards round at a county Fair judging.

"I learned a great deal in the judging discussion. One wine was a marceration carbonique style which I thought was really well done. Other people didn't consider it a serious wine. There was a lot of persuasion going both ways."

Damian Chouinard

Damian CL

CL

DAUMÉ WINERY

Still in his 40's, John Daumé is fairly young to be Godfather to fifteen California wineries, but as owner of the main winemaking shop in Los Angeles he has inspired that many amateurs to "go pro." His Cellarmasters Club consists of 150 dedicated home winemakers who buy over 20 tons of grapes a year from John and use his equipment and expertise to make everything from apricot wine to first-class Chardonnay. The club holds festivals and contests all year long. Judges are recognized wine authorities and several hundred entries are normal for any of the Club's competitions. John says, "When our winemakers get ribbons, they know it is a meaningful accomplishment."

An interesting transition is the way home beer making has grown in the last 6 years. John points out that beer making supplies were 20% of his business in 1982 and closer to 80% of it today. "It parallels the growth of upscale beers and micro-breweries," he says. "My customers aren't trying to save money. They are trying to make something at home which is better than what they can buy in a store." The wine industry diversified during the last 15 years to provide a multitude of distinctly flavored products at good prices. By contrast the beer industry is consolidated into 5 or 6 major breweries making product for the mass palate. John's beer club, the Maltose Falcons, was one of the first in country, and may be the largest with 150 members.

John grew up in Detroit and left medical school to pursue a career in retailing. He bought furniture for Gimbels in New York and then radios for Bullocks in Los Angeles. Tired of being a small cog in a big wheel, he took over the Wine Art store in North Hollywood in 1972 and began selling supplies to home wine, beer and cheese makers. In 1982 he opened his own winery, specializing in Burgundian-style Chardonnay, Pinot Noir and Vin Gris. The winery occupies 1,600 square feet of an industrial park in Camarillo. He has the capacity to produce 2,000 cases a year. Equipment is small and labor-intensive, but John can recruit plenty of help from his home winemaker customers.

For Pinot Noir, Daumé says that he wants cold climate vineyards with clones "that haven't reverted to the Gamay side of the family." He takes off half the juice for his Vin Gris in order to use twice as many skins in the fermentation for the Pinot Noir. "Think about it," he says. "The French have their grapes planted on 4' x 4' spacings with maybe 7 buds per vine. California spacings are 12' x 10', so even if the tons per acre are the same as the French, the pounds per vine are much higher." Daumé does not use any stems. He points out that in Burgundy the stems left in the fermentation are brown and dried out. "The green stems on California fruit give you a bitter taste," he adds with a grimace.

John likes a hotter fermentation than most Pinot Noir makers and a lot of cap punching to get extract from the skins. His style is to get as much flavor as possible during maceration, and then to let the bouquet develop in the bottle. He believes that vintage differences show up most obviously in the fruity aromas of young wines. That aromatic period is replaced by smells that come from the winemaking process. "Those smells are pretty reliable in my wines," he says. "The big, gutsy style is more work, but ultimately less chancey. It is not subject to a lot of bottle variation."

John also leaves the wine on the lees for a long time in what the French call "controlled filthiness." "We want layers of complexity rather than fruitiness," he explains. "I make dinner wines, not cocktail wines. My Pinot Noir is like an additional course at the meal instead of merely being a palate cleanser." Furthermore, he keeps his prices moderate to appeal to a value-oriented market. "I can afford to because I don't have any advertising expense," he deadpans, "and I have to because LA consumers are barracudas."

1984 Pinot Noir

A charming companion at your dinner table, this fine wine is reminiscent of the red Burgundies of the Cote de Nuit.

Soft, velvety, yet intense. Layers of developing flavors suggest dark chocolate, rich black cherries, vanilla and perhaps the earthy aromas of the forest after a rain.

Our friends at the Paragon Vineyards in the Santa Maria Valley are the exclusive growers of this select, classic clone of Pinot Noir.

A full year's aging in small french oak barrels harmonizes this handcrafted wine and contributes to its complexity.

Enjoy.

John E. Daumé

DAUMÉ

1984
PINOT NOIR
SANTA MARIA VALLEY

PRODUCED AND BOTTLED BY THE DAUMÉ WINERY
CAMARILLO, CALIFORNIA BW 5123
ALCOHOL BY VOLUME 12.8%

1986 Pinot Noir   300 cases
Paragon Vyd, Santa Maria   750 ml

Grapes from rolling hillsides and flat mesas near Sisquoc River. 15-yr-old vines picked 1st wk of Sept at 23.5°Brix, .95 acid. Frmtd 15 days with Assmanhausen yeast, punched down, on heavy lees 10 mos with lees stirred each time barrel is topped. Aged in Seguin-Moreau barrels with light toast, 25% newly shaved. Btld Aug '87 at 13.2 alc, 3.4 pH. Gold Medal at Central Coast Wine Judging.

1987 Chardonnay   1,200 cases
Pleasant Valley Ranch   750 ml

15-yr-old vines near Estrella River east of Paso Robles (vyd produces Bella Sauret label). Picked end Aug at 23.5°Brix, .8 acid. No SO_2 at crusher. Frmtd at 55-62°F using a walk-in cooler, Chanson yeast in French oak barrels, 25% of which are newly shaved. No racking, full M-L, lees stirred when topping. 9 mos barrel age, btld 4 July '88 at 13.2 alc, .8 acid, 3.3 pH.

1986 Fumé Blanc   300 cases
Nepenthe Vyd   750 ml

Picked end of Aug from 10-yr-old, dry farmed vines in rolling hills near Paso Robles at 22.5°Brix, .75 acid, 3.3 pH. No skin soak or SO_2 at crusher. Barrel frmtd entirely in Seguin Moreau barrels at 60°F in walk-in cooler with Pasteur white, no M-L. Aged 9 mos in French oak, topped and heavy lees stirred 2x/mo. Btld July '87 at 12.5 alc, .9 acid, 3.1 pH. Silver medal Orange County, Bronze at State Fair.

Do you control temperature in barrel fermentations?

"I use a 20 x 15 foot walk-in cooler that used to be an old flower box. The barrels are stacked 3 high, and it holds 50 of them. It takes a long time to cool, but when you get it down it stays there. I hold it at 50°F. Inside the barrel, the wine goes through a fermentation curve which may go up to 60°F. At end I let everything warm up to finish malo-lactic in the Chardonnay.

"The cold room is a lot of work. You have to carry all the barrels in by hand. They have to be empty, of course, to move them around. It takes days for two of us to set it up. Then I have to fool with it several days a week for about a month. We put 50 gallons in each 60-gal barrel, but some are always more active than others. It can get messy because there is no drain in the box.

"Barrel fermentation gives middle body and soft wood tannins. I call it a cheesecake flavor in the middle of Chardonnay. Stainless fermentations followed by aging in oak gives more of a hard tannin which is bitter and astringent. The cold room permits barrel ferment without losing fruitiness. At the same time you get a nice temperature curve. Optimum complexity seems to develop at age three; not at age one."

I always add yeast nutrient because Chardonnay tends to be deficient. It is the only grape that is that way. I don't think residual sugar in Chardonnay is a conscious decision by most winemakers. In many cases they just failed to get it to go dry."

John Daumé

BM

DION

Denis Kelly is one of the most engaging wine educators in America. He tells great stories (in the Irish tradition), and communicates his enthusiasm visually by rubbing his hands together rapidly in a conspiratorial fashion. In 1972 Denis was teaching a course in the East Bay suburb of Moraga. All of his students enjoyed the class, but two of them got more out of it than the others.

Joy and Jerry Dion (a French-Canadian name pronounced "dee OWN") were just average folks. "We drank wine recreationally," Joy says, "but really didn't have many friends who did." Jerry had been a Navy pilot. He got out of the service in 1963 and enrolled at U.C. Berkeley. The student politics of the time didn't suit him very well. "I was unhappy," he says. "I didn't want to be there." He left school to take a pilot's job with Pan American Airlines and continued flying in the Naval Reserve. He met and married Joy, who was a Navy nurse at Alameda Naval Air Station, in 1964. After Kelly's class in 1972, the Dion's tried a home winemaking course from Wine and the People to learn more technical information. Meanwhile, Jerry's job was putting him in Germany, Italy and France on a regular basis. He found that his emerging wine knowledge opened doors and introduced him to a great deal of history. He was starting to really like it. When a couple of his amateur wines won medals at a competition in London, he was hooked.

On a lark in 1976, the Dion's took a ride to investigate a piece of property advertised for sale in Sonoma Valley. They didn't like the piece being offered, but did take a shine to another parcel the owner thought he might like to keep for himself. This 7 acre hillside had been a vineyard at one time. In 1976 it was just raw land. They bought it and had their Chardonnay vineyard planted by Warren Dutton in 1978. "I thought I knew all the answers," says Jerry. "Turns out I didn't even know the questions. Things like layout, roads and terracing are very subjective." They had luckily found water right away and drilled a successful well in the middle of the '76/'77 drought. "However," explains Jerry, "we had to water everyone of those 3,500 vines by hand."

They built their house on the property in 1980. It includes a 3,200 sq. ft. cellar with a 10 foot ceiling. The cellar is cut into the hill and insulated to R-22 in order to maintain temperature control. Jerry wasn't sure, but he thought he might want to put a small family winery in that space some day. His first crop in 1981 was sold to Kenwood. Same with '82. The '83 through '85 crops went to Adler Fels. Then in 1986 Jerry was piloting a trip from San Francisco to New York. His co-pilot that day was Bob Ellis, owner of Mark West Vineyards near Healdsburg. Jerry started gripping about the meagre return from selling his grapes, and Ellis asked him why he didn't make the wine himself. A light went off (figuratively) and Jerry had the '86 crop custom crushed under his direction at Ellis's winery. When Joy and Jerry got together with Denis Kelly to try the wine, they decided they had a winner. So they bottled it under their own label and began planning for a winery of their own in the Dion's cellar.

"Right now flying pays for my avocation," Jerry says. "Some day I'll be able to switch those roles." One of the Dion's sons is a sophomore studying Enology at U.C. Davis and working summers at Mark West Vineyard. The other is a Philosophy major at Santa Clara. "He's not very interested in the bucolic life at this point," smiles Jerry, "but trying to turn a Philosophy degree into a job may open his mind."

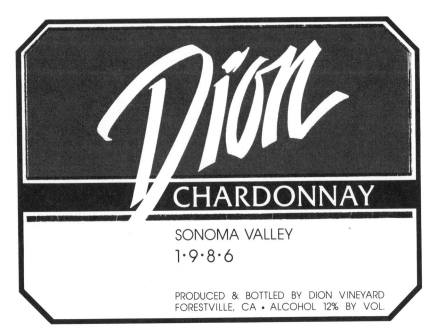

Dion
CHARDONNAY

SONOMA VALLEY
1·9·8·6

PRODUCED & BOTTLED BY DION VINEYARD
FORESTVILLE, CA • ALCOHOL 12% BY VOL.

1986 Chardonnay	1,830 cases
Estate	750 ml

Picked first week of Sept at 22°Brix. Overnight skin soak, 50 ppm SO₂ at crusher. 30% barrel frmtd with Pasteur White yeast. No m-l. Aged in Allier oak. Sterile filtered, then btld at 12% alc, .85 acid, 3.3 pH.

What have you learned about your vyd since '78?

"The weather is cooler than you might expect. We get a Venturi effect around the north face of Sonoma Mountain. That is when the speed of the air flow increases as you close down the aperture. You can see it when the fog rolls in past Petaluma. We are right in the middle of Region 2 at about 2,500 degree days. We rarely have frost because of the air drainage down the hill, although occasionally the grapes at the bottom may get nipped.

"Getting uniform ripeness in the grapes is an issue as well because we are on a steep hill. There may be as much as 4°Brix difference from the top of the hill to the bottom. The top is 525 feet elevation and the bottom is 400 feet. So we pick sequentially from the top down to get the grapes at the same point. Pruning technique can help somewhat. We have 3 guys who come in to prune for us every year. It takes them 20-30 days.

"Birds are an issue for us. Linnets can cause a lot of damage and there seem to be several colonies of them nearby. There is a huge flock of starlings that live up near Windsor that come down here in October, but we've already picked by then. Actually we like the starlings because they clean up the grape remnants that may still be on the vines. I've never had much of an insect problem. I think I've got a lizard under every vine, and that may explain the lack of insects."

Jerry Dion

RB

DONATONI WINERY

The roar you hear when talking wine with Hank Donatoni is most likely a 747 landing across the street at LAX. Making wine next to an airport is not so strange for the Donatonis, since Hank and his wife Judy have nearly 50 years between them flying for United Airlines. Hank was born and raised in Santa Monica, entered the Navy as an aviation cadet in 1952, and became a pilot for United upon leaving the service in 1960. Judy joined the airline as a stewardess one year later.

Hank's winemaking memories go back to childhood. His interest was rekindled when he and Judy bought a house in Topanga Canyon in 1968 which included a half acre of Zinfandel vines. He found Philip Wagner's book on winemaking and began his career with 12 gallons of Estate Red. The next year he pruned the vines and

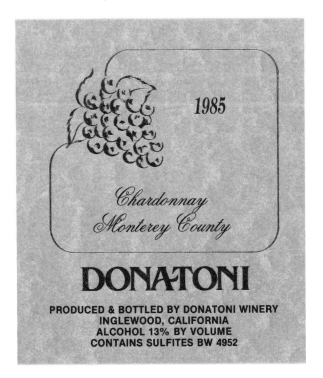

**PRODUCED & BOTTLED BY DONATONI WINERY
INGLEWOOD, CALIFORNIA
ALCOHOL 13% BY VOLUME
CONTAINS SULFITES BW 4952**

1985
*Chardonnay
Monterey County*

DONATONI

stepped up production with a ton of Zinfandel. As home winemakers in Los Angeles inevitably do, Hank found his way to the Cellarmaster's Club and started entering competitions. In 1979 he bonded space in a small industrial park near the airport and opened a winery. Hank Donatoni has an air of unflapable good humor about him and an endless inventory of jokes. His enjoyment in retelling stories with a group of visitors, and his understated delivery, make him one of the most congenial hosts in the wine business. "We don't have an elegant estate to show off," he says, "but we don't have any advertising expense either. Our prices can be lower. It's interesting how prestigious restaurants in Los Angeles agonize over our wine being priced too low compared to other items on their wine list."

Most of Hank's grapes come from Paso Robles. Cabernet is picked in the late afternoon or evening and trucked to the winery in half-ton bins at 2 a.m. so it arrives cool. Donatoni has maintained a definite Cabernet contract with Nepenthe Vineyard since his home winemaking days in 1968. The price is set 5 months after harvest when average prices paid for Cabernet in the North Coast regions of Napa And Sonoma are published by the California Crop and Livestock Reporting Service. The price is high because the grower limits production to around 2 tons/acre, but Hank likes that concentrated flavor. "Plus," he says, "Jensen always delivers on time and in great condition." The whole relationship is conducted with a handshake.

Donatoni made an adroit decision to stay out of the Chardonnay market in '87 and '88. Grape prices were rising so rapidly that he didn't think he could make the wine and sell it for the $10 price point he thinks is fair. Given the volatile price of Chardonnay grapes, Hank would like to

build up his inventory when grape prices are down and he can pick top quality. Then he can reduce his inventory and stay aloof from the grape market when prices are crazy. "I don't know how well this strategy is going to work," he reports. "I'm real low on Chardonnay and the grape market hasn't turned around because '87 and '88 were such small crops. Ventana Vineyards is getting $2,000/ton for Chardonnay this year. That translates to $20/bottle. I've got to look for a Chardonnay contract for '89 and I don't see any evidence that new plantings are going to bring the price down by then."

Hank's winery is a 2,200 sq. ft. insulated building, which is certainly adequate for Donatoni's 1,400 case production each year. They started in one quarter that much space and had to set everything up in the parking lot whenever they wanted to crush or press. They have air-conditioning, but rarely have to use it because of their proximity to the ocean. He has no plans to increase production or to switch from his normal 60/40% mix of Cabernet and Chardonnay. Hank says, "Cabernet sales have always been relatively stable. The mid-'80s bust occurred in reds like Zinfandel and Pinot Noir. As soon as the weather turns cold and restaurants start lighting their fireplaces, Cabernet sales go up." Donatoni uses a hydraulic basket press and an Italian stemmer/crusher with a must pump. He gets used barrels for his Cabernet from Ch. Lafite in France. They bottle the Chardonnay themselves with a six-spout filler, but have the Cabernet bottled by one of the mobile bottling lines. Hank does most of the analysis and lab work...and he tells ALL the stewardess jokes.

1985 Chardonnay   **500 cases**
Arroyo Seco Vyd   **750 ml**

Picked 10 Sept from Salinas Vly vyd at 23°Brix, .96 acid, 3.1 pH. No SO₂ at crusher, 24 hr skin soak, no M-L, racked off lees. 6 mos in Limosin barrels with light toast, btld Sept '86 at 12.9 alc, .91 acid.

1984 Chardonnay   **500 cases**
Bien Nacido Vyds   **750 ml**

Large vyd owned by Bob Miller just east of the town of Santa Maria in northern Santa Barbara County. Flat terrain with rich, sandy, deep soil. 3.5 t/a harvested at 22.9°Brix, .79 acid, 3.4 pH. Crushed at Corbett Canyon Winery. 40 ppm SO₂ at crusher, 12 hrs skin soak, 3 wk frmt at 48°F in stnls with Chanson yeast. Transferred at 10°Brix to 60 gal oak barrels for 10 days frmt at 75°F. M-L completed in the spring. Aged 50% in new Seguin-Moreau barrels with medium toast and 50% in 1-yr-old Demptos barrels with light toast. Fined with bentonite and gelatin prior to btlg July '85 at 12.9 alc, .89 acid, 3.15 pH.

1982 Cabernet Sauvignon   **850 cases**
Nepenthe Vyd   **750 ml**

Vyds on east facing slope near San Miguel. 12-yr-old vines on their own roots in sandy soil with no irrigation. Picked 15 Sept at 24.3°Brix. Frmtd with Montrachet yeast 10 days on skins. Pumped over, M-L completed by Xmas. Aged in Demptos Limosin barrels obtained 2 yrs old from Ch. Lafite. Gelatin fined, btld March '85 at 13.4 alc, .75 acid.

What's happening to your costs?

"Equipment is about the same, but the price of new French barrels has gone from $215 to $415. That makes it very hard to stay under $10/btl. I suspect a lot of American oak barrels are being used. French coopered American oak is becoming popular. So are inner staves and shaved barrels. Chips and saw dust give a different flavor, but I bet we'll see more of them too. You really have to ask $16/btl to justify investing in a new barrel these days.

"Then there is the price of grapes. The total wine crop was up in '88 because of production from the Central Valley; they're getting 13-14 tons/acre to supply the White Zin market. I've heard that 50% more 'Zinfandel' was crushed than was grown. BATF sent a notice around last year saying we couldn't refuse an inspection during crush any longer. But tonnage at Nepenthe Vineyard, where I get my Cabernet, was down 20%. They thought they were going to have a good crop when they counted the clusters, but the weight never showed up in the bunches. It took the pickers about 50% longer to harvest those small bunches too.

"Chardonnay has gone from $500/ton in '85 to over $1,500/ton. I didn't think we would ever see $2,000/ton because I figured growers would get out their chainsaws (for grafting) before then and supplies would increase. Unfortunately, tonnage was off in both '87 and '88. Now, even junky little bars are getting $3.75 for a small glass of mediocre Chardonnay.

"I've been thinking about making a Sauvignon Blanc. I have tank space. It is just so hard to figure out how to commit barrels at today's prices."

Hank Donatoni

BM

EVENSEN VINEYARDS

Richard and Sharon Evensen (pronounced EE-ven-sen) own 80 acres of duck hunting refuge between Gridley and Colusa in the Butte Sink. They have a seven bedroom clubhouse and usually take their black Labrador Retrievers up for a visit at least once a week during the late October to mid January hunting season. Other times they go up after frogs. Sharon has made painting a hobby for the last fifteen years and has done several works for donation to Ducks Unlimited, a national conservation group.

The Evensens live in Napa Valley right across the road from Robert Mondavi Winery. When they acquired the property in 1966 it was an old Italian-style vineyard with grapes like Portugese Blue and Early Burgundy. They sold to the Napa Co-op for many years, then decided to make a change in the mid '70s. "I liked a dry, spicy Gewürztraminer with wild duck," explains Richard. "Besides, the Gewürz harvest is always over before duck season starts."

Alsatian style Gewürztraminer is the speciality at Evensen Vineyards. Richard and Sharon appreciate the variety's rich, floral flavors so much that it is now the only grape they grow on their 8 acres. And the 700 cases of Gewürz they make annually is always bone-dry, in contrast to most popular California versions. The Evensen's audience is small, but sophisticated and evangelical. New converts show up every day. "We strive for perfume and spice that is clear and definite on the palate," says Richard. "We want plenty of aroma and character without the bitterness that often dominates the finish in dry styled wines. Residual sugar covers up this bitterness in a lot of Gewürztraminers, but sweetness ruins the wine's role with food. Since aroma and bitterness both come from the skins, we have to walk a tightrope in terms of skin soak. As the grapes ripen they also start to turn pink. Too much skin contact will color the wine."

The Evensens have a big advantage over other Gewürz makers. They live in their vineyard and make wine just a few feet from the house. In fact, their first wines were made in their 700 sq. ft. basement complete with head trauma from the six foot ceiling. They recently moved the winemaking operation to a new building in the backyard. It has 18 foot ceilings. They must wait for the optimum moment to pick their Gewürztraminer since there is only a short "window" when the smell is at it's peak. The Evensens recognize this moment by getting up in the morning to walk in the vineyard. It only takes two days to pick. The grapes are crushed quickly and kept cold in jacketed stainless steel tanks. "Our friends get mad if they're not asked to help bottle," Sharon says.

Both of the Evensens are wine country natives and Richard served 11 years on the California Highway Patrol. Matching Gewürztraminer with food is never far from their minds. "We like to give the wine a few years of bottle age," Sharon says. "When we release it, there isn't as much rose petal and melon aroma, but there's more complexity. It's perfect for oriental food, lightly curried BBQ chicken, Veal Scallopine and, of course, duck or holiday turkey." Sharon's most unique suggestion is Chili Verde. She sautes pork and makes a salsa from tomatillos, jalapeno and serano chiles, cumin, onion, garlic and cilantro. Then she adds Gewürz to the salsa. "The perfume and lingering finish add a new dimension," she concludes with a conspiratorial wink.

1986 Gewürztraminer	600 cases
Estate	750 ml

9-yr-old vines on St George rootstock in Bale loam soil of the vly flr. 8'x12' spacing, drip irrigation, cordon-pruned to 2 wires. 2 t/a picked early Sept at 22°Brix. 60 ppm SO_2 at the crusher, 12 hr skin soak, settled 2 days. Frmtd 40 days in closed stnls with Steinberg yeast at 50°F. Racked into stnls, bentonite fined, sterile filtered. Btld June '87 at 12.6 alc, .63 acid, 0.2% rs.

I understand you have a Stony Hill connection.

"My husband's best friend from school is Emil Chelini who lives in Sonoma. Emil's son Mike has been resident winemaker at Stony Hill for about ten years. Mike is devoted to Eleanor McCrea and doesn't move around like a lot of winemakers. He got his interest from his grandfather who made wine at home. Mike worked for Ric Forman at Sterling when he first started, and then got a great opportunity at Stony Hill.

"Mike really encouraged us in the beginning. We liked the Stony Hill Gewürztraminer and appreciated their dry style. He still comes to taste our wines and make suggestions. In '86 we bought 10 tons of Howell mountain grapes through Mike to make 560 cases of barrel fermented Chardonnay. I got my nose a little out of joint about taking on a second variety, but Dick was excited about the project and I've come around now. The grapes are from Bancroft Vineyard."

Sharon Evensen

Editor's Note: The owners of Bancroft Vineyard are descended from a giant of Western American history. Hubert Howe Bancroft established a bookstore in San Francisco in 1852. He went on to personally organize the most extraordinary documentation of how the West was settled. His work is now the foundation of Bancroft Library at U.C. Berkeley. Ironically, he received very shabby treatment at the end of his life. The politics of the situation were similar to the way Theodore Judah was cast aside after he singlehandedly conceived, designed and passed legislation to fund the transcontinental railroad.

JR

GARY FARRELL

Gary Farrell's wines have exploded onto the California scene since 1985 with a number of prestigious awards. The organization of his business is unique in that he owns neither winery nor vineyard property. He uses a Burgundian model of identifying select portions of a vineyard reflecting special regional character. His rise to prominence has paralleled consumers' recognition of the viticultural area Gary has chosen.

This area is located along the Russian River as it runs west of Healdsburg and out into the ocean at Jenner on the Sonoma coast. It is a rich and diverse viticultural district. The soils range from sandy river bottoms, through fertile alluvial loam on benches, up to steep hillsides. The climate is warm and sunny during the mid-day hours, but tempered by cool breezes in the evening and overnight fog which follows the river in from the coast and often hangs around until late morning all summer long. There is an extensive history of grape growing in the area dating back to the original colony of Italian and Swiss immigrants at nearby Asti. It is beautiful country which has long been prized as a tourist destination even though its viticultural splendors were something of an afterthought.

Gary Farrell grew up in Pasadena and feels that his migration to Sonoma County should be self explanatory. He took an undergraduate degree in Political Science from Sonoma State and then went to work at a series of western Sonoma wineries including that of wine consultant Robert Stemmler. In 1978 Gary began working at Davis Bynum Winery on Westside Road overlooking the Russian River. He learned from the excellent palates of Davis and his son, Hampton Bynum, and also got to perform the more laborious tasks of the winery. His legacy from this period is a deep respect for particular vineyards in the area, excellent grower relations and a sterling reputation for making Pinot Noir.

Today Gary still works at Davis Bynum, but he has consulting relationships with several other wineries. He makes about 2,500 cases each year for his own label. Technically the wine is made for him on contract at different wineries. Given the fact that he is simultaneously employed by these wineries as a consultant, Gary's authorship of the product is not some flight of press agent imagination. Gary owns all of the barrels that his wine goes through. He says he does not want to own vineyards and cites Pinot Noir as an example of his reasoning. "About 2/3 of the grapes I've been using come from the Howard Allen Vineyard. It has a northeast exposure and fairly rocky soil. I pick at about 23°Brix and always get good acidity. These grapes provide lots of body and an intense fruit to the nose. The other 1/3 has come from Rochioli Vineyard which is in loam near the river. Those grapes are usually harvested at 22.5°Brix and provide more of an earthy complexity to the blend. Tom Rochioli farms both vineyards and I think his viticultural practices are excellent."

For his own wines, Gary is partial to grapes from the coolest sections of the Russian River. He is always seeking out slow ripening vineyards even though they run the risk of catching a late season rain storm. "I'm fascinated by the Burgundian varietals," he says, "and this is a perfect place to work with them."

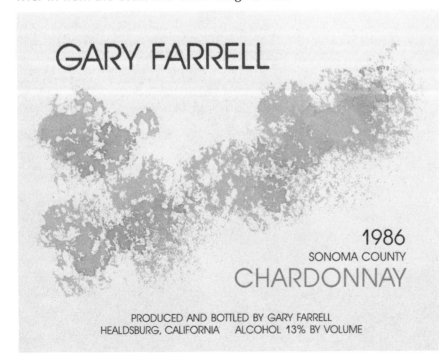

GARY FARRELL

1986
SONOMA COUNTY
CHARDONNAY

PRODUCED AND BOTTLED BY GARY FARRELL
HEALDSBURG, CALIFORNIA   ALCOHOL 13% BY VOLUME

1986 Pinot Noir   300 cases
Howard Allen Vyd   750 ml

Vyd next door to Rochioli farmed by Tom Rochioli. Cool growing season. No SO$_2$ at the crusher, 60-75% whole berries but no stems. Frmtd in 500 gal open stnls at 85-90°F with Pasteur Champagne yeast. Punched down 4x/day, pressed at dryness. On lees in oak uprights until M-L completed.

1987 Sauvignon Blanc   650 cases
Laurel Grande Vyd   750 ml

Vyd on Westside Rd 5 miles west of Healdsburg. Picked late Sept at 22.7°Brix, .93 acid, 3.18 pH. Btld Mar '88, Gold medal LA Fair, herbaceous style.

1987 Chardonnay   300 cases
Aquarius Vyd   750 ml

Grapes from western Sonoma County along Russian River. No SO$_2$ at crusher, 48 hrs settle at 45°F. Frmt started in stnls with Epernay 2 yeast, transferred cold to barrels at 19°Brix. 30% new barrels, on lees until Feb, no m-l. Btld in June. Gold medal LA Fair. Also '87 Chardonnay from Hafner Vyd in Alexander Vly vinted identically.

Are you making a move into Chardonnay?

"Sauvignon Blanc, Zinfandel and Cabernet are relatively easy to make if you get good grapes. Chardonnay is a challenge. It involves a lot more variables. Plus, there isn't much financial margin in Sauvignon Blanc.

"I've had my eye on the Chardonnay grapes from Aquarius Ranch since I began using them as a portion of much larger blends in my consulting business over the last 12 years. The owner, Will McIlroy, is a good friend of mine. DeLoach uses Will's grapes, and look at the success Cecil has had. I think Aquarius is one of the coolest pockets along the Russian River. It is in a little canyon running away from the river surrounded on the south and west by hills. The fog gets stuck there and burns off later than in other places. Will picks 2-3 weeks later than other vineyards in the county. There are 3 blocks to the vineyard. The oldest vines are next to the river, but I think the middle block has produced the best fruit. It is planted on AxR1 and grafted to the UC 108 Chardonnay clone. Everything is cropped to about 2 tons/acre.

"As an educational exercise in '87, I wanted to compare the wine from Aquarius to one made exactly the same way from grapes grown in a warmer area. I'd had good experience with Hafner grapes, so I tried them. The result was definitely a more lush, buttery style. In '89 I think I'll try the same experiment with Chardonnay from the Howard Allen Vyd as a mid-point toward the Aquarius which was my favorite of the two '87 versions."

Gary Farrell

RG

35

FENESTRA WINERY

Fenestra owner and winemaker Lanny Replogle is a busy man, especially at harvest time. He has been a Chemistry professor at San Jose State University since 1960. He teaches a full load during the Spring semester, but cuts back to 3/4 time each Fall to handle the crush. Lanny's wife Fran also works full time at Fenestra managing sales and publicity for the winery. Lanny grew up in Hayward and attended UC Berkeley. Wine wasn't very popular in his home, since his mother was allergic to yeast and yeast products. Lanny and Fran met at the University of Washington while he was getting his doctorate and she was studying for a BS in microbiology. Fran's father was a Geography professor at the University who became involved with Associated Vintners, one of the early wineries in the Seattle area.

After moving to San Jose, the Replogles leased two vineyards to get a supply of good wine grapes for themselves and a circle of winemaking friends. The group became organized as P.H.E.W., the Peninsula Home Enologists Workshop and many professional winemakers emerged from its ranks over the years including Nat Sherrill (Sherrill Vineyards), Tom Kruse (Tom Kruse Winery), Lee Sobon (Shenandoah Valley Vineyards) and Ben Zeitman (Amador Foothill Winery). Fran says that leasing the two vineyards was a necessity back then, because "growers hated home winemakers who were always so fussy about such small quantities."

In 1976 Fran and Lanny leased part of the old Ruby Hill Winery run by Stony Ridge and launched Fenestra. In 1980 Stony Ridge expanded production and the Replogles had to look for another site in the Livermore Valley. This was a lucky move for Fenestra, because two years later ComputerLand bought the Ruby Hill property from Southern Pacific and ended all winery operations. Fenestra settled in one of the valley's "ghost wineries," founded in 1889 by George True near Vallecitos Road. The winery had sealed its tanks during Prohibition, but continued to sell to Livermore residents "who had a doctor's prescription." The site was owned by Stephano Forni until the early 1960's and produced wines under the Pacific Coast and Golden Rule labels. Originally 750 acres, the property is currently owned by the Catholic Church, which uses most of it as a farming project for Laotian refugees. Fenestra leases the partially restored 8,000 sq. ft. winery building. They have three 1,500 gallon jacketed stainless steel tanks and use mobile bottling lines.

When you first meet him, Lanny Replogle appears to be the type of individual given to careful planning. He is a tall, thoughtful man. Sort of your basic Chemistry professor. Close scrutiny, however, will uncover a barely perceptible bounce creeping into his gait each September. Fenestra would like to be a 2,400 case, 4 varietal winery. Fran knows her problem is how to restrain her husband when growers with top quality vineyards get him on the phone during harvest. Lanny's mind unconsciously slips into gear and processes the fruit into wine before he's able to hang up. "The man's easy," Fran sighs shaking her head in resignation. "He just can't say no to good grapes. We've got 3,500 cases in 10 varieties fermenting away down there right now. "Plan" is a four letter word at our house." Lanny won't admit to these indiscretions, but an involuntary smile reveals his fond regard of the excitement at crush.

FENESTRA

1987

SANTA CLARA COUNTY

WHITE RIESLING

PRODUCED & BOTTLED BY
FENESTRA WINERY, LIVERMORE, CA
ALC. BY VOL. 10%   CONTAINS SULFITES

1984 Cabernet Sauvignon	580 cases
Smith & Hook Vyd	750 ml

1,300 ft vyd on westside bench above Salinas Vly just north of Soledad. 15-yr-old vines picked 9 Oct at 23.2°Brix, .62 acid. 8 days on skins at 81°F with Pasteur Champagne yeast in a open half ton fermentors. Settled 1 wk then aged in 52 gal American oak. Egg white fining, pad filter. Btld April '87 at 13.6 alc, .7 acid. Two puffs Connoisseur's Guide.

1986 Chardonnay	360 cases
La Riena Vyd	750 ml

Picked at 23°Brix, 1.08 acid, 3.5 pH from grapes in the Salinas Vly at 300 ft elevation on a westside bench opposite Gonzales. 14 yr old vines. Frmtd in stnls at 55°F with Pasteur Champagne yeast, then transferred to 60 gal French oak at 12°Brix. No M-L. Sterile filtration. Btld Nov '87 at 13.6 alc, .9 acid.

1984 Merlot	400 cases
Narsai David Vyd, Napa	750 ml

Are you converting to lees contact?

"I did an experiment with my '86 Chardonnay. Half was racked off the lees as soon as the barrel fermentation finished. The other half stayed on the lees 8 months with the lees stirred up once per week. I had a group taste both portions out of the barrel and got a pretty clear concensus of opinion. The portion which had remained on the lees was smoother, more easily drinkable and it had richer flavors.

"Your biggest worry with lees contact is that H_2S will develop. When the wines finish fermentation, they are in a highly reduced state. Due to the yeast enzyme systems, and the way the wine has been loaded with CO_2 for so long, no oxygen is available. If elemental sulphur were in the wine from the grapes, it could be reduced to H_2S quickly. Stirring the lees may introduce oxygen and help prevent off-odors. If you recognize off-odors quickly enough in the barrel, aeration will usually eliminate them. Copper sulphate is available if a winemaker lets H_2S problems go on too long.

"As I've moved toward lees contact, I've moved away from skin soak. Although some skin soak occurs by default when you have crushed grapes waiting for the previous press load to be completed. Dave Ramey at Matanzas Creek has influenced me to think that skin soak may result in tannin which makes the wine bitter and astringent. Eliminating skin soak also reduces the risk of getting elemental sulphur into the wine."

Lanny Replogle

THOMAS FOGARTY WINERY

If you thumb through a surgical supply catalogue, you'll understand why Dr. Thomas Fogarty is eminent in his field. You will find several pages devoted to his inventions. He went to school in Cincinnati and trained in Oregon before coming to Stanford in the late 1960's to work with Dr. Norman Shumway pioneering heart transplants. He also had the foresight in 1968 to purchase 300 acres running from the ridge of the Santa Cruz Mountains down into the Portola Valley.

In 1980, Fogarty planted 14 acres of Chardonnay and half an acre of Pinot Noir at the top of the property about 2,000 feet elevation. The vineyard has one to six feet of topsoil, with several diverse types. Vines are protected from frost by the ocean and get a cool breeze every afternoon. Winter comes late to this location, and winter rains may vary from 30 to 100 inches. Separate five-acre plots will be planted to Chardonnay and Pinot Noir over the next six to ten years, for a total of between 50 and 60 acres of grapes. The plots will be scattered around the property. Vines will come into production steadily and allow for gradual replacement in the middle of the next century.

Winemaker Michael Martella expects the Estate vineyards to be at their best in warm years and foresees a lot of variation year to year. For instance, 1984 and 1985 produced little fog cover, and the grapes ripened in September. But in 1983 they picked their first Chardonnay on November 3rd. Martella says, "the grapes are on the vine for a long time, they come in with sugars over 23°Brix and the acids are double what you find elsewhere. It has something to do with potassium in the soil. We get very reasonable pH, combined with very high acid. Yield is the only factor that troubles me. For the last three years, we have gotten less than a ton per acre because of freak fogs that inhibit pollination. It will be sunny for months, then foggy for two weeks during flowering, then sunny again. We end up with very scraggly clusters." The goal in Fogarty Chardonnay is full flavor. They try to accentuate fruit and balance it with an ample amount of oak. They always put the Estate Chardonnay through malo-lactic fermentation. Even so the acid rarely drops below .9%.

Fogarty got Pinot Noir from the Carneros region while waiting for their own vineyards to mature. Martella liked the cherry fruitiness of Carneros grapes, but says, "if they're too ripe, they get prune-like flavors." He has taken small crops from a half acre on the Fogarty property since '83, but none has been released commercially yet. He says the Fogarty Pinot Noir is a little earthier than the Carneros with more of a spicy quality."

Fogarty's winery sits on top of the ridgecrest, with a commanding view of San Francisco Bay. A short stroll west provides an excellent view of the Pacific as well. Their international selection of equipment includes a French Demoissey crusher-stemmer, a Swiss Bucher tank press, a German Schenk filter and a 3-inch must pump a l'Italiano. They do their own lab work. Fogarty has two formally trained winemakers. Michael Martella graduated from Fresno State in 1971 and has been with Fogarty since the beginning of the wine operation. He is the intuitive one with the abstract art collection. Jim Varner is a Davis grad with experience at Krug and Rutherford Hill. He is the lab man. For a premier heart surgeon, Dr. Fogarty is surprisingly active in the daily affairs of the winery. He lives on the property and even takes part in things like pruning. Before starting the winery, he had been a home winemaker for many years and he has an extensive wine collection.

Then there is the story about Dr. Fogarty and his friend Tennessee Ernie Ford. They introduced the first Fogarty Chardonnay at an elegant society party in a prestigious French restaurant, paired with catfish.

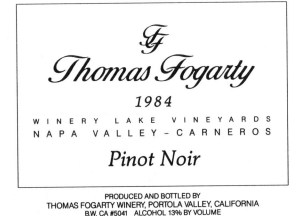

THomas Fogarty

1984

WINERY LAKE VINEYARDS
NAPA VALLEY - CARNEROS

Pinot Noir

PRODUCED AND BOTTLED BY
THOMAS FOGARTY WINERY, PORTOLA VALLEY, CALIFORNIA
B.W. CA #5041   ALCOHOL 13% BY VOLUME

1984 Pinot Noir   **1042 cases**
Winery Lake Vyd   **750 ml**

Picked 7 Sept on hillside reserved for Fogarty in this well known vyd in Napa's Carneros region at 22°Brix. No whole berries, 30 ppm SO_2 at crusher. Frmtd in 500 gal open top stnls 5-6 days at 85-90°F with Montrachet yeast. Punched down 4x/day. Settled 1 mo in stnls, aged 50% new Francois Freres 60 gal Troncais barrels with medium toast. On fine lees 14 mos. Btld Feb '86 at 13 alc, .7 acid, 3.3 pH.

1986 Chardonnay   **800 cases**
Ventana   **750 ml**

Picked in Ventana Vyd near Soledad in Salinas Vly on 10 Oct at 23.3°Brix. 30 ppm SO_2 at crusher, no skin soak, settled overnight and frmt started in stnls with Prise de Mousse yeast. Racked into 60 gal French oak barrels at 15°Brix. 6 mos on fine lees, 33% new wood. No M-L. Bentonite fining, sterile filter, btld June '87 at 13 alc, .7 acid, 3.31 pH. Also 800 cases of '86 Carneros.

1986 Chardonnay   **1,213 cases**
Santa Cruz Mtns   **750 ml**

Picked 27 Sept at 23.5°Brix, 1.4 acid. Made as above, but with M-L induced during alc frmt and 9 mos on fine lees. Btld Aug '87 at 13.7 alc, .95 acid, 3.35 pH.

1985 Chardonnay   **1,100 cases**
Edna Valley   **750 ml**

Are you concentrating on restaurant sales?

"Not exclusively, but we recognize their importance just like all wineries do. We're concentrating on sales within 100 miles of the winery. We would like to be thought of as the winery in the Peninsula's backyard in contrast to such a large number of places in Napa and Sonoma. We also think we can treat local accounts in a classier way. 6 to 12 times a year we try to bring the wait staff from restaurant accounts to the winery. Dr. Fogarty attends and we serve a meal. We start with available wines, then do upcoming releases. Finally, we open some older vintages to show them how the wines develop.

"We also have two-month selling contests in bigger restaurants that use a wine-by-the-glass program. The prize is usually a weekend at a house here on the winery property. Some restaurants will do 50-100 cases during the contest. An individual waitperson might win by averaging 2 bottles a night over the two-month period. Normally wine-by-the-glass programs are tough for us to get into because high end wines end up priced at $4-5/glass. Nevertheless, I'd estimate there are 2 or 3 times as many by-the-glass programs around today as there were 5 years ago.

"Beverage managers have become much more knowledgeable in that same period. They know more about wine, but they are more confused because the number of wineries has grown enormously. The other thing that strikes me is the rapid increase of women in these various sales positions. Whatever bias may have held them back before must be starting to crumble."

George Burtness

Dr. Thomas Fogarty   KF

CL

FREY VINEYARDS

Imagine a scene out of the movie *Deliverance*. Everybody is rawboned and barefoot. That is the first impression you get at Frey (pronounced fry) Vineyards. Then the friendliness and self-sufficiency become clear. "We're glad you came," they say. "Visitors are a treat, because we don't have television." By the time you are ready to leave, you will have discovered that the Frey clan is exceptionally well educated, with a preference for learning because the subject is fascinating rather than for some practical advantage.

Paul Frey was originally a minister, but quit in disagreement with the church over military service in World War II. He went on to become a psychiatrist. His wife Marguerite is an obstetrician, which seems appropriate since they have twelve children. Six of these kids live on the ranch, three with families of their own.

Their 100-acre property was purchased in 1961.

The family began planting Cabernet grapes in 1966. Their motivation was to raise the land value and discourage proposals for a local dam site. The Freys soon discovered that their ranch had viticultural advantages. It is at 1,000 feet elevation on a high bench at the northern tip of the Russian River watershed. The soil is not deep, but it is well drained with a sandy composition due to an adjacent stream bed. Many producing springs on the property give it an abundant water supply even in drought years. Redwood trees mark the eastern boundary of the coastal fog which comes through the mountains at a gap near Willits. 10 acres are planted to Cabernet which has some virus. Five acres that were originally Grey Riesling have also been budded over to Cabernet, and in 1979 eight acres of Sauvignon Blanc were planted. Recently the Freys bought the 20-year-old Easterbrook Cabernet vineyard next door. They have also planted 5 acres of Chardonnay. Their friend Ernie Butow has had such success with his 3 acres of Syrah that he recently budded 13 more acres to that variety.

Jonathan, the oldest Frey child, attended UC Santa Cruz. In 1978 he met winemaker Keith Hohfeldt through a friend from school. Keith made a Cabernet from Frey Vineyard grapes for Sunrise Winery that received tremendous critical acclaim, although a miniscule amount was all that was produced. Jonathan decided to enter the wine business. He and his brother Matthew built a

6,000 sq. ft. winery out of wood salvaged from the old Garret Winery in Ukiah. They welded their own stainless steel tanks and achieved temperature control by wrapping them with 1" irrigation tube. They bought used barrels which they scraped and retoasted themselves. Everything at the winery seems rough hewn and home-made and it all fits together beautifully. The main house has a twenty foot long hand-made dinner table that seems to symbolize the Frey's solidity and sense of community.

After college, Jonathan apprenticed himself to British organic horticulturalist Allan Chadwick. This early training in organic gardening led to the Freys' decision to use only certified organically grown grapes and no SO_2 in winemaking. Half the Frey's production is sold in health food stores. "Fermentation cures a lot of ills in a wine that may have come from negligent handling of the grapes. We think we can be extra careful at our size and avoid the need to add SO_2 as an anti-oxidant."

The winery operation doubled in size each year for six years to reach its present capacity of 6,000 cases per year. Jonathan says that his parents were not overly pleased when he took out the first loan in the history of the property to finance this expansion. The winery has now stabilized in size, however, and the debt has been paid off. For grape processing they use a Howard Rotapress and an Italian Stemmer-crusher "which takes only one lug box at a time." They have the capacity to sterile filter and do their own bottling with a semi-automatic line and liberal use of family power. "Things here look rustic," Jonathan explains patiently, "but we are not nostalgic for a return to the past. I'd happily accept a high-tech image. We want to employ new ideas while getting benefit from that historic wisdom which can usually be seen most clearly in hindsight."

Frey

1984

MENDOCINO

CABERNET SAUVIGNON

Uncle Bob's Vineyard

GROWN, PRODUCED & BOTTLED BY FREY VINEYARDS
REDWOOD VALLEY, CALIFORNIA, U.S.A. BW CA 4979 ALC 11.8% BY VOL
CONTAINS NATURALLLY OCCURRING SULFITES
NO SULFITES ADDED

This is a soft, delicate wine grown in a small vineyard in the Mendocino foothills. 188 cases produced. All Frey natural wines are made using 100% ORGANICALLY GROWN GRAPES (in accordance with sec. 26569.11 of the California Health & Safety Code) • Member, CA Certified Organic Farms • Harvest October 10 • Naturally processed wine with no preservatives • Store in a cool place

1984 Cabernet Sauvignon	900 cases
Estate Vyd	750 ml

Dry farmed, 17 yr old vines, picked at 5 Oct 22.5°Brix, no SO₂ at any time during production. No acid adjustment. Frmtd with Pasteur Red to 80°F, on skins 7 days. Aged 18 mos in American oak. Btld May '86 at 11.7 alc, .65 acid. Also '84 Cabernet Sauvignon from Easterbrook plot next door.

1986 Syrah	500 cases
Butow Vyd	750 ml

7 yr old, irrigated vines east of the Russian River in Redwood Valley on well drained bench of alluvial gravel. Picked 30 Sept at 23°Brix. Frmtd with Pasteur Red yeast 4 days, racked off lees. Aged 18 mos in French oak. 65 filter, btld May '87 at 12 alc, .75 acid, no SO₂.

1986 Zinfandel 1,400	cases
	750 ml

Blend from 3 Redwood Valley vyds on the benchland age 6-25 yrs. Picked 10 Sept. Frmtd with Pasteur Red yeast, on skins 5 days. Half American and half French oak. Btld May '88 at 13 alc, .75 acid, no SO₂.

What is "long pruning?"

"A lot of the old dry-farmed vineyards up here don't have any frost protection. So we prune vines in January, but leave an extra foot of wood on each cane. That first pruning takes a lot of time because you have to judge which bud sites will fruit best and how much crop the vine can carry. I figure between 40 and 100 snips at each vine when pruning initially. At the end of March we hustle through the vineyard cutting off that extra foot of wood on each cane. It takes about a tenth as long because all the cuts are obvious and there are only about 10 snips at each vine. The result is a delayed bud break of about 3 weeks.

"Long pruned vines also flower 3 weeks late. In '88 that made a big difference because there was such a 'shatter' problem caused by weird weather at the normal flowering time. The Easterbrook Cabernet is in a little cold pocket. In '85 its normal 20 tons went down to 5 tons because of frost damage. So we long pruned it in '88. It produced a real heavy crop, while our Estate vineyard right next door had the crop cut in half by shatter. Long pruning delays harvest as well, so you can employ it to spread out the crush season and make more efficient use of your equipment.

"Pruning takes some intuition. You have to recall how each vine did during the previous season and study the size of the canes. You prune for fruit or wood. Leaving lots of buds will give you lots of fruit and very little foliage. Few buds mean lots of wood and leaves, but a small crop. It's not a bad idea to alternate back and forth. And the pruner must do this; grapes are not like nut trees which have evolved to fruit irregularly as a reproductive defense against animal predators (i.e., squirrels eating all the

nuts). Wood growth produces healthier vines. Slightly heavy crops will stress the vines, but produce less juicy berries and make better wine. In young vineyards it is best to err on the side of wood growth and root development. Older vines can draw on resources in the root system and produce more even crop sizes every year."

Jonathan Frey

JR

FRICK WINERY

The bold brush strokes of Frick Winery's handsome wrap-around label bring to mind Japanese calligraphy with Zen monks writing haiku in mountain retreats. The connection with mountains, art and the Orient is not too far off the mark. Bill Frick and artist/wife Judith collaborated with Dave Bhang to design the label. The Fricks also began their winemaking operations in the Santa Cruz Mountains. They currently own an 8 acre vineyard of 40-year-old vines in the hills which separate Dry Creek Valley from upper Alexander Valley.

Bill grew up in the orange groves of Southern California, and Judith is a third generation San Franciscan whose grandfather made wine in the basement. In the early '70s they were living in Los Angeles and commuting up Hwy 5 looking for winemaking property in Northern California. By 1975 they had moved to Bonny Doon and begun making wine in an 800 sq. ft. building on property that had formerly housed a gas station. From '79 through '87 they operated out of 2,100 sq. ft. in downtown Santa Cruz, making 3,500 cases a year.

Throughout this period Bill and Judith had always wanted a vineyard of their own. In 1988 their two children had gone away to college and

the timing looked right. Price, however, played a role in where they ended up. Napa Valley was prohibitively expensive. Bare land in Santa Cruz cost as much as an established vineyard with a house in northern Sonoma County. They already owned a small office/apartment in San Francisco, so they viewed a parcel several miles north of Pedroncelli as relaxing rather than remote. They knew that Zinfandels from the area could be outstanding and began to wonder how other hearty varieties might do. The move disrupted their winery considerably. Very little wine was produced in '87 and '88. But the Fricks are quite excited about their acquisition and anxious to explore the artistic expressions it will inspire.

Judith, a painter and weaver, designed Frick's striking label for the 1979 vintage. "I wanted something different," she says, "and I didn't want it to be boring." Judith sees a parallel between the creativity of her art and winemaking and cooking. "All these forms of art are seasonally rhythmical," she points out. "Just as the light changes for a painter and fresh ingredients change for the cook, the grapes give you a particular perspective to start from. A lot of wineries use the same grapes, just as tapestry

weavers start with the same warp and weft in the fabric on their looms. Then creativity comes to the front." Judith's view of the importance of the creative impulse comes through when she says, "I don't use recipes when I cook, and I almost never sketch before I paint."

It would be inappropriate to call the Fricks present location "their **new** place." One of its primary attractions for them was that it came with generations of effort already in place. Luigi Muzzini's parents had homesteaded the property when they arrived in the U.S. from Tuscany. The soil is very rocky with gravel, sand and rounded river cobbles throughout. It is also 40-60 feet deep. The impression is one of a creek bed that has been thrust upward to form a gently rounded hill 150 feet above the valley floor. Many of the vines are an old black mix of Petite Sirah, Carignane and Zinfandel dating from the 1940's. A separate block of Gamay vines was planted in the '60s. There is a 3-year-old house on the property and one that is 40 years old. A barn will be outfitted with insulation, crush pad and stainless steel tanks for the Frick's first official crush in 1989.

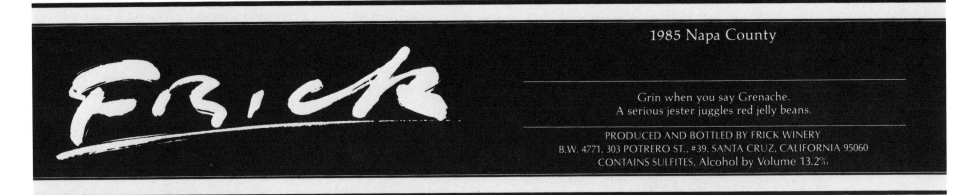

1985 Napa County

Grin when you say Grenache.
A serious jester juggles red jelly beans.

PRODUCED AND BOTTLED BY FRICK WINERY
B.W. 4771, 303 POTRERO ST., #39, SANTA CRUZ, CALIFORNIA 95060
CONTAINS SULFITES, Alcohol by Volume 13.2%

1984 Pinot Noir — 400 cases
Ventana Vyd — 750 ml

Grapes from back part of Ventana Vyd with special clone mix selected by Frick. 15-yr-old vines on sandy and rocky soil next to the Arroyo Seco. Frmtd with 10% whole berries in open 500-1100 gal redwood tanks at 90°F for 10 days. Cellar blend of yeasts with Assmanhausen predominant. Punch down 6x/day, pressed at 1°Brix. Settled 1 mo in stnls, spontaneous M-L. Seguin Moreau barrels. 12.6 alc, 3.37 pH, .7 acid. Also 150 cases of '84 Santa Maria Valley.

1985 Petite Sirah — 450 cases
Ventana Vyd — 750 ml

15-yr-old Ventana vines. 6 days on the skins with cellar blend of yeasts in small redwood tanks at 80°F, punched 4x/day. No fining, polish filtration. partial carbonique

nv Zinfandel — 800 cases
Coyote Creek — 750 ml

Blend of '84 and '85 vintages. Grapes from 60 to 80-yr-old vines in a 5 acre vyd near downtown San Jose which is part of a truck farming operation. No SO₂ at crusher, 10% whole berries. 8 days on skins in open redwood tanks at 88°F with wild yeast. No M-L. Aged in 4 yr old French barrels. Polish filter, btld Sept '87 at 13 alc, 3.09 pH, .833 acid.

1985 Grenache — 250 cases
Napa County — 750 ml

Mountain vyd planted in '50s off Sulphur Springs Rd on west side of valley near St. Helena. Reddish clay/loam and volcanic soils, head pruned vines, under 2 t/a. Frmt in open redwood at 85°F, punch 4x/day, pressed at dryness, inoculate for M-L. Settle in small stnls, aged in new 120 gal French oak puncheons. Fine filtration, btld April '87 at 13.5 alc, 3.47 pH, .71 acid.

What does your new vineyard need?

"We have a lot of vines where all the foliage has been removed by deer. We are the end of the vineyard plantings up out of the valley and along this road. It is to be expected we would get most of the deer's business. So I guess I'll have to see where they are coming through or over our fence. I've talked to my older Italian neighbors and they all recommend your three basic pieces of equipment, which they refer to as 'Luigi's Deer Control:' a spotlight, a shotgun, and a freezer. I had hoped my trusty companion (Luna the wonder-dog) would scare deer off, but she has chosen to specialize in rabbits, rock chasing and poison oak.

"This winter I will prune severely and pay close attention to cane size. Next spring I will sucker all the vines and replace those that are missing. I pump water from the creek to a storage tank in the tower, but I'll need some 300 foot hoses to water the replacement vines. I want to consider a pond in the creek bed someday, and maybe I'll plant a few vines of a white variety there. Primarily we will be sticking to reds though. If I had the pond, I might consider doubling up on my vine spacing.

"I need to get some experience with these old, hillside vines before I make long-term decisions about wine styles. We have some 50-year-old Gamay that could make a wonderful light-bodied, aromatic style for early consumption. By the same token, the Italians that have made wine here for the last century knew that planting on the hillside enabled you to get long-lived wines with great character. I need to pick several small batches at different sugar/acid levels to see what happens. It may be that blends from different harvest times will produce the best results."

Bill Frick

RG

GAINEY VINEYARDS

Daniel Gainey's father was a founder of the Arabian Horse Registry. Today Gainey Fountainhead Arabians are one of the top pure-bred lines in the world. The 2,000-acre Gainey Ranch is the largest diversified farming operation in the Santa Ynez Valley. The 22,000 sq. ft. winery and visitors center was designed from the beginning as an educational tour. Visitors start with a minicourse in viticulture. The demonstration vineyard has two rows of 50 vines for each of the six varieties grown on the property. This allows guests to see the progression of bud break in different varietals, cluster and berry size, six different pruning and trellising techniques, overhead versus drip irrigation and clean-till versus groundcover weed control. The rest of the tour follows the route of the wine from grape to glass. Robin Gainey, Dan's wife, furnished the building with 18th and 19th century French antiques. She also drew on her extensive knowledge of fine cooking to design eight-

person, hands-on culinary classes at the winery, featuring top chefs from Los Angeles restaurants.

The winery itself occupies 10,000 square feet and features state-of-the-art equipment throughout. "We wanted to give ourselves every chance to produce top wine," say Barry Johnson, "and also show our visitors examples of the best technology." The first complete crush at the Gainey Winery was supervised by a winemaking consultant in 1984. 100% Santa Barbara County grapes were used. The winery is air conditioned and enjoys 45,000 gallons of jacketed stainless steel tanks cooled with a direct expansion freon system. They have a German bottom-filler bottling line with a membrane filter. A Bucher press, lees filter and Healdsburg crusher-stemmer process the grapes. Gainey says they plan to make only 10,000 cases a year. In February of 1985 Ric Longoria was hired as winemaker. Ric graduated from UC Berkeley in 1973 with a degree in Sociology. He worked at Buena Vista, Firestone, Chappellet, Rancho Sisquoc and J. Carey wineries before taking the job with Gainey.

The Gaineys planted 54 acres of grapes in 1984: 19 Chardonnay, 18 Sauvignon Blanc, 5 Cabernet Sauvignon, 6 Johannisberg Riesling, 4 Semillon and 2 Merlot. Longoria describes Gainey's location, near the airport in the eastern third of Santa Ynez Valley, as a warm Region II. Using Sauvignon Blanc as an example, Ric says, "Grapes grown at the winery produce a fine wine with melon/fig overtones, but little of the varietal herbaceousness. To get complexity, I also use grapes from regions closer to the coast which do have the grassy character." Longoria considers Cabernet and Merlot to have super potential in Gainey's location. He thinks they don't ripen well closer to the coast. Gainey's vineyards consist of gently sloping gravel and clay soils about five feet deep. Grapes are

planted on their own roots with 12' x 6' spacing. They use water from Lake Cachuma for overhead sprinklers. Frost protection is essential. Barry Johnson says the temperature can drop as low as 12°F.

Recently Longoria has been "fooling around" with botrytized grapes. He says it's hard. "My '85 LH JR started fermenting right away, but there is some anti-microbial enzyme called botrycine which inhibits the yeast. We kept the fermentation perking along for nearly four months just to get up to 7% alcohol. I started to run the wine through a membrane (sterile) filter, but gave up when I only got 3 gallons in the first hour." Ric doesn't always find the fruit he wants either. Growers would rather not let botrytis get a strong foothold in their vineyard because it can play havoc with all their vines the next spring.

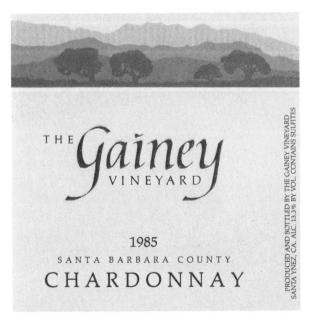

THE Gainey VINEYARD

1985

SANTA BARBARA COUNTY

CHARDONNAY

PRODUCED AND BOTTLED BY THE GAINEY VINEYARD
SANTA YNEZ, CA. ALC. 13.3% BY VOL. CONTAINS SULFITES

1986 Sauvignon Blanc   1,800 cases
750 ml

Four Santa Barbara County vyds. 33% barrel frmtd, Pasteur White yeast. 3 mos in French oak. Sterile filter, btl Aug '87 at 12.3 alc, .76 acid, 3.22 pH.

1987 J. Riesling   2,400 cases
750 ml

Grapes from Estate Vyd and Rancho Sisquoc. Steinberg and Epernay. Frmtd at 47°F. Btld May '88 at 2.8 rs, 10.9% alc.

1985 Cabernet Sauvignon   1,500 cases
750 ml

13% Merlot from Brander and Rancho Sisquoc vyds, 3.5% Cab Franc from Joe Carrari's vyd in Los Alamos. Cab Sauv from La Cuesta Vyd and Valley View vyd which is 2 miles west of Solvang. Frmtd with Pasteur Red, 7-9 days on skins. 18 mos in French barrels. 12.2 alc, .64 acid, 3.55 pH.

1986 Chardonnay   446 cases
Limited Selection   750 ml

85% Whitegate Lane Vyd, 8% Sweeney Cyn Vyd, 7% Santa Maria Hills Vyd. Barrel frmtd with 70% new oak, 9 mos in oak on lees, no m-l. 13.2 alc, 3.2 pH, .88 acid. Also regular Chardonnay.

Do you buy from those cold climate vyds near the coast?

"I'm always interested in new vineyards, particularly in Chardonnay from the very cool sections of the county. I had several years experience with one I call Sweeney Canyon when I was making Chardonnay for my Longoria label. That program has now been melded into Gainey's Limited Selection Chardonnay. You probably know Sweeney Canyon (the road it is located on) as Rancho Dos Mundos. It is a 12 acre vineyard planted in 1980 and owned by some people from Long Beach (hence the reference to their two worlds, city and country). They never have any problem getting the grapes to 23°Brix, and they always have good acid. We picked at 22.5°Brix, 3.28 pH and .93 acid this year ('88) during the last week of September.

"We barrel ferment in 75% new oak from the Vosges, Trancais and Alliers forests. I'm particularly pleased with some barrels coopered by Dargaud et Jaegle that Mel Knox has been introducing to this country. One of the keys in our barrel fermentation is to elongate the period to 10 or 12 days. The flavors from short, hot fermentations are too coarse. My technique is to use a sparing amount of yeast inoculum and air-condition the ambient temperature to less than 60°F. For these wines I use about half the normal 2.5 pounds of dry yeast per 1,000 gallons that is normally recommended. After fermentation we cut down to 50% new oak for aging on the lees. We don't feel the need for malo-lactic fermentation because we're seeking a lean, austere style. Eventually this cool climate wine will be blended with warmer climate grapes picked August 19 at 21.8°Brix (in '88) from Whitegate Ranch.

"The dilemma I find is between wanting to slow barrel fermentations of Chardonnay down, and making sure they go dry. I'm a purist. When I judge wine competitions, I'll refuse to give Gold or Silver medals to Chardonnays with perceptible residual sugar. Yeast nutrient makes them go dry, but it also speeds the fermentation up."

Ric Longoria

Dan Gainey   RL

GOLDEN CREEK

60 miles from Vienna, in the little Czechoslovakian town of Skalica, Ladi Danielik grew up surrounded by vineyards. His grandfather had planted one in 1910. The rolling hills and heavy clay soil produced tannic red wines much beloved by people living in this relatively cold climate. Ladi's father owned a shoe shop, and the whole family worked hard in both the vineyard and the store. Then came World War II. Born in 1935, Ladi was just a baby when the Nazis occupied his country and barely a teenager when the Communists supplanted them. Nevertheless, he speaks forcefully of the oppression that followed.

GOLDEN CREEK

1985
Sonoma County
CABERNET SAUVIGNON

GROWN, PRODUCED AND BOTTLED BY GOLDEN CREEK VINEYARDS
4480 WALLACE RD., SANTA ROSA, CA 95404 • (707) 538-2350
ALCOHOL 12.8% BY VOLUME. CONTAINS SULFITES.

"All the unemployed people in town became communists," he explains. "They were all given positions as policemen. They called my father a capitalist because he had worked to own something. Everything was taken away from us, and I was sent to dental technician school in 1951. An acre or two of vineyard was overlooked because communists like to drink too. Everybody works from 6 a.m. to 2 p.m. They want some entertainment in the afternoon. We made wine in the basement, but it was always secret. You couldn't get barrels so you used the same ones your grandfather had used. Bottles and corks were out of the question, so people would pick up wine in 5 gallon demi-johns. No vintage ever saw its first birthday."

In 1968, Russian tanks rolled through Skalica to crush the freedoms initiated by Alexandre Dubcek. They may have had a point. Prior to the advent of Dubcek's reforms, Ladi had never even considered asking for a passport to travel outside Czechoslovakia. While the Soviets were in the process of snuffing that candle, Ladi obtained permission to visit friends in Austria at Easter. He never went back to Skalica.

After 4 months in Austria, he immigrated to New Jersey with his wife. Ladi's sister had preceded him and settled in New Jersey. Now he says, "I am kicking myself every day for not coming straight to California." Ladi worked for dental labs until 1975 when he was able to set up a lab of his own and buy a house. This security unleashed artistic yearnings which had long lain dormant in him. He wanted to work outside. And he wanted to make wine. He looked around New Jersey, but could not find land he considered suitable for a vineyard. In 1977 he visited Napa Valley for ten days. He returned to New Jersey armed with real estate brochures. When he phoned an agent in California, and was told about a potential listing, she had to

talk him out of flying out the next morning to look at the property. He bought 77 acres of rolling hills 5 miles northeast of Santa Rosa. "I knew it was the place the minute I saw it," he says contentedly.

He has planted a 12 acre vineyard on the property at the 400 foot elevation. Another 10 acres is plantable. The rest is quite steep, rising to 800 feet of elevation. He has a good well and drip irrigation. Merlot, Cabernet Sauvignon, Gewürztraminer and Sauvignon Blanc were planted in 1980. The whites do well in his location. He got a Silver medal on his Sauvignon Blanc at the Orange County Fair. But his soil is heavy clay just like he knew in Skalica, and he thinks it favors red wines. He also doesn't have temperature control equipment in his winery. So in 1986 he had the white grapes grafted over to Merlot and Cabernet Sauvignon.

When Ladi built his house, he put a 1,300 sq. ft. cellar underneath it. Since 1983 he has made 1,000 to 3,000 cases a year from his own grapes. "Depends how it is selling," he explains. "I don't like to beg people to buy my wine." Ladi continues to run his dental lab. Even former clients in New Jersey send him business. For fun, he works in the vineyard. "I don't need a hobby if I can be outdoors working in this beautiful place," he says. His 24-year-old son and 74-year-old father help with the winery and the vineyard.

1985 Cabernet Sauvignon	230 cases
Estate	750 ml
1984 Merlot	40 cases
Estate	750 ml
nv "Caberlot"	30 cases
Estate	750 ml

Do you make blends?

"We make a Cabernet and a Merlot separately. Then we make a 50/50 blend we call "Caberlot." It has won 20 medals. We don't fertilize the vineyard, and we don't spray anything after flowering. We are on the skins about a week in an open topped former dairy tank. Everybody is using Prise de Mousse yeast. Me too. We punch down 5 times a day. I don't like to use new oak. I stay in the barrel 2-3 years depending on the wine.

"My mother, father and son help me bottle. We use a 6 spout gravity filler. It takes us 1 day to bottle 120 cases. We put labels on as we sell the wine so that we can afix our medals to the labels. At first we were bottling as the wine sold, but these wines need more than a week of bottle age. We don't do much selling. Most of the wine goes to old accounts who tell other people about our wines.

"I don't want to get big. I haven't had a vacation, or even a weekend off since I came to the U.S. We only use our own grapes and that keeps it fun for me."

Ladi Danielik

RG

GRANITE SPRINGS WINERY

Granite has both positive and negative connotations for Les and Lynne Russell. The positive side is the intensity of flavor in grapes grown on the weathered granitic soils of their vineyard. The negative part came when Les began excavating a hillside location for his winery building and had to use dynamite to blast through ten solid feet of granite.

Les grew up on a ranch in El Dorado County. In the late '70s he was working as Director of Parks and Recreation for the City of Novato. Lynne was a civil engineer. Proposition 13, which reduced local taxes, made working for city governments less appealing, and Les had long held a desire to return to the Sierra Foothills. Having worked for the David Bruce Winery after college, Les thought about establishing a vineyard. His original idea was to sell Lynne on a five year plan with a gradual transition from the Bay Area to the vineyard property.

To investigate land prices, they drove blindly up to a house near Somerset and asked if anything in the vicinity was for sale. The lot next door was. They fell in love with the property and made an offer that was accepted three days later. Their five year plan disintegrated as they began planting grapes in 1980. The winery building was completed in 1981 just days before grapes began arriving for the earliest crush in this century.

The Russells have planted Cabernet Sauvignon, Zinfandel and Sauvignon Blanc. Chenin Blanc, Petite Sirah and Muscat are grown by neighborhood families nearby. The first wines were released in 1982, totaling 2,700 cases. Annual production will probably peak at about 9,000 cases. Les tends to the winemaking duties and manages the vineyard. Lynne handles record keeping and marketing. They emphasize that their wines are primarily "food beverages," and opt for only moderate alcohol levels in order to enhance food compatability.

The new tasting room at Granite Springs "with its honest-to-goodness flush toilet" hosts people from all over the country. Lynne feels a certain type of wine enthusiast enjoys going to out-of-the-way places. "Some people won't go to Napa any more because of the crowds," she reports. "We'll get as many as 100 people on weekend days in early spring when 'cabin fever' takes over. We don't see as many White Zin devotees as we did two years ago either."

One of the most difficult Granite Springs wines to find is their Petite Sirah. It comes from a well drained, "decomposed" granite vineyard at 2,300 feet. Hot days and cool nights are typical of the area's climate. They pick the grapes at 22.5°Brix with acid in the .8% range which they say is "good for the variety, but not phenomenal." They ferment at 65°F which is low for red wines. In 1986 they started using

jacketed stainless tanks, but earlier years were fermented in open redwood tanks cooled by well water running through a stainless coil inside the vat. They press the Petite off the skins after 4 or 5 days, usually at 8-10°Brix. "The idea is to conserve the peppery aroma as well as the fruit," says Les, "and to keep the tannin level low. The grape is so darkly pigmented we never have trouble extracting good color. Our Petite Sirah is drinkable much earlier than traditional styles and suitable for food match-ups." The '83 Granite Springs Petite Sirah was chosen American Champion in the U.S. Gold Medal Taste-off conducted by Wines & Spirits magazine, a tasting that included all of the Petite Sirahs that had won Gold Medals in 1986. Les thinks the '84 was a step up and the '85 is better still.

VINTAGE 1985

GRANITE SPRINGS

EL DORADO

Petite Sirah

GRANITE HILL VINEYARDS

PRODUCED & BOTTLED BY GRANITE SPRINGS WINERY
BW 5073 SOMERSET, EL DORADO COUNTY, CALIFORNIA
ALCOHOL 13.0% BY VOLUME

1988 Chenin Blanc   1,000 cases
750 ml

Several El Dorado County vyds. Picked end Aug at 22.5°Brix, .88 acid, 3.38 pH. 4 wks frmt in stnls at 50°F. Btld end Nov '88 at 12.3 alc,1.5% rs.

1985 Zinfandel   200 cases
Higgins Vyd   750 ml

75-yr-old vines. Picked mid-Sept. Frmtd 9 days on skins. Aged 1 yr in oak uprights, then 16 mos in small American oak cooperage. Btld Apr '88 at 13 alc, 3.3 pH.

1985 Petite Sirah   700 cases
Granite Hill Vyd   750 ml

Picked late Sept at 22.7°Brix, .6 acid, 3.5 pH from vyd at 2,400 ft elevation. Cool frmt, off skins at 5°Brix. Aged French and American oak. Btld Feb 88 at 13 alc, 3.3 pH, .63 acid.

1987 Sauvignon Blanc   600 cases
Estate Vyd   750 ml

Picked end Aug at 22°Brix, 3.45 pH. Barrel frmtd and aged in Limousin oak. Btld June '88 at 12.5 alc, 3.21 pH, .67 acid.

1985 Cabernet Sauvignon   451 cases
Estate   750 ml

Picked end Oct at 22.5°Brix, .85 acid. 11 days on skins. Aged 1 yr in oak uprights, then 18 mos in small French barrels. Btld May '88 at 13 alc, 3.4 pH, .62 acid.

What was the 1988 vintage like up there?

"Variable. Real tough for some growers, but close to normal for others. White varieties were down 20-30% overall. Reds were only down 10%. Everyone wants to say it is due to the weather during flowering. First it was warm, then it got real cold. Pollination probably has something to do with it, but we haven't seen very much shatter in our vineyard. Our bunch count is down. The bunches are small and the berries are very small. We even had a batch of Cabernet from our vineyard that couldn't be pumped out of the crusher because there wasn't enough juice for the amount of skins. These factors would indicate that drought is part of the problem. We had lots of hot weather too. Acids are low. The entire summer was hot and there were several periods at least a week long with days consistently over 100°F. Everything ripened at about the same time. We have picked our Cabernet as late as November in the past, but had it in the fermenter before the end of September this year.

"Our vines must have roots down pretty far because they don't look stressed at all. It is an unirrigated block, and I'd bet the top 6 or 7 feet of soil is bone dry too. With our well we could only irrigate a small portion of them anyway. Ground water is obviously important to vine production. Many growers this year irrigated heavily in the spring when they realized it wasn't going to rain. They still ended up with reduced crop sizes."

Les Russell

CL

CL

49

GREEN & RED VINEYARD

When Joseph Chiles, a genuine Kentucky Colonel, arrived in the valley that now bears his name, he knew he'd found the perfect place to carry on his favorite activities — farming, trapping, and making fine sour mash whisky. There was plenty of good soil, wooded hillsides full of game and hardly any people to interfere with the operation of his still.

That was in the 1850's. Even today Chiles Valley seems pretty remote, in spite of the fact that it's just a few miles east of the hustle and bustle of Napa Valley. There are few residents and fewer tourists. In the early morning hours, you can travel the entire length of the valley without running into another person.

Unless you happen to arrive at Green & Red Vineyard during the crush. Things start real early there when they're harvesting grapes. Jay and Pam Heminway have things hopping. They want to get fruit in before the sun comes up over the canyon wall and warms the grapes. All the picking is done by hand into lug boxes and moldy or unripe bunches are sorted out on a conveyor belt. The must is chilled before going into the fermenters. In '87 they even added the capacity to cool their open topped tanks during the red wine fermentations. Jay feels this is the best way to preserve fresh fruit flavors in his wine.

"Our Zinfandel is a modulated style," he says. They try to harvest just as the acid starts falling, at about 23.5°Brix, 3.2 pH and .9 acid. They use Assmanhausen yeast for 50% of the must. Jay thinks this yeast produces a spicy character. Recently, the remaining wine has been fermented with a new yeast isolated by Lisa Van der Water from wild strains found on Zinfandel grapes in York Creek Vineyard. This uniquely California yeast emphasizes the fruity aroma of the grapes.

The Heminways do all all their own pruning with the help of one hired hand. It takes about 6 weeks. Jay does a different section himself each year. He tries to prune in the coldest part of the winter when there is no sap in the vines to avoid any risk of *Eutypha,* or drop-arm disease, which is like an infected wound. "We began pruning more heavily in '84," he reports. "Each vine has two cordon arms, and we cut back to 4 spurs on each cordon with 1 bud per spur. The result was to drop our yield from 4 tons/acre in '83 to less than 2 t/a in '84. The yield has started going back up as the vines continue to mature, but it was still under 3 t/a in '87."

Jay has also added an additional cross arm and 2 extra trellis wires about a foot above the existing side wires in his vineyard. This arrangement extends the foliage vertically. It adds two weeks before the weight of the canes causes them to turn and slump downward across the top wire. Apical dominance naturally puts the most vigorous growth at the tips of the canes and at this bend, so it is helpful to position the curve further out along the cane. This new canopy position also means the fruit is shaded in the middle of the season while the sun is high, but that sunlight can penetrate vines from the side at harvest when the sun is low on the horizon.

Heminway first planted grapes in 1970 and bonded the winery in 1977. He started out small, making just a few hundred cases of Zin in a single wooden barn on the property. As production grew, outbuildings were tacked onto the original structure to accommodate the winemaking and storage operations. "The result is not," says Jay, "an architect's dream, but it is practical and in its own way it has a lot of charm." Big leaf maples, live oaks and walnut trees shade the grounds near the winery.

The Heminways own 160 acres, but only about 16 are planted, all in Zinfandel and Chardonnay. Even though the vineyards are not far apart, they are actually in two very different micro-climates. The Zinfandel, with a western exposure is shaded from the afternoon sun by nearby mountains. The terraced Chardonnay vineyard is on a steep slope with a northeast exposure and is even cooler than the Zin. The winery is named for the soils that make up the vineyard: red iron laced with green serpentine. The grapes get 2-3 applications of water from a drip irrigation system each year. Jay won't come right out and say that 1987 was a drought year, but he did drill a new well on the property.

Heminway was a Fulbright scholar in 1969 who taught sculpture at U.C. Berkeley before he embarked on his winemaking career. He married Pam in 1986. Jay chose the work of another artist to decorate his labels. Exekias' painting of Dionysus originally decorated, appropriately enough, a kylix or wine cup that dates from the 6th century B.C.

GREEN & RED

VINEYARD

1987

NAPA VALLEY

CHARDONNAY

ESTATE

GROWN, PRODUCED & BOTTLED BY GREEN & RED VINEYARD
ST. HELENA, CA : ALC. 13.0% BY VOL. : CONTAINS SULFITES

1985 Zinfandel	1,400 cases
Estate Vyd	750 ml

13 yr old vines picked 5 Sept at 23.5°Brix. Vines have a SW exposure at 1,000 ft. Planted on own roots in Olympic clay/loam and iron oxide shale. 50% frmtd with Assmanhausen, 50% with York Creek yeast. Aged 18 mos, 25% French barrels, 75% air dried, fire coopered American. Btld Aug '87 at 13.5 alc, .67 acid, 3.36 pH.

1987 Chardonnay	550 cases
Estate Vyd	750 ml

1,500 foot elevation, east facing slope, mixture of soils, 5-yr-old vines, Wente clone along with a clone from Monticello Vyd. Picked 18 Aug at 22.7°Brix. No skin soak, no SO₂ at crusher. 80% frmtd in stnls, 20% barrel frmtd. No m-l, on fine lees 5 mos. Aged 7 mos in French oak with medium to heavy toast. Sterile filtered, btld June '88 at 13.0 alc, .78 acid, 3.15 pH.

Are you considering anything new in rootstocks or canopy mgmt?

"Most new research on rootstocks involves restricting growth in deep, heavy soils. We have such light shallow soils and low production I don't feel it applies.

"We do sucker vines each spring when new growth gets out some 8". That means taking sprouts off the trunk, underneath the cordon arms, and removing any second or third shoots that may have come out at the spur position. Zinfandel tends to put out a lot of extra shoots. All this labor is aimed at limiting crop size and allowing more air into the vine in case of a rain before harvest. We also limit crop size by pruning to one bud per spur. I've seen some Zin vineyards leaving entire canes tied to their trellis wires in an effort to double production for White Zin sales. It works if you have enough water, but old timers tell you the vines just give up after a couple years of that treatment.

"We don't physically remove leaves before harvest because we prune and trellis for vertical growth and an open center to start with. We also stop irrigating in July. On our thin soils, the vines begin to stress a month later and big leaves near the trunk drop off. It's a great technique, but it wouldn't work for vineyards with deep, heavy soils. Those guys would have to cut off water two years ahead of harvest. After we pick the grapes each fall, we give the vines about 5 gallons of water each. That reduces stress and lets the vine pull carbohydrates back into the trunk as cold temperatures induce dormancy. When water stressed, vines put carbohydrates out into the canes in a last-ditch reproductive effort and they will be lost when dormancy occurs.

Jay Heminway

RG

RG

GREENWOOD RIDGE VINEYARDS

Greenwood Ridge was logged over in the 1880's and then became a sheep ranch, but by the turn of the century lumbermen were taking the train from Elk up into the mountains to buy good red wine, most probably Zinfandel. The Du Pratt Vineyard's 65 year old Zinfandel vines are still putting out first rate grapes in the same area 1500 feet up and only six miles from the Pacific. In 1972 Tony Husch planted a vineyard on Greenwood Ridge seeking a level above the fog of the valley floor.

Allan Green bought the 700-acre ranch on the ridge in 1971 as a retreat from the pressures of a successful graphics design business and purchased the Husch vineyard in 1973. Allan comes from a fourth generation San Francisco family and remembers drinking Prohibition vintaged wines from the family's cellar. His great-great grandfather was a marketing man for Inglenook in the 1890's. In June 1976, Allan finally succumbed to his need to escape the city and built himself

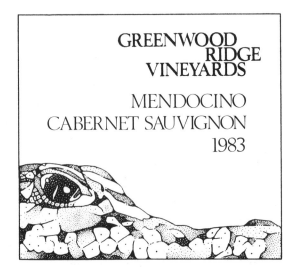

Grown, produced and bottled by Greenwood Ridge Vineyards, B.W. 4960, Philo, California. Alcohol 12.5% by volume.

a redwood home on the property. The house has since undergone three additions as Allan struggles to find space for his beer can collection.

The vineyard consists of 2.5 acres of Johannisberg Riesling, 4.5 acres of Cabernet Sauvignon and 1 acre of Merlot. The clay soil is shallow with less than six inches of top soil in some spots. The drip irrigation system is fed by a run-off pond that plays an important role, since Riesling is particularly vulnerable to water stress in the shallow, hillside soil. Allan says that another 150 acres of the property would be suitable for vineyards, but access to irrigation water is a limiting factor. The present grapes are planted on their own roots. The ground is left bare and the vines trained fairly low to get as much reflected heat as possible. Vines are trellised on a four-wire system to give them extra support against the wind.

Cabernets from Greenwood Ridge are evolving to reflect their cool climate location. The '80 was all Cabernet and very tannic. In '81 they did not remain on the skins as long, but still used 95% Cabernet. In '82 they used 20% Merlot as those vines caught up to the Cabernet in production level. "The Merlot definitely softens the wine and makes it drinkable earlier," Allan says. They harvest Merlot at 24.5°Brix and Cabernet closer to 22.5°Brix so that the Merlot will contribute a ripe fullness to the nose right away. Recognizing this effect, they released the '82 ahead of the '81 and took Best Cabernet of the Region with it at the State Fair.

Greenwood Ridge's 1,000 sq. ft. concrete block winery was built into a hill above the irrigation pond in 1978. In 1982 an 1,800 sq. ft. warehouse and bottling facility was added. Both buildings have R-30 insulation in the roof and use night air cooling. Equipment includes a small Zambelli crusher-stemmer and a hydraulic basket press along with 5,000 gallons of jacketed

stainless steel tanks. The winery buys 25% new barrels each year. Four hundred cases per day can be bottled on the premises with the help of friends. Harvesting has been done by the same nine man crew from Cloverdale since 1980.

Allan made all the wines through 1984 himself with consulting help from Jed Steele (now at Kendall-Jackson) and lab work by Vinquiry of Healdsburg. Fred Scherrer was hired as full-time winemaker for the 1985 crush. Fred has an Enology degree from U.C. Davis and worked as Assistant Winemaker at Fieldstone Winery for two years.

Every July since 1983 Greenwood Ridge hosts a competition for wine tasters. The basic format is identifying grape varietal in wines tasted blind. There's a day for singles and a second day for partners. They have novice, amateur and professional divisions each day. The competition is great fun in much the same manner as a three-legged race. They had over 200 entries in '87 and got written up in Newsweek. Wine writers have been fairly supportive about giving them publicity, but few have ever taken part in the competition. "They know identifying varietals blind is a chancey thing," Allan explains. "Most of them feel they have something to lose and nothing to gain. I'd like to attract more participants in the professional division, but the ambiance and good-time spirit of the event is more important. It is similar to why we want to remain a small winery."

1984 Cabernet Sauvignon	1,200 cases
Estate Vyd	750 ml

5% Merlot. Cab picked end Oct at 22.5°Brix, .9 acid, 3.21 pH. Merlot picked early Oct at 24.7°Brix, .9 acid, 3.4 pH. Frmtd separately in open stnls 5 days at 90°F with Pasteur Red yeast. Punched 2x/day and pressed at 4°Brix. Aged in Nevers oak from Demptos and Nadalie with med toast. Btld June '86 at 12.5 alc, 3.5 pH, .76 acid.

1987 White Riesling	550 cases
Estate Vyd	750 ml

Crop 1/3 normal due to rain in June during flowering. Picked on 25 Sept at 22°Brix, .95 acid. Cold frmt in stnls. Btld Feb '88 at 11.5 alc, 3.07 pH, .85 acid, 1.6% rs.

What do you do about weeds and pests?

"Part of the reason people think we have a good looking vineyard is because the surrounding land is so picturesque. Weed control is not too hard because the soil is so infertile. We've done 15 years of strip spraying with a hand held sprayer called 'Herbi.' It has a spinning head which micronizes droplets to reduce the volume necessary. You can cover an acre with a small amount of Roundup diluted in a gallon of water. I stroll through the whole vineyard on a couple of windless mornings in February after the weeds have started to come up, but before the vines have pushed buds. You get the Harding grass and Filigree underneath the rows and then disk the centers of the aisles.

"To avoid mildew we spray sulphur from the air with a crop duster. He'll come up here for $50 plus materials to get DuPratt and us in one load. In these mountains it looks pretty dangerous, but you know these guys. He used to fly under the power lines until we put them underground. Once the vines are fully leafed out, we spray sulphur by hand to get good coverage on the sides.

"We rarely have much of an insect problem. That's probably because we are so remote from other fruit crops, or maybe because of our cold nights. I did have thrips once. They are barely visible, but in huge numbers they eat a lot of leaves. If the weather is warm, the vines will grow faster than the thrips can eat. In cool weather the thrips get ahead of growth and require treatment. Otherwise I'm fairly naive. I drive through the Central Valley and see all these billboards for insecticides to use on grapes, and I don't even know what they are.

"Birds and raccoons are my biggest pest problems. The raccoons love our pond. They walk along eating all the grapes from 6" to 2' off the ground. Quail eat a lot of grapes too. So last night we ate some Riesling stuffed quail."

Allan Green

Allan (Stretch) Green scores with seconds left. The barrels go wild.　RG

JR

HAGAFEN WINERY

Wine has played an important part in religious ceremony throughout history. Jews inherit a particularly rich cultural tradition which naturally includes wine since the cradle of Jewish ritual and the cradle of viticulture occurred in much the same place and time (cf. *Numbers, 13*). It is noteworthy that this integration of wine into daily life over a period of centuries seems to carry a cultural buffer against alcohol abuse. Most Jews drink, but as a group the rate of alcohol related problems among them is extremely low.

Hagafen Winery contributes a valuable element to Winewright's panoply of artistic California winemakers. Not only do Ernie Weir and Zach Berkowitz make extremely good wine, but they make it under the rules and direct supervision

HAGAFEN

1987 NAPA VALLEY 5748

JOHANNISBERG RIESLING

PRODUCED & BOTTLED BY HAGAFEN WINERY, ST. HELENA, NAPA VALLEY, CA
ALC. 11.5% BY VOL.   CONTAINS SULFITES   K

of an Orthodox Rabbinical Council. In other words, it is kosher. That means no work on holidays, nor on the Sabbath, and all winemaking operations must be attended by a Mashgiach, representing the Council in San Francisco. They can not use animal products like gelatin or isinglass in the treatment of the wine. "It is most difficult during the crush," says Ernie, "because the High Holidays often correspond to the ripening of the grapes. Overall, we probably need someone from the Rabbinical Council for about 30 full days a year."

Hagafen Cellars does not intend to make wines to match specifically with traditional foods for Jewish holidays. They set out to make the best wines possible and want them to have broad appeal. The fact they make a dry, high quality wine that Jews can serve on religious occasions is a bonus, not a limitation. Once Ernie makes that point, however, he likes to draw a distinction between religious and ethnic origin. Jewish cuisine can be said to fall into at least two styles. One is Germanic, derived from northeastern Europe. The Hagafen Riesling and Chardonnay seem to go best with those foods. The other is Spanish, derived from the Mediterranean, and it is much more piquant. Their Cabernet usually matches up best with this latter style.

Weir and Berkowitz moved to Napa Valley after graduating from UCLA in 1971. Both went back to school at UC Davis for degrees in viticulture and both currently work as vineyard managers for Domaine Chandon. Both are married, and Berkowitz has two children. Neither are Orthodox Jews, but like many non-Orthodox Jews they like the idea of having well structured, dry wines to drink which are also kosher.

The third partner in Hagafen (which means vine in Hebrew) is Rene DiRosa, art patron and probably the best known grape grower in Napa Valley. Rene is not Jewish, but until 1986 he was the owner of Winery Lake Vineyards where he pioneered premium grape planting in the Carneros District at Napa's cool southern extremity. Rene has since sold most of his vineyard to Seagrams. Rumor has it that the price paid for each acre would finance an undergraduate tuition at Yale, Rene's alma mater. Hagafen used grapes from Rene's vineyard for many years and continues to buy fruit in the Carneros District. "We like Carneros because we look for low vigor in the vines and good acid in the juice," says Weir.

Hagafen's highly acclaimed Cabernet has a great vineyard pedigree. The Cabernet Sauvignon is from one of the best kept secrets in Napa Valley, Oak Knoll Vineyard. The Cabernet Franc is from Ernie's own property on Silverado Trail in the Stag's Leap District. Oak Knoll is on the west side of the valley just north of Yountville. Visually, Oak Knoll seems to be the southern end of the Rutherford Bench, and it is at least a mile further south than Martha's Vineyard at the Oakville Grade. Because Cabernet Sauvignon is Napa Valley's forte with grapes planted in excellent sites, Ernie decided Cabernet Franc would be a nice complement to have at his house. "My 4 acres of Cab Franc grow well and add a component of fruitiness to the wine," he says. "I pick it between 22.5° and 23°Brix which produces a chocolate note. Riper fruit tends to jammy or black current smells, which I think indicate dehydrated berries."

1987 J. Riesling	1,500 cases 750 ml

Grapes from the southern end of Napa Valley. Frmtd cold in stnls. 11 alc, .75 acid, 2% rs.

1987 Chardonnay	1,000 cases 750 ml

Grapes from the southern end of Napa Valley. A few hours skin soak, frmtd in stnls at 55°F with Prise de Mousse yeast. No M-L. 3-6 mos in combination of French and American oak. Btld at .7 acid, 12.8 alc.

1984 Cabernet Sauvignon	650 cases 750 ml

24% Cabernet Franc, 10 days on skins, 18 mos in barrels, 12.5 alc.

Does immigration reform make it hard to get harvest crews?

"There does seem to be a little attitude change, but the new law hasn't affected the labor supply. Those workers who have documents are now a special category. I've seen them walk off jobs this year when it really wasn't in their best interests to do so. When they are underpaid it makes sense, but wages are higher in Napa than any place else. I'll bet the average picker makes $85 a day. They all like to talk about that $200 day though, as if it were a fish they once hooked.

"The higher the tonnage/acre, the lower the price. Grapes like Cabernet are hard to pick, so they command a higher price. Large growers rarely negotiate. They publish the prices they will pay and stick to them. They never have trouble getting help because they are able to promise work for many weeks at a time. Small growers have to network with their neighbors. The labor supply is usually abundant in Napa because of the prices. Word gets out quickly about any shortages and people show up from other areas. There has never been any hiring hall type organization because there has never been any need. Of course, where these people sleep is not a topic of which anybody is particularly proud.

"On the other hand, I know lots of well educated Chicanos who have gotten involved in the industry as contractors doing vineyard work. Those businesses go through boom and bust cycles, so many of them move on to technical work like pest control consulting, or become hired guns like me. The United Farm Workers never took hold because the big growers paid more money and better benefits to non-union pickers. A lot of the harvest has been mechanized too."

Ernie Weir

Ernie Weir and Rabbi   RG

HANDLEY CELLARS

Having a career and raising a family at the same time may be the goal for many young women today, but it is always difficult. Wrestling barrels filled with fermenting Chardonnay while pregnant must be a special category. Milla Handley successfully completed that labor in 1985.

Milla says that being a homemaker and winemaker at the same time is not always possible. "If you saw my house right now, you'd know what gets neglected," she admits. Her husband, Rex McClellan, is a realtor and Milla calls him "real supportive." Rex worked at Navarro Vineyards when they first moved to the Anderson Valley, so we can assume that he is useful in the winery as well as the kitchen.

Milla grew up in the Los Altos Hills where she and her family acquired a taste for fine wine through a friend who owned a top retail store in the area. She went to U.C. Davis to study art, but switched to Fermentation Science early on. Brewing was a natural interest since her mother's great-great grandfather was Henry Weinhard. After graduating in 1975, Milla worked in the lab at Sonoma Vineyards and then was in charge of quality control at Chateau St. Jean for three years. From 1979 through 1982 she worked at Edmeades.

Milla and Rex bonded their own winery in

1982 in the 30 x 20-foot basement of their home. They made less than 1,000 cases a year and stored wine in the garage. In 1986 Handley Cellars moved to an historic site just up the road. They intend to plant 20 acres on a south-facing slope, two-thirds Chardonnay and one-third Pinot Noir. Plans include a tasting room and eventual expansion to 5,000 cases a year. They are also producing 400 cases of sparkling wine.

Anderson Valley is a very cool region, and Milla finds she has to pick grapes for her sparkling wine based on acid rather than on sugar. If she doesn't wait until the pH rises above 3.0, the grapes are still green. She likes Epernay II yeast for the primary fermentation because it works slowly and she can keep it under 63°F without refrigeration. She uses Prise de Mousse for the bottle fermention because it always goes dry and she likes the flavors. "We want the toasty quality you get from yeast autolysis," she says, "but I prefer fresh wines without the nose that often comes with French Champagne. I think that nose comes from age. You don't find it when you drink those same wines in France." Handley hopes to keep their costs reasonable by riddling the sparkling wine themselves. It is a specialized job because each bottle gets handled every day for 6 weeks. Mediocre riddlers just go slow. Good ones have to learn to match the riddling schedule to the individual wines because yeast moves differently in each different cuvée.

Handley makes both a Brut and a Rosé. The Brut is 72% Pinot Noir, but none is left on the skins. The Brut has no salmon color and no varietal taste characteristic. The Rosé is fruitier with Pinot Noir flavors. They are vintage dating the sparkling wines, but discussing a plan to hold back some wine each year as a reserve lot for blending into the cuvée. Right now the scarcity of Pinot Noir in Anderson Valley is the limiting

factor on their production. They would like to make 3,000 cases a year.

The time each bottle spends en tirage makes quite a difference according to Milla. "It takes 6 months to complete the secondary fermentation, and autolysis of the yeast doesn't begin right away. Therefore, a second year en tirage actually gives 3 times as much effect. We are leaving some lots en tirage longer than 2 years to see how they develop. We may do a 'Recently Disgorged' wine in the future."

Milla's father owns a 20-acre vineyard planted to Chardonnay and Sauvignon Blanc in the southern end of the Dry Creek Valley. Milla finds her father's grapes quite different from those grown in the Anderson Valley and thinks the difference illustrates why it is so hard to tell growers to pick at a specific sugar level. "At our own place the Chardonnay seems ripe to me at 21°Brix," she says, "but my dad's grapes need to get to 22.5° or 23°Brix before they show the same translucency in the skin. In Anderson Valley we get bud break, bloom and everything else at least two weeks behind Napa. It is rare for us to not have at least one rain before we pick Chardonnay. Fruit, to us, means an apple character rather than the tropical fruit aromas found in the Central Coast. We have lower alcohol, and balance requires wood be kept in the background. If I didn't use malo-lactic fermentation to provide some richness in the mouth, my Chardonnay might seem thin." Her string of Gold medals apparently indicates she has overcome that problem.

1984

HANDLEY

ANDERSON VALLEY SPARKLING WINE
BRUT

Produced and bottled by Handley Cellars, Philo CA
Contains sulfites. Alcohol 12.5% by volume.

| 1987 Chardonnay | 700 cases |
| Dry Creek | 750 ml |

Grapes from Family Vyd owned by Milla's father. 12-yr-old, dry-farmed vines on deep sandy soils in southern Dry Creek Vly at the confluence of the Dry Creek and Russian Rivers. Picked 13 Sept at 22.4°Brix. No skin soak, settle overnight. Frmtd in barrels with Prise de Mousse yeast. Portion put through M-L after alc frmt. Portion left on lees. Aged 6-9 mos in new to 2-yr-old French oak barrels. Sterile filter, btld Aug '88 at 13.1 alc, .73 acid, 3.3 pH.

| 1985 Chardonnay | 150 cases |
| Anderson Vly | 750 ml |

Grapes from two vyds in the valley floor. One is on a rolling knoll, the other is on a ridge. Picked 20 Sept at 22.8°Brix, .91 acid, 3.04 pH. Partial M-L. Btld Aug '87.

| 1987 Sauvignon Blanc | 1300 cases |
| Dry Creek | 750 ml |

Picked 20 Sept at 22.2°Brix, .9 acid. No skin soak, no M-L, no time on lees. 1/3 barrel frmtd and aged 6 mos in French oak, rest in stnls. Btld July '88 at 12.8 alc, .72 acid, 3.35 pH.

| 1985 Rosé | 100 cases |
| Sparkling | 750 ml |

90% Pinot Noir, 10% Chardonnay. 2/3 of the Pinot Noir on skins overnight. 2 yrs en tirage with Prise de Mousse yeast. Riddled with a gyro-pallet. Disgorged Aug '88.

What are fining trials?

"We take about 10 samples of a wine and test them with different treatments. Bentonite (a clay) stabilizes a wine by taking out excess proteins. Isinglass (sturgeon stomach), gelatin and egg whites take out bitter phenolics like tannin. Colorfine and Polychlor are agents which take out excess color phenolics. We're talking small amounts. You might use one-eighth pound of Bentonite in 1,000 gallons of wine. You mix them into the samples in different amounts and different combinations, let them settle overnight, decant off the sediment and then taste the wines blind. It takes about an hour once you get set up. You do it several times per year.

"Some samples will be markedly better than others. Isinglass, for instance, will round out the rough edges from the wood and bring up the fruit in the nose. But they don't work in a linear progression. Just Colorfine may strip the wine, while Isinglass and Colorfine may be fantastic. The additional problem is trying to predict what the wine will do 6 months down the road. The same technique applies to acid adjustments, or sugar in the dosage of sparkling wines. Tartaric acid may seem harsh compared to malic, or you may want tartaric to give structure for aging.

We usually have a panel of 4 tasters. Sometimes we go to consultants, and sometimes we do it at home as a little party. Generally there is a lot of concensus because the samples turn out so remarkably different. When we do cork trials (by submerging cork samples in 100 ml of wine), even my 10-year-old daughter, who by the way doesn't like wine, picks out the concensus winner immediately. If the results surprise me, I'll repeat them a week later. Occasionally a fining treatment will have such a beneficial effect that I don't trust it and end up using the traditional method anyway."

Milla Handley

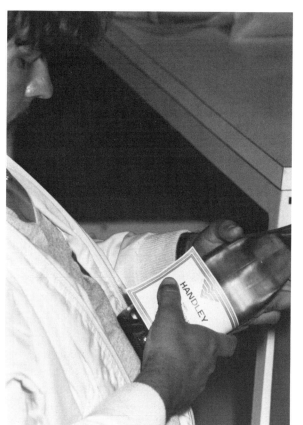

RG

RG

HART WINERY

Oddly enough for a winemaker, Travis (Joe) Hart was raised by tee-totaling parents. He was 22 before he had his first taste of wine while stationed in Germany during the 1950's. A trip to northern Italy introduced him to full-bodied reds and the enjoyment of pairing hearty wine with good food. Later in California, he and his wife Nancy, a Carlsbad schoolteacher, began to taste and collect wines seriously. They traveled to all the viticultural regions in California seeking to expand their knowledge.

Hart is a third generation Californian who grew up near Holtville in the Imperial Valley. He attended San Diego State University, taking a degree in Political Science. He taught school in Carlsbad for a few years and then, drawn by a

love of the sea, he went to work for the Scripps Institute as a Physical Oceanographer studying the topography of the ocean floor.

About this time he began to hear of the success of nearby Temecula as a grape growing region. In 1973 the Hart family and a partner purchased 12 acres next to Callaway Vineyards. On weekends Nancy, Joe and their three grown sons planted the Winery Estate with 4 acres of Cabernet Sauvignon and 3 acres of Merlot. "The Bordeaux varieties do okay here," Joe points out, "but there is a big difference in vine vigor from the top of our hill, which has pretty sandy soil, down to the bottom which retains water better. Our Merlot is on the herbaceous side of the spectrum as compared to the more berry-like character of Merlot I've purchased in Santa Barbara. I'm fully planted now, but I want to encourage local growers to give Cabernet Franc a try."

In 1979 Joe took "a year's leave of absence" to build the family winery and just never went back. By the summer of 1980, the winery was complete and the Harts crushed their first harvest of 350 cases. They originally planned to level off at 2,400 cases, but the hospitality of the Hart's tasting bar combined with the proximity to San Diego dictated a change. Today their production is constant at 6,500 cases per year.

Joe uses a Vaslin horizontal basket press. It has two plates that are driven toward the middle along a threaded (screw) shaft. It is programmed to exert pressure and then stop for awhile to let juice drain before exerting more pressure. It also has stainless steel chains inside to break up the cake and release pockets of juice. The Hart's Model 15 holds a little over 2 tons and takes about 2 hours to express around 300 gallons. Joe doesn't use pectic enzymes or press to the hardest cycles because he feels the extra juice becomes harsh with strange color and high pH. "You have to remember you are pressing seeds

as well as skins," he points out. 2 tons is a convenient size for Joe's operation because his grapes arrive in 2-ton gondolas. They usually work 5 or 6 loads a day on 6-8 days a year.

Hart is the first winery encountered by visitors to the Temecula area. As such Joe stands as a symbolic bastion against the encroaching development of Rancho California, and he fully understands the pressures that urbanization can cause. He keeps a pragmatic eye on other viticultural areas nearby. The most interesting one is at 2,500 feet in the coastal mountains 14 miles from the ocean. It is called La Cresta. There are volcanic soils at La Cresta on gently rolling, oak studded hills and a Region II climate compared to Temecula's Region III. Hart is getting more Cabernet from La Cresta every year. Unfortunately, there is a lot of development pressure for palatial homes up in the mountains, and Joe doubts that grape acreage will increase much in the next couple of years. The mountains on the eastern edge of San Diego County are also interesting because they are outside the area under developmental pressure and high enough (3,000 feet) to be cool.

1987 Sauvignon Blanc 400 cases
750 ml

Picked early Sept from Estate and Bear Creek Vyds in Temecula at 21° to 23°Brix. 50 ppm SO₂ at the crusher. Frmtd with UCD 595 yeast, small portion M-L. 40% aged in French oak. Btld Oct '88 at 3.0 pH, 12.5 alc.

1987 Chardonnay 375 cases
Murrieta Vyd 750 ml

Picked early in Sept at 23°Brix from Phil Hanson's vyd at La Cresta in Temecula appellation. UCD 595 yeast, some M-L. Aged in French oak. Sterile filtered, btld Oct '88 at .76 acid, 13.2 alc.

1987 J. Riesling 310 cases
750 ml

Chairman's Trophy at Orange County Fair. 2%rs, 2.82 pH, .9 acid. Temecula appellation grapes.

1986 Cabernet Sauvignon 600 cases
750 ml

Picked early Oct at 23.5°Brix. 20% from Estate Merlot vines, Cab from Murrieta Vyd in La Cresta. Frmtd in stnls at 85°F with Montrachet yeast. Pumped over 2x/day during frmt then left on skins an extra 2 weeks. Aged in 2-5 yr old American oak. Btld July '88 at 3.4 pH, .68 acid, 13 alc. Also 250 cases of straight '87 Merlot picked at 22.5°Brix, 3.6 pH, .7 acid.

Are you posting the birth defect warning in your tasting room?

"Yes. I don't want to lay myself open to the bounty hunters provided for in the law. People can turn in violators and receive 25% of the fine. Fines can be thousands of dollars per day when you are not in compliance. Some visitors have mentioned the signs and shaken their heads in disbelief. Just like some people look at the sulphites statement on the bottle and ask when we started putting sulphites in our wine. Most of them are very knowledgeable though. They tell me there is more sulphite on a salad bar than in any winery.

"Pregnant women have been coming in here with groups for years. They rarely tasted the wine, and those that did would use the spitoons we provide. They know a little wine isn't going to hurt them, but they are cautious anyway. Same way with most drivers in groups. They never drink much. We are right off Interstate 15. There are drunk driving accidents out there all the time, but nobody has ever even suggested a link to the winery tasting rooms here. Fine wine drinkers are simply not part of the problem.

"We've got ourselves in a Catch 22. We don't want wine seen as an elitist beverage, because we'd like to broaden the market. At the same time, existing wine drinkers are certainly elite enough to realize how silly these warning signs are.

"My initial reaction was to vote for Proposition 65 (the toxics labeling law whose interpretation has unleashed this bureaucratic warning sign binge). However, I didn't do so because it paints everything with such a broad brush. I suspect it will be changed when people see how ridiculous these measures are. They certainly aren't doing anything about toxic waste."

Joe Hart

BM

HONIG CELLARS

Parents in California may find something vaguely familiar about this label. You know the name, but not in the context of wine. Bill Honig has been State Superintendent of Public Instruction since 1982. He makes the papers regularly because his job entails wrestling with the Governor about money for schools. Louis Honig was his father. The other partner is a Municipal Court Judge in San Francisco named Daniel Weinstein. The Honigs and Weinsteins are in-laws. Viticulturalist Rick Tracy helped start the winery, then sold his interest back to the family in order to pursue other projects. Michael Honig, Bill's son, is in charge of marketing. Michael was married in September, 1987 to Elaine Arnold, an

Oklahoman who is taking an active part in sales for the winery.

The Honig vineyards and winemaking facilities are situated, quite literally, in the exact geographical center of Napa Valley. The property was originally part of the Caymus Land Grant held by George Calvert Yount, a trapper and mountain man from North Carolina who settled in the valley around 1836. The town of Yountville is named after him. Eventually the land was sold to the Wagner family, of Caymus Vineyards fame. In fact, Charlie Wagner was born on the property. Louis Honig bought the current 67 acre parcel in 1966. The winery released its first 500 cases of Sauvignon Blanc in 1980 under the HNW Cellars label. They changed the name to Louis Honig Cellars in 1982. The Weinsteins had remodelled an old barn on the property as a weekend residence in 1975, and an Earl Thollander painting on the Honig label depicts the vineyard viewed from the Weinsteins' window. The winery produces about 10,000 cases of Sauvignon Blanc annually.

The vineyards contain 29 acres of Sauvignon Blanc, 4 acres of Merlot, 6 acres of Chardonnay and 7 acres of Cabernet Sauvignon. Some of the Sauvignon Blanc is sold to Vichon Winery. Honig picks the Sauvignon Blanc for their own wine a week or two after they pick the grapes for Vichon in order to produce a fruitier style. Vichon likes their Sauvignon Blanc at 21°Brix, then they use Sémillon to soften the herbaceous nose. Honig has planted 11 additional acres to Cabernet and Merlot. In the past their Cabernet has been sold to Conn Creek Winery. In '87 Honig made 800 cases each of Cabernet and Chardonnay for themselves.

Rick Tracy had originally become involved with Honig after managing the vineyard next door which is owned by Austin Hills (as in Hills Brothers coffee and Grgich-Hills Winery). Rick

left Honig in March of '87. James Hall was hired to replace him. James attended U.C. Davis after a stint at U.C. Santa Cruz. Before Honig, he worked at Felton-Empire and Flora Springs. James thinks his wine interest first ignited in 1975 when he went to France during the harvest to visit his sister who had married a Frenchman.

Hall hasn't changed Honig's full bodied style of Sauvignon Blanc which de-emphasizes grassy smells in order to match up well with food. He is trying to maintain a "grapefruit and pear" nose, while increasing complexity. In 1987 he experimented with a small lot of Sémillon picked at 21°Brix. At that sugar level, the grape doesn't have much Sémillon smell, which was fine by him. "I'm not interested in the nose as much as the structure," he said. "The unique feature of Sémillon as a varietal might be its strong pH combined with weak acid. The ones I'll use came in at .6 acid and 3.2 pH. I'll make it like the Sauvignon Blanc except use Prise de Mousse yeast." He also tried a little experiment with canopy management to see if he could pinpoint alternative ideas for keeping vegetal character out of the wines. They went through one vineyard block hedging every fourth row and removing leaves. It was a fairly labor-intensive exercise. This experiment gave them two lots of grapes which they increased to four experimental samples by barrel fermenting half of each and doing the other halves in stainless.

One big change Hall has initiated is a move into Chardonnay and Cabernet. "It's a market driven decision," he says. "We're barrel fermenting 100% of the Chardonnay and 50% of the barrels are new. We'll avoid malo-lactic, but leave a portion on the lees. Should be pretty nice stuff."

HONIG

1987

Sauvignon Blanc

Napa Valley

Estate Bottled by Honig Cellars,
Rutherford, Ca. Alc. 12.5% by Vol. Contains Sulfites

1986 Sauvignon Blanc	10,000 cases
Estate Vyd	750 ml

Grapes from 9-yr-old, Wente clone vines on deep, Yolo series sandy loam soil. Picked 31 Aug to 14 Sept at 22.8°Brix, .85 acid, 3.1 pH. 25 ppm SO₂ at crusher, no skin soak, settled after pressing. Frmtd with Steinberg yeast, 40% frmtd in barrels from 7°Brix, no M-L. Btld Apr '87 at 13.6 alc, .75 acid, 3.3 pH.

How is your vineyard changing?

"The experiment with leaf removal in every other row of Sauvignon Blanc was inconclusive. There was very little difference in the wines. Our clone just isn't very 'grassy.' It has more of a muscaty note than other clones I've tasted. The Sémillon was grassier than our Sauvignon Blanc. So we grafted the Sémillon over to Merlot. We considered adding some Cabernet Franc, but our soil is too rich and sandy. Cabernet Franc needs stress on hillsides. Cabernet Sauvignon turns out to be softer, rounder and fruitier here by itself. We now have 4 acres of Merlot, 7 acres of Cabernet Sauvignon and another 11 acres of Cabernet Sauvignon which will begin bearing in 1990.

"We made our second vintage of Estate Chardon-nay this year; about 1,500 cases. It's 100% barrel fermented with 40% new barrels and 15% malolactic. The grapes came in at 23.2°Brix and .8 acid. Tonnage was off about 25% for the whole ranch. Sauvignon Blanc was the hardest hit. We didn't get a lot of shot berries, but there was a big second crop, which is typical of poor set years, and we dropped that. Acid levels were funny too. We had low sugar in the Cabernet and also low acid. Field samples were unpredictable throughout the Valley. They would test high, and then come in low. All the grapes stalled at 22°Brix. It might have had something to do with a series of 40°F mornings and overcast from wildfires in the hills."

James Hall

James Hall   RG

Michael Honig though window illustrated on label   RG

HOUTZ VINEYARDS

Here is a pop quiz. Who do you call when the neighbor's bull gets loose in your vineyard? Clue: It's not the police. Margy Houtz has found the virtues of a country home include discovering how to solve such problems on your own. It took her 6 months to get over an absence of classical music on the radio, but she has concluded the bucolic life is invigorating. "We're up here to have fun," she says. "The wine business is a career, but we've chosen to avoid the syndrome you are surrounded with every day in Los Angeles. Just because a little bit of something is good, does not mean that ten times as much will be better."

Dave Houtz has spent over 30 years building a real estate business in Santa Monica. His firm is small and personal and very successful. Margy

HOUTZ VINEYARDS

1986
santa ynez valley
sauvignon blanc

ESTATE BOTTLED BY HOUTZ VINEYARDS
LOS OLIVOS, CALIFORNIA B.W.C.A. 5201
ALCOHOL 12.2% BY VOLUME
CONTAINS SULFITES

was a systems analyst prior to their marriage in 1976. She's also an accomplished cook who studied Italian at UCLA and lived for a year in northern Italy. Dave and Margy came to the Santa Ynez Valley originally looking for a weekend get-away. They spent 4 years considering options, including cattle ranching. Viticulture and winemaking were ideas that only dawned on them as they began to meet people and consider the future of the Valley. "Santa Barbara County makes construction very difficult, and employment is limited," Margy explains. "It is unlikely that Santa Ynez will be over-run with people very soon."

They bought 35 acres of raw land in 1980 and planted 5 to Chardonnay, 6 to Sauvignon Blanc and 5 to Cabernet Sauvignon. They also planted 400 apple trees and a garden. They built a barn, a house and a gazebo. Then they acquired dogs, horses, sheep, chickens, cats, ducks, goats and a few peacocks. "So much for the weekend idea," says Margy. "I was a little shaky about caring for this menagerie, and Dave was uncertain about maintaining his business with just a couple days per week in Los Angeles. Everything, however, has worked out nicely. He enjoys wearing two hats, and he's learned how to delegate better. I'm busy, and that makes me happy." The Houtz label depicts an 18th century engraving of two lambs symbolizing a Bach Cantata, *Sheep May Safely Graze*.

Margy grew up in San Francisco. Wine was a regular event. In fact, it was her father who taught her to cook because he would come home and "relax by going out in the kitchen to chop and sing." But neither Dave nor Margy consider themselves wine connoisseurs. They shamelessly echo America's most frequently heard refrain on the subject of stylistic preference, "We know what we like." More importantly, they figure their taste is similar to

what most people enjoy. Having neither debt nor shareholders, they can keep prices in the low to moderate range. They have won prizes for their Sauvignon Blanc at County competitions, and they are confident that even better wines are waiting for release in 1988.

John Kerr is the consultant at Houtz. John was a helicopter door gunner in Viet Nam, and got shot down during the Cambodian incursion. When he got out of the service in 1971, he sold Hi-Fi equipment full time and wine on the side. But his interest lay in wine production, so he jumped at an opportunity in 1980 to work the crush at Chalone. He worked the next year with Dan Lee at Jekel and then several years at Ventana. His wife is in the Forest Service, and they moved to the Santa Ynez Valley in 1984. Since then, John has done consulting work with Babcock, Brander and Byron vineyards in addition to Houtz.

Although Dave and Margy are not peasant farmers, manual labor is very apparent at their winery. Grapes are picked into lug boxes, which are then lifted by hand into the Zambelli crusher. It is slow, but the press will only handle 2 tons at a time, so the crusher doesn't really hold up the process at all. The size of the winery also dictates how much barrel fermentation can be done. There is more room for barrels since 1987 when a case storage facility was dug into the hill the Chardonnay is planted on. Bottling is also labor intensive. They get the wine cold stable, then sterile filter into a set of two Gai six-spout fillers. Corks are put in with a hand corker, which gets pretty tiring after a few hours. It takes a minimum of 7 people to run the bottling line. They can only turn out 50 cases an hour. Even at that, they have to bring the bottles back later, and put the capsules and labels on as the wine is sold.

1986 Chardonnay   1,000 cases
Estate Vyd   750 ml

Davis 108 clone with good sized clusters yielding 5-6 t/a on a south facing shale/loam hillside. Picked at 22°Brix, .9 acid, 3.4 pH. Settled 2 days. 50% barrel-frmtd with Pasteur Champagne yeast, no M-L. Aged 9 mos in Allier and Vosges oak with medium toast, 20% new.

1986 Sauvignon Blanc   1,000 cases
Estate Vyd   750 ml

Grapes planted in '82. Hand picked over 5 days at 22°Brix into wooden lug boxes. Frmtd with an *S. Bayanus* yeast which finishes very strong. Aged 4 mos in French oak.

1985 Cabernet Sauvignon   800 cases
Estate Vyd   750 ml

Vines planted in 1982. Picked at 23°Brix, 3.5 pH. On the skins 10-14 days in open stnls, pumped over 3x/day. Aged 18 mos in French oak, 20% new.

How do you choose a time to pick?

"I do my own lab work. Generally I'm looking for lower alcohol and pH, but good flavor. I go through the vineyard with a refractometer around 10 a.m. when the sun hits the grapes and the sugar starts to rise. I go to every fifth row, because we have a sprinkler head at every fourth row, and then walk in 25 paces. I sample clusters on alternate sides; from the ends of canes, center of canes and next to the trunk.

"I'm trying to keep some consistency from year to year. We don't blend our wines from several sources, so I can only make what God gives us. We are on rolling hills which slope down to the north and west from a flat top. I don't use single berry selection. There can be as much as 5°Brix and .2 pH difference throughout the vineyard. Berries at the tip of a cluster can be 1°Brix sweeter than at the shoulder. Clusters next to the trunk can be 2°Brix sweeter than those at the ends of the canes.

"We don't pick second crop and we leave any bunch rot behind. I pay by the hour in order to get careful selection. It takes about 10 days to pick our whole vineyard with five guys. There is often a break of a week or two in the middle. That can make it difficult to get a crew. We have a man who has been with us since the vineyard was planted and he can usually find a crew if I give him a week's notice. He gets on a bicycle and rides around talking to people. If it looks like ripening isn't going to be spread out evenly, we'll hire more people. I'd even use gringos, but only as a last resort because they're not very good. This job takes experience."

Dave Houtz

BL

DOMAINE KARAKASH

The night after he took his final Master of Science examination at the University of Belgrade, Yugoslavia, Miles Karakasevic (pronounced kah rah KA shev ik) bolted for the West. His "emigration" was a clandestine crossing of the Austrian frontier and on to the Enology School at Geisenheim, Germany. It was 1962, and the stand-off between the U.S. and the Soviet Union over missiles in Cuba was intensifying the cold war. Soviet tanks had crushed an unarmed resistance in Hungary four years earlier, but the threat of external domination was nothing new to southern Slavs. Miles' family were Serbians whose trade in wine, brandy and pigs went back twelve generations to 1751. They had endured religious wars plus domination by Turks, Napoleon, Austrians, internal dictators and the Nazis before nationalization of their business under Tito. Miles valued his winemaking heritage, but figured his skills were more likely to blossom some place else.

He did synthetic organic chemistry for the pharmaceutical industry in Canada six years. Then he got an opportunity to make wine in Kalamazoo, Michigan. He met his wife Susan there. However, refering to the "foxy" smell of *V. Labrusca* grapes, Miles ruefully admits, "Methyl anthranilate drove me out of Michigan. It was like garlic in an Italian kitchen. Everything you made smelled of it." He came to California in 1970 to work for United Vintners before becoming assistant winemaker at Beringer. Eventually he went off on his own as a consultant to Tijsseling, and later Baccalla, in Mendocino County. Throughout this period he dreamed of a Karakash winery with a label drawn from a 14th century icon of Demetrios, the family saint.

Miles bought 17 acres on Spring Mountain Road above St. Helena in 1982. Chosing to grow slowly rather than let bankers dictate his life, he makes his wines at facilities where he is the consultant. Grapes are chosen from Mendocino appellations. His teenage son Marko helps out in the winery, while Susan and daughter Lara handle marketing. It is a family operation, and Miles is determined to keep it that way.

The wines are "instantly recognizable" and definitely not standard California fare. "We're not trying to make lemonade," Miles says emphatically. Chardonnay and Sauvignon Blanc are pressed from whole clusters of fully ripe grapes which are neither crushed nor destemmed. He uses a bladder press which is very gentle. No separation of the juice into press factions is allowed. Most wineries separate the free run juice from the later press fractions which may have 10% solids and many harsh phenolic components. Miles gets 170 gallons/ton with only 2% solids out of his press. He uses Montrachet yeast and says, "I never have problems with H_2S because I don't introduce sulphur in the form of SO_2 prior to fermentation. My growers don't apply sulphur in the vineyard for at least 2 months before harvest. If they have a mildew problem in August, it is too late to do anything about it anyway."

All Karakash wines go part way through a spontaneous malo-lactic fermentation during the alcohol fermentation. "The wild M-L bacteria are not as strong as a pure strain inoculae," Miles explains, "and they succumb to the alcohol before consuming all the malic acid. That is important because malic acid eventually forms some of the fruitiest esters in wine." All of the wine is barrel fermented at warm temperatures in Burgundian Vosges and Allier oak. It spends significant time in contact with the lees. Miles does sterile filter to stabilize the wine, but filtration does nothing to reduce the wine's massive body and very strong flavor. Somehow you know that will be the case given Miles' background and the enthusiastic Karakasevic family. Their name means "black eyebrows."

In addition to making 4,000 cases a year of table wine, Miles has imported an alembic pot still from Cognac and begun producing 500 cases a year of fine brandy. He blends barrel fermented Chardonnay with brandy liqueur in a proprietary dessert wine called Charbay. It is so popular with restaurants which have wine-only licenses, that he sold his first batch out in less than a month. Even the Peninsula Hotel in Hong Kong is a customer.

Karakash

VINTAGE 1983
MENDOCINO
CHARDONNAY

PRODUCED AND BOTTLED BY DOMAINE KARAKASH
UKIAH MENDOCINO COUNTY CALIFORNIA U.S.A.
ALCOHOL 13.4% BY VOLUME

1985 Chardonnay	1,800 cases
Mendocino	750 ml

Vyds 10 mi south of Ukiah in Russian River benchlands with deep, well drained gravel. 3.5 t/a picked 16 Sept at 23.2°Brix, .87 acid, 3.29 pH from 7-yr-old, dry farmed vines. No SO_2 until after frmtn, Montrachet yeast, spontaneous M-L. Frmtd and aged in dense, hardwood oak from the Vosges mountains, heavy toast, 40-60% new.

1984 Sauvignon Blanc	1,400 cases
Mendocino	750 ml

Picked 15 Sept at 22.9°Brix, .9 acid, 3.3 pH. Barrel Frmtd 12 days at 54°F through 68°F. No SO_2, spontaneous M-L. 36 days on lees, 5 mos in Vosges and Allier barrels. Btld June '85 at 12.9 alc, .79 acid, 3.27 pH.

nv Charbay	650 cases
Sonoma County	750 ml

Family secret proportions of 4 yr old barrel-aged brandy liqueur and barrel-fermented '83 Chardonnay. 18.0 alc, sweet.

How do you pick a yeast?

"In the wine I will distill for brandy to use in our Charbay I want one that has been isolated for low production of aldehydes. Distillation will concentrate any aldehydes 10-12 fold. Some yeasts produce a lot of them. Dr. Ralph Kunkee at Davis has recently bio-engineered a new strain that produces virtually no aldehydes. It is most applicable to huge distillers who do not have the opportunity to control their fermentations and distillations the way I can at my small scale.

"For the table wines, I don't like fruity or per-fumey strains. I like bottle age character. I use Montrachet because I'm a traditionalist. I haven't had any H_2S problems. In think H_2S production is a function of temperature. It tends to form at high temperatures, although you wouldn't always notice it since vigorous fermentations can vent it with all the CO_2 that's evolving.

"Prise de Mousse is very fashionable. It is a strong fermenter and many people have been having trouble with stuck fermentations in Chardonnay. It is a *S. Bayanus* which basically indicates it has traditionally been used to conduct the secondary fermentation inside bottles of Champagne. One of the reasons it has become so popular all of a sudden is that Red Star brought it out in dry form this year. I suspect there will be a new popular strain next year."

Miles Karakasevic

RB

KATHRYN KENNEDY

This part of the Santa Clara Valley was known as the Westside in the 1800s. Cabernet Franc grew here then, and it won international awards as a "Medoc style" wine. Even Louis Martini once concluded that the best red wines in California came from Santa Clara's Westside before attention turned to Napa. In the 1950s and '60s, Martin Ray was one of the wine industry's most progressive spokesmen. He was the first vintner to produce 100% varietal Chardonnay and label it as such. He pioneered cane pruning, and budwood from his Mt. Eden vineyard has been widely propagated throughout the state. Saratoga has a rich viticultural heritage. Unfortunately the gentle slopes of these hillsides have largely been developed as homes over the last 30 years.

Following a divorce, Kathryn Kennedy found herself with 10 acres of property in 1971. An adjacent farm had just been turned into 30 homes. The developer approached the City Council to say that every subdivision needed two access roads for fire trucks. Therefore, he coyly pointed out, Kathryn's property needed a road through the middle of it. She fought this intrusion, and simultaneously embraced a plan to put the property into grape vines. The Knight-Smith Vineyard across Pierce Road from Kathryn had been planted to Cabernet Sauvignon in the '40s. Kathryn decided she rather liked the wine Gemellos Winery was making from the Knight-Smith grapes.

Kathryn's vineyard was planted in 1973. It is entirely Cabernet Sauvignon, following in the Martin Ray tradition. The vines are planted on their own roots from cuttings taken in David Bruce's original Estate vineyard. Kathryn commuted to and from U.C. Davis for an entire semester in order to master recommended viticultural techniques. Martin Ray made wine from the '76 crop. The '77 and '78 crops became the MEV label from Mt. Eden. Kathryn Kennedy Vineyards bonded themselves as a winery in 1979.

Bill Anderson was the first winemaker. Kathryn's son Martin graduated from college at about this same time. He had majored in International Relations, but reached the conclusion that he already missed the opportunity to work out of doors. Martin took over as vineyard manager, learned from Anderson and became the winemaker in 1982.

Martin has some interesting ideas about the possiblility of planting additional vines in his limited space. They planted the last 1.5 acres available in spring 1988 using a close (6' x 10') spacing of vines because that particular piece of land is quite rocky and the vines are likely to show low vigor. Another 30% of the property is similar, except the vines in those areas are planted to 8' x 12' spacing. Martin thinks he might be able to raise his production 20% by interplanting the rows in those areas. "We would rather put in more plants than start irrigating," he says.

Kathryn and Martin have long been aware of the choice between cash and the agricultural heritage of the Westside. Two more homes were recently built on property adjacent to their vineyard. The land alone for each one cost $285,000. There are homes in the area built on quarter acres. "We tell each other daily how much we appreciate this lifestyle of raising something out of the earth," Martin explains, "but we wonder how long we will be able to maintain it."

1985

KATHRYN KENNEDY

CABERNET SAUVIGNON
SANTA CRUZ MOUNTAINS APPELLATION

ESTATE BOTTLED

BY KATHRYN KENNEDY WINERY IN SARATOGA CALIFORNIA
ALCOHOL 13.7% BY VOLUME · CONTAINS SULFUR DIOXIDE

| 1985 Cabernet Sauvignon | 770 cases |
| Estate | 750 ml |

Picked 18 and 28 Sept and 5 Oct at 23.8°Brix, .90 acid, 3.24 pH. Frmtd with Champagne yeast in 3/4 ton bins, punched down 3x/day, on skins 14-20 days. Aged 18 mos in 80% Nevers and 20% American oak, 25% new wood. 13.7 alc.

How has your vineyard production been recently?

"Our soil is unique. We have a creek and I suspect the whole area was influenced by that drainage long ago. Generally it is loam with clay, underlain by sandstone and golfball sized river rock. The good soil has largely washed off the higher hill tops. We dry-farm and in drought years the water just drains away. We have 8 acres. This year we will do just under 300 cases. That is about 3,000 bottles from 3,000 vines. We've had 3 years in a row under 400 cases. The price has to go up and allocations are getting tight. Our best year was '82. We got 860 cases. That '82 wine won a Gold along with Best of Region at the State Fair.

"We are the warmest vineyard in the Santa Cruz Mountains appellation. U.C. Davis calls it a Region 2. The coolest years are best for us. '80, '82 and '85 were spectacular. Years like '84 provide a 'thrilling' harvest because maturity comes early and quickly.

Martin Mathis

Debbie Egner, winery asst.   CL

Kathryn Kennedy vyd & winery in Saratoga with Knight-Smith vyd across the street   RG

LAMBORN FAMILY VINTNERS

Robert Lamborn was designated a journalist by the 15th Air Force in Africa and Italy during World War II, and assigned to intelligence gathering. For the last 25 years he has been a private investigator. He continues to combine writing with investigative work as a consultant to several media companies who want a police perspective when the police "won't or can't talk about a matter." Bob and his partner were agents for the Hearst family when Patty was kidnapped, and recently they were hired to investigate aspects of the Iran-Contra hearings.

Lamborn chuckles when asked to compare his life to the one Tom Selleck portrays on TV. "I drive a Dodge; not a Ferrari," he says. "I'm usually home at 9 pm, reading, in bed, alone. I only carry a gun under duress, and I haven't been in a fist fight since Junior High School." Far from being hard bitten or cynical, Bob speaks gently and is a very supportive listener. "We're usually hired in cases that require extreme discretion," he says of the image question. "The thrill of the hunt is exciting, but the hunt is an analytical exercise."

Lamborn came to Howell Mountain seeking an escape from the "crisis mentality" of his job.

The tiny village of Angwin was ideal. It seemed to be a "window in time," with a pace and attitudes straight out of the 1800's. Seventh Day Adventists at Pacific Union College are a majority of the citizenry. They are not inclined to trendiness. There's no booze, no meat, no tobacco and no condiments to be found in town. "Finding the town is hard enough," Lamborn relates. "I rarely feel compelled to search locally for mustard and cigars." There is no Saturday mail delivery, but there is one on Sunday. Angwin sits in the cup of an old volcano, and the college gets live steam heat from holes drilled a couple thousand feet down. Lamborn thinks that whole system was built in the 1920's.

Bob's interest in wine occurred after he acquired his hide-away property. He had grown up in a hard drinking family of miners in northern British Columbia. In Italy, he converted to vermouth with a twist. But on Howell Mountain, table wine was a prudent social choice. "You can hardly go to dinner at Randy Dunn's house and not drink wine," Bob points out. Dunn is a neighbor whose winery newsletter Lamborn has written for five years. "Before moving here, becoming a winegrower seemed about as likely for me as becoming an astronaut. I caught the fever of Howell Mountain's wine renaissance when I discovered remnants of the old Ferazzi Vineyard on my property. Now the rejuvenating process of pruning nude vines in bone-chilling drizzle is magic to me. It's a love affair, some neurotic addiction, alternately seducing and abusing my citified body."

Lamborn's vineyard is flat

as a pancake, but his driveway ends at an edge of the mountain and looks right down the throat of Napa Valley. He planted his 9 acres of Zinfandel in 1979. Being a rookie viticulturalist, he figured he'd stick with a variety which had reputedly won prizes in Paris before the turn of the century from grapes on his land. He was amazed at the way his neighbors would drive over, rest a foot on the bumper of their pick-up truck and offer detailed advice about everything from rootstock to the proper grip on pruning shears. Bob wrote it all down. Then he started entering all the information he could find on Zinfandel into his computer. "What I got," he reports, "was an almost spiritual sense of proportion about the subjectivity of the whole matter. There is no correct position and rarely any concensus. It is art. There's a certain amount of science, but in the end answers are very personal." Lamborn found this pursuit rather soothing when juxtaposed with his weekday activities.

At first most of Lamborn's crop was vinified by Kent Rosenblum whose winery is near Lamborn's Oakland office. Grapes were also sold to Sattui Winery. Bonded himself now, Bob has hired Larry Langbehn (former Freemark Abbey winemaker) as consultant. Lamborn seeks a "user friendly wine that I'll live long enough to enjoy. Something I can drink without my knees buckling or my Fruit of the Looms smoking." Bob's son Michael owns a vineyard next door, and Bob says, "I'll let him make the family's nuclear mountain Zin." Lamborn also has 10 acres facing southwest which he would like to terrace and plant to Sauvignon Blanc and Sémillon. "I'm going to do it as soon as I win Lotto," he says unexpectedly.

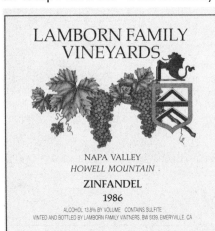

LAMBORN FAMILY VINEYARDS

NAPA VALLEY
HOWELL MOUNTAIN

ZINFANDEL
1986

ALCOHOL 13.8% BY VOLUME   CONTAINS SULFITE
VINTED AND BOTTLED BY LAMBORN FAMILY VINTNERS. BW 5139, EMERYVILLE, CA

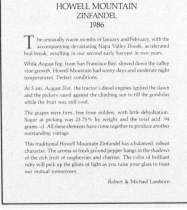

HOWELL MOUNTAIN
ZINFANDEL
1986

The unusually warm months of January and February, with the accompanying devastating Napa Valley floods, accelerated bud break, resulting in our second early harvest in two years.

While August fog, from San Francisco Bay, slowed down the valley vine growth, Howell Mountain had sunny days and moderate night temperatures. Perfect conditions.

At 5 am, August 31st, the tractor's diesel engines ignited the dawn and the pickers raced against the climbing sun to fill the gondolas while the fruit was still cool.

The grapes were firm, free from mildew, with little dehydration. Sugar at picking was 23.75% by weight and the total acid .94 grams/cl. All these elements have come together to produce another outstanding vintage.

This traditional Howell Mountain Zinfandel has a balanced, robust character. The aroma of fresh ground pepper hangs in the shadows of the rich fruit of raspberries and cherries. The color of brilliant ruby will pick up the glints of light as you raise your glass to toast our mutual tomorrows.

Robert & Michael Lamborn

1987 Zinfandel	800 cases
Howell Mtn	750 ml

Vyd at 2,200 ft on Red Aiken-volcanic soil, high plateau planted in '79. Old Napa Valley clone on AxR₁ rootstock with some scions taken from old Ferazzi Vyd vines. 2 t/a picked 31 Aug 23.7°Brix, .94 acid. Frmtd with Montrachet yeast at 90°F, punched down 3x/day, on skins 11 days. Aged in French and American oak. Btld Oct '88 at 13.8 alc.

Are you going to make a late harvest Zin?

"The words Late Harvest are attractive when applied to German types of wine. Zin is not so lucky. Its image went downhill hand-in-hand with deteriorating quality during the early '70s. I've spoken with several retailers about LH Zin. They say that an educational effort could bring it back just as there is a new interest in good red Zinfandel throughout the marketplace. The criteria seem to be modest residual sugar (<2%), don't fortify it, and introduce it as an accompaniment to social things or food items.

"I've been making small amounts for my own use for some time. I get to 17% alcohol and 0.5% rs; just a suggestion of sweetness. I age in 3-year-old French oak used for Chardonnay by Acacia Winery. When served at Christmas with hot minced pie, the wine is lusciously extravagant. I also like it with those Italian cookies which contain cloves and currents. Or after-dinner cafés.

"Of course, the people I've been talking to also suggest that LH Zin needs to be called something else. I'm starting to consider proprietary names a little tiresome at this point, so I'm fresh out of ideas. It's a little pretentious for a winery my size to talk about promoting a name that the whole industry would adopt."

Bob Lamborn

(When phoned unexpectedly for this interview, Bob Lamborn anwered the phone, "Hiroshima Vyds. This wine will blow you away.")

RG

LAUREL GLEN VINEYARD

Harvard education, several years in a Zen commune, three lovely daughters, a professional violin career and now a "classic" Cabernet vineyard in the Valley of the Moon. Patrick Campbell may not have it all, but he's had a lot of it. He even has a wife named Faith.

After graduating from Pomona College in 1970 with a degree in English, Patrick went to Harvard for a Masters in Philosophy and Religion. He abandoned his notion of a career in academia to come to the Bay Area and play violin. Until 1987 he continued to hold down a "union" viola chair with the Santa Rosa Symphony. When he lived in the commune, they collectively owned a vineyard. That is where he discovered the joy in working vines.

Patrick and Faith bought Laurel Glen Vineyard near Glen Ellen in 1976, retaining the historic name. Seven vineyard parcels totaling 27 acres are grouped together on the eastern slope of Sonoma Mountain. They get full morning sun, but only oblique rays in the afternoon which gives them a very even ripening day. There is a marine influence from the ocean across the

Santa Rosa plain, and also from San Pablo Bay to the south, but both currents of cooling air have to come around the mountain to reach Laurel Glen. As a result, the grapes are usually out of the fog in the summer. Sonoma Mountain is an approved viticultural appellation with nearly 700 acres currently bearing. It also has a long history going back to pioneer German winemakers like Kohler and Froehling, who planted land which later became famous as Jack London's ranch.

The Campbells sold their grapes for a couple of years. Chateau St. Jean used them for vineyard designated Cabernets in the mid '70s. Then their fruit was a major component in the Kenwood "Artist Series" Cabernets from '78 through '82. Patrick built his 4,000 sq. ft. winery in 1980. "You can't make enough money to service a mortgage by selling grapes to other people," he says. "From a creative standpoint it is a little like raising kids to adolescence and then turning them over to someone else. I figured any winemaking mistakes might as well be mine." Having collected gushing reviews from all the top publications in the last three years, Patrick can make these remarks rather casually.

Besides Cabernet Sauvignon, Laurel Glen grows Cabernet Franc. The cuttings came from Mt. Veeder. They tried Malbec, Petite Verdot and Merlot, but didn't like the results. "I thought they diluted my wine rather than adding anything to it," Patrick says. "They also didn't grow well in my thin soil. I think Merlot needs heavy clay,

and the other two were just junk in my location. But Cab Franc grows well, sets a good crop, comes off early and adds a spicey dimension without sacrificing intensity or aging ability."

Campbell does not change the style of his wine from year to year. Cabernet Sauvignon is always the backbone, and he has introduced a second label (Counterpoint) for wine which he thinks departs from the style and standard of his primary marque. But he keeps a progressive eye out for improvement possibilities. He met Serge Hochar, a third generation Lebanese of French extraction, on a trip to New York. Serge makes Ch. Musar by blending Syrah and Cabernet Sauvignon. Campbell was impressed by someone who has to pick grapes while dodging bullets, and he liked the wine. Patrick got to thinking about grapes which might add a dollop of additional fragrance to the Laurel Glen Cabernet. Having already given the traditional Bordeaux varieties a fair shot, he decided to experiment with Syrah, Tempranillo (makes R. Parker's favorite, Pesguera brand in Spain) and Mataro (Mourvédre from the Rhone Valley). In 1988 Patrick grafted 150 vines on his property to each candidate. "I'll give them a 7 year trial," he says. "If any of them grow well and add a positive dimension to my wine, I'll try them out in Counterpoint for a couple years while considering them for Laurel Glen. If not, I'll give 'em the hook."

Shaking hands with Patrick can be startling. He weighs less than 130 pounds, but has hands like an NFL lineman. He hires one man full-time in the vineyard, plus a helper once a week to top barrels in the winery. Otherwise Patrick does all the work himself. It would be an extraordinary accomplishment for most people. To Patrick, who had polio as a child and performs this labor on crutches, it's just like another day at the office.

ESTATE BOTTLED BY LAUREL GLEN VINEYARD
SONOMA MOUNTAIN, GLEN ELLEN, CA
TABLE WINE • CONTAINS SULFITES

Laurel Glen

SONOMA MOUNTAIN
1986 CABERNET SAUVIGNON

1984 Cabernet Sauvignon — 4,200 cases
Estate — 750 ml

8% Cabernet Franc. Estate vines were planted in 1968 on red, rocky, thin, volcanic soil with NE aspect at 1,000 ft near Glen Ellen. They are on St. George rootstock and yield 3 t/a. Picked end Sept through first week of Oct at 22.9°Brix, .89 acid. Frmtd in 2,000 gal open stnls tanks at 92°F with Montrachet yeast. Punched down 4x/day, on skins 10 days. Aged 22 mos in new Nadalie Nevers oak with light toast. Egg white fined, btld Aug '88 at 12.8 alc, .68 acid, 3.45 pH.

1983 Zinfandel — 300 cases
Sonoma Mtn — 750 ml

100-yr-old vines from property just above the Estate Vyd. One-time-only wine as the vyd was pulled out by a new owner in '84. Picked 10 Oct at 22.5°Brix. Made like the Cab above altho aged in neutral Nevers and American oak. Btld June '85 at 12.6 alc, .7 acid, 3.4 pH.

1985 Cochino de Oro — 120 cases
LH Sauvignon Blanc — 375 ml

Botrytized Sauvignon Blanc from the northern Dry Creek Vly. Patrick, who speaks spanish well, told the pickers to bring him the "cochino" (lit. pig or hog) grapes. The phrase is idiomatic for filthy or dirty, and it corresponds roughly to the German "edelfaule" or the French "pourriture noble" which both mean noble rot. 38°Brix, 1.2 acid at harvest. No SO₂, but the must was fined with Sparkloid. Frmtd at 65°F with a special late harvest yeast. Aged 2 mos in Nevers oak. Sterile filtered, btld Aug '86 at 14 alc, .9 acid, 3.6 pH, 9% rs.

Do you pay pickers by the hour?

"I used to pay $7/hour in order to get the crews to go carefully. Now I pay $90/ton because most of my guys have been with me long enough to know what is acceptable and what isn't. We do a lot of selection in the vineyard. Then I personally do some selection at the crusher. They don't want to pick and carry fruit that I'm going to throw out, because they won't get credit for it. Plus, they don't want to sit around and wait for me to paw through their buckets, which happens if I start finding poor quality clusters.

"I don't use raisins, and I don't use the unripe fruit on severely virused vines. We also avoid 'water berries.' Those are clusters with light red colored berries you can see through. We also leave what the pickers call 'pachichis.' They look like large clusters, but the berries are withered.

"Second crop, the small clusters that form further out along the canes, is worth considering, but not every year. It depends what happens during the extra two or three weeks necessary for them to ripen. I didn't take them in '87 because of the October heat wave. I let a home winemaker come in and pick them for himself. When the first crop is below average size, the seconds will usually be above normal. Sometimes they amount to half a ton per acre. If I go back for them, I use the wine in my second label, Counterpoint."

Patrick Campbell

JR

LOLONIS

Tryfon Lolonis grew up in Tripolis, Greece. His parents raised grapes. So did a lot of their friends. But 1914 wasn't exactly a great year to be a young man picking grapes on the Greek peninsula. World War I had just broken out in the Balkan countries to the north. Tryfon and his brother William "wanted to come to the country that has everything." They landed at Ellis Island and then came west working on the railroads and in the Colorado mines. When they hit San Francisco, they took the Northwest Pacific Railway to Ukiah on the inland side of the coastal mountains in Mendocino County.

A real estate man took them to see some forest property on a bench high above the east fork of the Russian River. The bought 120 acres. As they cleared the land they sold firewood in Ukiah. Tryfon built a house and wrote to his father in Greece. Before leaving he had noticed a comely 17-year-old girl named Eugenia. Of course, Eugenia had never met Tryfon. But Tryfon's father made a convincing case to Eugenia's father about the splendors of life in California's

Redwood Valley. She accepted his proposal and traveled to California to meet her future husband.

In short order the Lolonis brothers had cornered the firewood market in Ukiah. At one point they had 50 wood choppers working for them. They were able to maintain a firewood monopoly in a town surrounded by redwood forest because they had mules and wagons to move the product. They bought the first Model T in Ukiah. They planted wheat and oats as they cleared the land. They also planted grapes. Prohibition limited the sale of wine, but they shipped grapes to San Francisco and the east coast. They made some wine for the Christian Brothers. Most of their grapes were the dominant black varieties of that era, Zinfandel and Carignane. In the mid-'20s an arsonist nearly wiped them out, destroying all the buildings on their property, plus 100 cords of firewood. The only structure remaining was the original house Tryfon had built for his mail order bride. They started over.

Today Tryfon and Eugenia's children run a thriving farm business. The Lolonis vineyard covers 300 acres of gradually sloping land at 1,000 feet elevation. On the west side their property drops off sharply to the valley below. Lake Mendocino was formed by damming the east fork of the Russian River. It is just 2 miles south of Lolonis Vineyard. Their land is a farming masterpiece. Deep soil with virtually no frost danger because of their position on the side of the mountain. They only average 24 inches of rain a year, half of what the coastal Mendocino mountains expect, but their soil is extremely well drained anyway because the water just runs through and off the bench. They have buried drain pipe in the vineyard to avoid erosion. Their elevation makes them cooler than Ukiah. They grow Cabernet Sauvignon, Petite Sirah and Zinfandel on the southwest side of the

property where the slope is steepest and the sun shines longest. Pinot Noir, Sauvignon Blanc and Chardonnay grow on the cooler northeast side. The vines range from 5 to 50 years old. So many wineries have been anxious to pay a premium for these grapes, and designate Lolonis Vineyard on the label, that Tryfon's 3 sons decided in 1980 to start making wine for themselves.

Ullysses is the vineyard manager. He lives on the property nearby his mother's house with his wife Jofrid. Nick is a U.C. Davis graduate and a classmate of Dimitri Tchelistcheff. Petros and his wife Maureen handle the marketing. They have purchased their own barrels and stainless steel tanks, but rent space at Mendocino Vineyards to make their 8,000 cases. Chardonnay is their claim to fame. They also sell grapes to Kendall-Jackson, Fetzer, Mondavi, David Bruce, Dolan and Parducci.

Petros left the family farm to become president of AMC's shoe division. For 25 years he bought shoes for 30 major department store chains. Each year he would go to London and Paris to see the shoe shows. Then he would continue on to Florence and to Spain to talk with manufacturers and designers. As Hong Kong was added to this itinerary in the last decade, the pace began to wear on him. "If I was going to kill myself," he says, "I decided it should be for my own ticket." He now works out of Walnut Creek, but figures he will move back to the family property before too long.

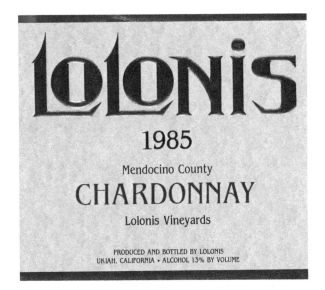

Lolonis

1985

Mendocino County

CHARDONNAY

Lolonis Vineyards

PRODUCED AND BOTTLED BY LOLONIS
UKIAH. CALIFORNIA • ALCOHOL 13% BY VOLUME

1986 Chardonnay	4,000 cases
Estate	750 ml

Picked third week of Sept at 23°Brix. 80% cold frmtd in stnls. 20% barrel frmtd. No M-L. Aged 4 mos in small cooperage.

1987 Fume Blanc	4,000 cases
Estate	750 ml

Frmtd in stnls. 60% aged in small barrels of which 80% are Nevers and Limousin oak.

1983 LH Sauvignon Blanc	200 cases
Estate	375 ml

Picked at 32°Brix. 13.8 alc, 8.7% rs.

Tell me about your Dukakis connection.

"My wife was in Boston. She just walked into his office. He is rarely there, so it was a piece of luck to find him sitting behind his desk. She gave him a bottle of our Chardonnay. I guess they liked it because he wrote us a letter about how much he and Kitty had enjoyed it with dinner. Then we met them again at a fund raiser here in Los Altos. As you may imagine, we are Dukakis supporters. Next time Maureen was in Boston she went to his office again to leave a bottle of the new vintage with a note. He walked in while she was writing the note and said, 'Are you following me. Where are we going next?'

"Then Art Agnos (new Mayor of San Francisco) took a lot of our Chardonnay to the Convention in Atlanta to give to delegates. Liking wine is sort of an ethnic obligation for Greeks. Since then, one of the Dukakis aides has contacted us regularly to get wine for events they hold.

"We would like to have Lolonis Chardonnay served at the Inauguration."

Petros Lolonis

Eugenia and her 3 sons, Petros, Ullysses and Nick   RG

Tryfon (on truck), William, eldest daughter Nicki and the Model T

LUCAS WINERY

Lucas Winery is the kind of operation that any wine growing region needs. They are also a bit of an anomaly. They are the prototype hands-on, artistic winery, but their location is surrounded by fields of stainless steel tanks owned by the world's largest producers. Lucas ignores this image and concentrates on the area's advantages. Lodi has deep soils, lots of sunshine, a breeze most afternoons and low overnight temperatures.

Dave and Tamara Lucas recognized the deep berry smell of Lodi Zinfandel was extremely attractive, but the heavy tannins and high alcohol were turning off American consumers. They knew they could solve the problem as long as they stayed small. The secret is simple. It just requires three times as much work. First, they limit irrigation to their 60-year-old vines which cuts the production down to 4 tons/acre. Then,

Estate
Bottled
100%
Zinfandel

LUCAS
1985
Lodi
ZINFANDEL
ALCOHOL 13.1% BY VOLUME
GROWN, PRODUCED, & BOTTLED BY THE LUCAS WINERY
LODI, CALIFORNIA

they pick the vineyard once aiming at grapes between 18° and 19°Brix. This batch of wine gives them good acid and longevity. The next third of the grapes are harvested around 22°Brix to contribute a freshness component and lively color. Finally the vineyard is harvested a third time at 24°Brix to add body and the distinctively aromatic smell of ripe Zinfandel. The batches are fermented separately in stainless steel and then aged in French oak. All this labor would be impossible were it not for the fact that Lucas Winery produces only 1,000 cases a year.

Dave and Tamara met at Cal Poly. Dave had just returned from three years in India advising remote tribes on rice and potato production. Tamara was studying Wildlife Resouces. They married in 1971, and later trekked to Iran where Dave directed the Peace Corps Agricultural Management Program and Tamara taught English and Mathematics. They returned to purchase their 30 acre Lodi property in 1977. It had 18 acres of 50 year old Zinfandel, 12 of Tokay and a number of farm buildings — all in dilapidated condition. Dave restored the vineyard while Tamara took classes in construction and transformed the buildings. Today Dave is employed as the "fieldman" buying grapes for Robert Mondavi's Woodbridge facility. The job has always involved a lot of travel. Rumor has it that Woodbridge crushes 15% of the Sauvignon Blanc grown in California. When Mondavi became financially involved in the huge Tepusquet vineyard of Santa Barbara County, Dave began commuting 300 miles one-way each week.

Tamara has built a new house. "I hired three guys to frame it for me because it has two stories with 2x6 construction," says the wine industry's most attractive carpenter. "The overhanging eaves make it look like a white tailed hawk hovering in the vineyard. I got the tiles laid on the roof so it was water-tight, and I've been taking my own sweet time finishing the inside. I'm sort of a tempermental builder."

Lucas Winery crushed their first grapes in 1978. Tamara recalls Dave bursting into the house demanding a virgin to bless the harvest. "Some primitive notion he probably picked up overseas," she adds. Their two-month-old daughter Mitra was pressed into service and her heel dipped into the fresh Zinfandel must. The next year was their first commercial harvest, yielding 300 cases. Many of the grapes were sold to home winemakers as far away as Canada and Boston. Today, they restrict production on the best 5 acres of their old Zinfandel vines to make wine for their own label. The rest of the grapes are sold to the highest bidder, primarily to fuel the White Zin boom. "Prices have quadrupled in 4 years," reports Tamara. "As the fieldmen come by, I just sit on our front porch telling them it isn't enough. Seems like they call back every hour. The deal usually turns on who is willing to eat our Tokays in order to get our Zins."

Lucas has a clone of Zinfandel which predates the U.C. Davis program to introduce high yield vines. Tamara says she can see the difference because her grapes have much smaller berries than those in more recently planted vineyards. The soil is also quite sandy compared to most areas of the Delta. "We use ditch irrigation on the Tokays," she explains, "but it is hard to get the water to flow past ten vines because it sinks in so fast."

1985 Zinfandel	1,130 cases
Estate	750 ml

Picked in three lots: 25 Aug at 19.5°, 31 Aug at 23.2° and 12 Sept at 23.5°Brix. 13" of winter rain. Sandy soil, one irrigation via furrow every other row. Vines planted in 1917, head pruned to 4' stakes. Field crush and at the winery within 15 min. Frmtd in 600 gal stnls 5 days at 85°F, punched down 5x/day. 20% left on skins 21 days. Individual lots kept separate and aged 16 mos in four varieties of French oak. Egg white fined, btld June '87 at 12.6 alc, .75 acid, 3.34 pH.

How's the grape market?

"The price went up so rapidly this year ('88), we only made a small amount of wine for ourselves. We had a balloon payment due. We watched the price climb, and finally said 'if it gets to $1,000/ton, we'll sell the grapes.' A winery offered me $950/ton and I said, 'Why not make it an even $1,000 so I can do the multiplication quickly?' Four days later they called back and said 'one thousand.' You always get excited when you're making the wine, so we had some second thoughts as we made our little batch, but I know we did the right thing.

"We pulled our Tokay out. I'll probably plant Cabernet, but I won't plant anything without a contract. My neighbor Stanley was just offered a contract on his Cabernet which looks pretty good. It is 5-15 years at his option, guaranteed $400/ton but rising to match the district average if it goes higher.

"My neighbor on the other side, however, is crying the blues. He had 40 acres of young, vigorous Zinfandel. He was getting such high tonnage the sugar barely went to 22°Brix — perfect for white Zin. He ripped them out in 1985 when Gallo said they didn't want them. 40 ACRES! He replanted Burger. Now nobody wants them."

Tamara Lucas

KF

MACROSTIE

The Army could have been worse for Steve MacRostie after being drafted at the end of the '60s. He was sent to Vincenza, Italy, between Venice and Verona to do communications work. The first thing he did was learn the language. The second was develop an appreciation of wine.

Upon discharge and return to the U.S., he conciously began looking for a career direction. A gentleman farmer friend from South Carolina noted his college training in natural sciences, and pointed out that wine was an acscendant industry. Steve didn't need much persuasion. He had grown up in Sacramento. Enrolling in U.C. Davis's Enology M.S. program was just like going home. Upon graduation in 1974 he took the one job he would hold until going off on his own in 1987. He became the winemaker at Hacienda. The title may not have changed much during those 13 years, but the job sure did.

When Steve arrived, Hacienda was a tiny one-man operation. Frank Bartholmew had come up through the ranks of United Press International to become President and Chairman of the Board. He had an illustrious career covering key events during WW II and bought the historic 400 acre Buena Vista property at an auction (reportedly sight unseen). He sold the winery building in 1968 and wanted to recapture use of the 45 acre Estate vineyard when he hired Steve in '74. That vintage amounted to 1,000 cases. "Frank and his wife were older people from a different era," Steve says. "They were conservative. You had to be resourceful and do things as inexpensively as possible."

Dr. Cooley bought Hacienda from the Bartholmew's in 1976. By the time Steve left, Hacienda was making 25,000 cases. Steve got to try his hand at a lot of jobs. He conducted extensive experiments with outside vineyards aimed at developing blends. Hacienda was making 8,000 cases before help was hired in the cellar. They were making 20,000 cases in '81 when they hired their first winemaking assistant. Dr. Cooley and his son did most of the marketing. They never had a vineyard man.

"Deciding to do it for myself was an economic reality," MacRostie explains. "I was a stockholder, but it never amounted to much. There isn't much money to spread around." His knowledge and relationship with growers helped Steve immediately. He was able to get the Chardonnay grapes he wanted from Angelo Sangiacomo (no relation to the infamous San Francisco landlord) whose family had grown pears around Sonoma for 40 years. The Sangiacomo brothers had moved into Carneros District grapes 20 years before, and they were delighted to help Steve produce the artistic wine he wanted.

Winemaking facilities were also straightforward. Steve went right to Vinwood, the custom crush facility started by Alan Hemphill and managed by Kerry Damsky at the Gauer Ranch in Geyserville. "I'd like my own place," Steve says, "but I need to get big enough. There aren't many small guys at Vinwood. They crushed 25,000 tons in '88. I'm very happy with the way I'm treated though." Steve goes to Vinwood every day. He does his own analyses. Labor policy precludes clients from doing their own cellar work, but he writes the work orders and supervises. He owns his own barrels.

In the future MacRostie is thinking about a vineyard designated Chardonnay and a Pinot Noir. He is also intrigued with the idea of a proprietary red. It might be a Bordeaux blend, or something even more adventuresome. "I've been through every possible style of winemaking," he says. "I've settled on the notion of fruit as the strong center point. I'll aim for accompaniments, but fruit will always stay in the forefront."

1987 Chardonnay   1,300 cases
Sangiacomo Vyds   750 ml

50% from Southern Sonoma ranch, 25% from Caterina ranch and
25% from Home ranch. Picked 10 and 12 Sept at 23.3°Brix, .95 acid.
No SO_2 at crusher. Entirely barrel frmtd with Prise de Mousse yeast.
60% M-L, 5 mos on lees stirring every 3 wks. Radoux and Francois
Allier barrels with medium to heavy toast, 35% new. 7 mos in
wood, sterile filter.

What are the differences in Sangiacomo's vineyards?

"Their southern Sonoma ranch is down by the airport. It has a clay soil and is planted to an old clone. The fruit is intensely varietal. Somewhere between pineapple and herbaceous. With aging, the herbaceous smell comes around to add complexity. I like it as a blending element.

"Caterina ranch is on the west side of Sonoma Creek. It has a deep, loamy soil and produces much more heavily. It is planted to a clone called the Hopland clone which has a lot of citrus character.

"The Home ranch is the one by their offices around the bend from Ravenswood Winery. Except for Caterina, the areas have fairly thin soil over hardpan. They have to be watered to maintain the viability of the vines. I get to select certain areas for my wine. I have some say over the viticultural practices too. Generally, they wouldn't do something if I told them I didn't like it."

Steve MacRostie

RG

MADROÑA VINEYARDS

Dick Bush chose the name Madroña because he believes the tree (like oak and poison oak) is an excellent indicator of good growing regions for wine grapes. At 3,000 feet his vineyards are the highest in California, but he studied temperature records for various sites and decided that El Dorado County might gain an advantage from the cooler weather at this high elevation. Dick has a PhD in Materials Science from Stanford, so one might assume this decision was a reasoned analysis rather than a hunch.

He planted his vineyards six miles east of Placerville in 1972. All of his neighbors grew apples. He put in Chardonnay, White Riesling, Gewürztraminer, Zinfandel, Merlot and Cabernet Sauvignon. In 1981 he added Cabernet Franc from UC Davis cuttings. The winery was built in 1980. Aside from the concrete slab, steel beams and split level block wall, Dick and his family did all the construction work themselves. They don't seem to understand sitting around very well. In 1973, while they were waiting for the grapevines to come into full production, they went to Africa and taught school in the Congo during the exciting times just before the revolution that created Zaire.

In 1985 Dick decided to concentrate on the vineyard and hired Mark Foster as winemaker. Mark has a BS in Enology from U.C. Davis and was assistant winemaker at Smothers and Chalone before coming to Madroña. Actually, winemaking is Foster's third career. He holds a Masters in Zoology from Cornell and spent four years as a limnologist in Arizona. He then returned to school to take a second Masters in Computers before working three years on jet aircraft systems as a programmer.

White Riesling was the first grape from Madroña to catch consumers' attention because anything east of California's coastal counties was considered too hot for the variety. That notion was dispelled when Bush produced several delicate, award winning wines. A botrytized Riesling which won a Silver Medal at the State Fair in 1987 weakened the notion further. But the cool climate characteristics of high elevation vineyards became irrefutably clear when several Madroña Merlots and their '85 Chardonnay hit the market. The Chardonnay sold out in a matter of weeks after taking a Gold medal at the San Francisco Exposition, a Gold medal at the American Wine Competition and Best of Region at the CA State Fair.

Foster is increasing the winery work load on Chardonnay several fold. He thinks the fruit grown at Madroña has a natural buttery character. He would like to add complexity. They are cutting back on malo-lactic so that half the wine is now fermented in stainless, a quarter is barrel fermented and a quarter is barrel fermented with malo-lactic. They are picking at 22.5°Brix because their conversion rate (sugar into alcohol) is extremely high. "It has something to do with our high percentage of malic acid," Foster thinks. "We are also trying different yeasts. I wasn't particularly knocked out by Epernay, but I love Montrachet in our barrel fermented portions. Champagne seems to bring out a pineapple fruit in the stainless portion. In '86 I tried a new one called Wadenswill that seems to emphasize certain citrus notes."

Madroña's '86 White Zin got two puffs in Connoisseur's Guide, but Foster and Bush only make a little bit. "I prefer red Zin," says Foster. "White Zin is pressed off the skins right away. It doesn't use the color from skins, nor flavoring and smell ingredients that take time to be extracted. We don't want to waste these valuable components. The raspberry fruit and low tannin we get at our altitude is different than a typical Zin from down lower in Amador." In '85 Foster began taking Zinfandel skins, after pressing off the juice for white Zin, and putting them into fermentation vats with other Zinfandel grapes being made into red Zin. It raises the skin to juice ratio about 50%. They want to avoid extracting too much tannin. However, color and fruity aroma are extracted first during fermentation, with tannin coming in later stages. So, they press "augmented red Zinfandel" earlier than usual. Tannin levels are normal, but berry smell is enhanced. They also use open fermenters, believing that punching down is gentler than pumping over. At their elevation, ambient air temperature in October can keep red fermentations below 80°F. They suspect the fruitiness of Zinfandel is improved by combining low fermentation temperature with their augmentation technique.

Madroña started producing 1,500 cases of a Bordeaux blend in 1986. The wine will be Cabernet Sauvignon with approximately 10% Merlot and 5% Cabernet Franc.

Madroña

1985
EL DORADO
RIESLING
SELECT LATE HARVEST

ESTATE PRODUCED & BOTTLED BY MADROÑA VINEYARDS, CAMINO, CA
HARVEST SUGAR 43° BRIX RESIDUAL SUGAR 21% BY WT. ALC. 10.7% BY VOL.

1983 Cabernet Sauvignon   792 cases
Estate Vyd   750 ml

5% Merlot. 11-yr-old, high mountain vyd. Frmtd with Pasteur Red yeast at 75°F. Aged 2 yrs in American oak barrels. Btld Sept '85.

1983 Zinfandel   382 cases
Estate Vyd   750 ml

Picked 18 Oct at 23°Brix. Aged 18 mos in American oak barrels. Btld June and Sept '85 at 12.8 alc, .69 acid.

1986 Chardonnay   1,000 cases
Estate Vyd   750 ml

Picked early Oct at 3.3 pH, .9 acid, 22°Brix. No SO₂ at crusher, 8 hrs skin soak. 50% frmtd in 60-gal French oak barrels, balance in stnls at 50°F. Chanson yeast, M-L 34. Aged 10 mos in 60-gal Seguin-Moreau barrels, new to 2-yrs-old, medium toast. Btld Sept '87 at 3.5 pH, .72 acid, 12.6 alc.

1983 Merlot   400 cases
Estate Vyd

Picked end Sept at 23°Brix. Frmtd with Pasteur Red at 72°F. Aged 2 yrs in American oak. Btld May '86 at 12.6 alc, .73 acid.

1985 J. Riesling   673 cases
Estate-Select Harvest   750 ml

100% botrytized bunches picked 5-8 Oct at 43°Brix. 1.55 acid. Frmtd at 56°F with Champagne, Epernay and Steinberg yeasts. Btld July '86 at 10.6 alc, 1.3 acid, 21.1% rs.

How are the Bordeaux varieties in your vyd?

"We have much deeper and richer soils than most people expect from mountain vineyards. We are on a ridge with gentle slopes. As long as there is ground cover, erosion is never severe. The soil is primarily volcanic in origin. Volcanics break down into top soil faster than erosion has taken place. Historically, this land produced prime timber, which is a good indication of nutrients. In the early years I put fertilizer on the vineyard, but my vines weren't very vigorous. Then Dr. Kasimatis came up from U.C. Davis and diagnosed my problem as nitrogen toxicity. I get improved growth by simply leaving the soil alone.

"The Cabernet Franc does very well here. It grows vigorously and produces a wine with notable spice. Merlot has been more difficult. The vines show reasonably good vigor, but they don't set much crop. We get small, loose bunches. You have to give those grapes special attention in the winery. If you vinify them in the standard way, you'll end up with an inky, tannic, impenetrable wine. You couldn't use much wine like that in a blend without degrading the whole thing. We had to learn special techniques for handling the Merlot from our vineyard. Once we did that, we became quite excited about the blending possibilities.

Dick Bush

Dick Bush   CL

Mark Foster   KF

MERRY VINTNERS

In the early '70s Merry Edwards was one of Maynard Amerine's best pupils at U.C. Davis. Her reputation for exquisite Chardonnay became firmly established during three years as winemaker at Mt. Eden Vineyards when consumers elbowed each other out of the way to pay $20 a bottle for her wines. Merry moved to Matanzas Creek Winery in 1977. During the next 7 years she was besieged by a California phenomenon that raised certain chefs and winemakers to superstar status in the media.

This glare of publicity was hardly diminished by an extraordinary event in 1983. A PBS television crew filmed Merry as background for a show on small wineries that would conclude with the San Francisco Exposition Wine Judging. When Merry's '81 Matanzas Creek Chardonnay won

THE MERRY VINTNERS

1986 CHARDONNAY
SONOMA COUNTY

VINTAGE PREVIEW

A TABLE WINE PRODUCED & BOTTLED BY
THE MERRY VINTNERS, SANTA ROSA, CA • CONTAINS SULFITES

the Sweepstakes Award over 2,000 other entries, the cameramen were so shocked they could not hold the cameras steady. Her '79 Matanzas Creek Chardonnay had won the Sweepstakes Award at the Sonoma Harvest Fair two years before, but the coincidence of building a program around Matanzas Creek and then documenting their march to the top prize in a major blind tasting was something only fiction writers would have dared to imagine.

Merry, herself, is not a media hound. She's no shrinking violet, but public appearances probably rank somewhat behind her family, and doing field samples, and actually "touching the wine" in her list of priorities. Merry has always been a crackerjack scientist. It is charming to watch her downplay her technical competence in order to encourage conversation among wine consumers. She will demonstrate showmanship when it is requested of her, but it is hardly a compulsion. One gets the impression that she has found the connection between presentation and expertise in the artistry of wine to be a matter of curiosity.

In 1984 Merry left Matanzas Creek to launch a family venture on her own. Merry Vintners is a collaboration with her husband, Bill Miller, and her parents, Charles and D.J., who have moved out from Colorado. They own 18 acres northwest of Santa Rosa. Merry considers it a great opportunity to integrate motherhood with her career. In fact, her warmest memory of her relationship with Matanzas Creek was the time Sandra MacIver offered to hire full time child care when Merry decided she wanted to have a baby. It is a situation which applies to a big part of our society. "It's crazy," Merry says, "for Americans to risk taking ambitious and talented women out of the gene pool."

Merry Vintners concentrates on making Chardonnay. They buy grapes from several vineyards around Sonoma County, seeking a diversity of clones and growing conditions. This effort to enhance complexity in her wines is an example of the way Merry's ideas have evolved. "At Mt. Eden," she explains, "we had a single, rather monochromatic, clone. The grapes were marvelous because of their age and location, but they were best suited for showing off winemaking techniques like fermenting in new barrels. At Matanzas Creek all the grapes were eventually going to come from the Estate vineyard, so we tried different clones. I was impressed with the complexity that could be achieved that way." Merry has also moved toward inducing malolactic fermentation early when she wants it in a wine. "Otherwise," she says, "you get too much of the buttery characteristic. That is not good for extended aging."

Two Chardonnays are made each year at Merry Vintners. Their "Sonoma" bottling is designed to showcase fruit, although crisp acid and a disdain for residual sugar indicate that Merry wants this wine consumed with food. Only a small portion of the wine is barrel fermented, and it is bottled early to keep the price low. Grapes for the Reserve bottling mature on the vine longer to enhance body. This wine is completely barrel fermented and aged in oak about 7 months. They also give it a year of bottle age prior to release. The goal is more complexity and aging potential around 7 years. An educational label on the Reserve bottling changes every year. In '85, for example, it was a drawing of microscopic wine sediment done by Louis Pasteur in 1865. A portion of the sale price on the Reserve wine is contributed to a scholarship in the Enology program at U.C. Davis.

1986 Chardonnay   2,000 cases
Sonoma   750 ml

Picked at 22.1°Brix, .86 acid from 4 different Sonoma County vyds. No skin soak. Frmtd with a proprietary yeast from Domaine Chandon. No M-L, 40% barrel frmtd. Polish filter, btld April '87 at 13.1 alc, .79 acid, 3.34 pH.

1986 Chardonnay   4,700 cases
Reserve   750 ml

Grapes from vyds in Sonoma Vly, Alexander Vly, and Sebastopol. Picked at 23°Brix, .89 acid. No skin soak, same yeast, partial M-L, completely barrel frmtd. 67% aged in new Sirugue barrels with low toast, remainder 1-yr-old. Polish filter, btld June '87 at 13.3 alc, .82 acid, 3.29 pH.

Did you drink wine when you were pregnant?

"I have two children. During the first couple months of each pregnancy, I had no interest in drinking wine whatsoever. Didn't have much interest in food either. As a winemaker and wine-lover, this change was quite clear to me. I'm around fine wine all the time, and it is often in conjunction with good food. The smells and flavors lost their appeal. I went about my work with much more of an academic interest. I drank small amounts on occasion, but I got the message that our bodies regulate these matters on their own. Toward the end of each pregnancy my interest returned. I didn't drink bottles by myself, but I didn't hesitate to have a glass with dinner. Both my kids are perfectly healthy.

"I'd also like to draw your attention to a couple of studies about wine and nutrition. Janet Tribe MacDonald at U.C. Berkeley took an exhaustive look at the way minerals, vitamins and other nutrients are absorbed by humans from the food they eat. Her variable was the beverage they consumed with the meal. Wine was significantly better than anything, i.e. water, liquor, milk, etc., in promoting uptake and metabolism of nutrients from food in the large and small intestine. There have also been several recent studies that demonstrate the increase in high-density lipoproteins in the blood due to wine consumption. HDL is positively correlated to reduced risk of heart attack.

"The point is that wine is not just safe. In moderate amounts, it is good for you."

Merry Edwards

RB

MT. VEEDER WINERY

Mount Veeder Winery earns its name. The hillside vineyards are on precipitous slopes with elevations from 1,000 to 1,600 feet. The topsoil of "rotten" shale mixed with volcanic ash produces a strength of flavor that defines mountain grapes. Winemaker Peter Franus likes the ability to pick earlier than on the valley floor and still get intensity. Mount Veeder's berry size is small and their yield is low, about 3 tons per acre for Cabernet. They get more rainfall than the valley, are above the fog, have a slightly warmer climate and avoid extremes of hot or cold. Their vineyards face east and get sun in the cool morn-

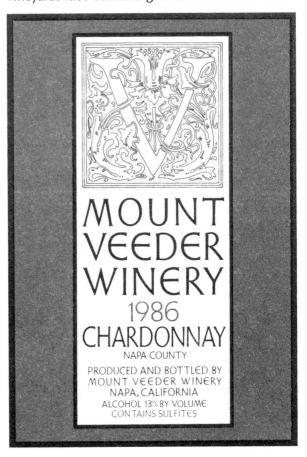

ing instead of baking in the afternoon. "The drawback to mountain vineyards," Peter points out equitably, "is that everything's a pain in the ass. From pruning to cultivating to picking, nothing is easy up here. Erosion is a problem too. In the winter of '85/'86, we had part of a vineyard just slide away down the hill.

Owners Henry and Lisille Matheson purchased the vineyard and winery from Michael and Arlene Bernstein in 1982. Henry's great grandfather had owned Key Biscayne. After college in 1969 Henry did a year of draft counseling with the Quakers. He then returned to school for a business degree and entered the family real estate business. By 1982 he had been looking for agricultural property for several years. "We wanted to do something with the land other than manipulate the investment," says Henry. "Our daughter, Harper, had just been born and we decided to find something before we became too entrenched in Miami." As compensation for being bumped from a flight in Ohio, Henry received an airline ticket for his first visit to California. Six months later the Mathesons moved to Mt. Veeder.

Grapes on the property date back to 1963 when attorney Bernstein fled life in San Francisco to establish a vineyard in a former prune orchard in the mountains above the Napa Valley. There are 100 acres on the property with 22 planted to grapes. The original Zinfandel vines have been budded over to Chardonnay and Matheson expects to plant another 4-6 acres to that variety. 90% of the remaining acreage is Cabernet Sauvignon, with Merlot, Cabernet Franc and other red Bordeaux varieties making up the difference. In fact, many of the Cabernet Franc vines currently enjoying a surge of popularity among California wineries trace their original cuttings back to Mt. Veeder.

The 1,500 sq. ft., air-conditioned winery was

built in 1973. It quickly established a reputation for mouth filling Cabernet Sauvignons. In the early years the wines were big and brawny, following the style popular at the time. By the mid '70s, however, consumers started looking for more complexity and elegance. The percentage of Bordeaux blending varieties in Mt. Veeder Cabernet has increased steadily since then. Harvest sugars have also gone down. 25°Brix was the average then, 22.5° is more the norm these days. In addition, Mt. Veeder has started using a "submerged cap" fermentation and giving their wines more bottle age prior to release. "This style evolution is an improvement," Matheson says. "Our wines will never be timid."

In 1986 Mt. Veeder started a "Reserve" program. They only did 2 or 3 barrels the first year, but they are up to 350 cases in '88. The idea is to use a higher percentage of Merlot and Cabernet Franc. Such wines should be more aromatic. The blend in '86 was one-third each of the Estate's red grapes. In '87 it moved to 40% Cabernet Sauvignon, 40% Cabernet Franc and 20% Merlot. It is made entirely made from free run juice. It will be left for a shorter period of time in newer wood. In fact, they are using new château barrels to get a more rapid effect of oxygen through the wood. Château barrels have thinner staves than "transport" barrels. They are also better looking with willow hoops and cross pieces in the heads.

1984 Cabernet Sauvignon	2,600 cases
Estate	750 ml

Steeply terraced, dry-farmed vyd with an east aspect planted between 1965 and 1972. 85% Cabernet Sauvignon, 5% Cabernet Franc, 5% Merlot, 3% Petite Verdot and 2% Malbec. Picked early Sept to mid-Sept at 23°Brix. Frmtd with Assmanhausen yeast, on the skins 10 days. Aged 2 yrs in 1 to 5-yr-old French oak barrels. Filtered and fined. Btld Dec '86 at 13 alc, .73 acid.

1987 Chardonnay	1,500 cases
Estate	750 ml

4th crop of Chardonnay grafted on to vines planted in 1973. 30% from other vyds on Mt Veeder. Picked first two wks Sept at 22.8. No SO₂ at crusher, no skin soak. Entirely frmtd with Epernay 2 in Damy barrels from Meursault, 25% new. No M-L, 6 mos on lees. Aged in new to 2-yr-old. Sterile filter, btld July '88, .82 acid.

Are barrels a hassle?

"I love barrels. They are one of the most aesthetic aspects of the whole business. Getting new ones is always exciting, and the smell of new wood is wonderful. I lived in Los Angeles and worked as a moving man. When I got into the wine industry, I thought the most physical part of my life was behind me. It had just begun. What irony that barrels would be so beautiful and such grief to move around.

"We must conserve space in our small winery. So barrels must be lifted into the stacks in very close quarters. And then lifted down for washing every time we rack the wine. You don't want to let the labor involved affect your philosophy about racking schedules. We do the first racking after 6 weeks because the new wine throws a lot of sediment. Even when red wines have cleaned themselves up there is a beneficial effect from the aeration on a young wine.

"Some coopers have a better reputation for the structural aspects of their barrels than others do. It is totally unrelated to the flavor aspects you want. Building barrels is an art. A top cooper can select wood and read the grain when splitting staves so that the barrels don't leak. We haven't had a leaker in 3 years out of the 50-75 barrels we buy every year. An occasional twig borer hole can be fixed with a toothpick, but we haven't even had those."

Peter Franus

Peter Franus   RB

Henry Matheson at winery   RB

NEVADA CITY

Nevada City Winery is a reflection of its community. In fact, it was started with the specific goal of supporting Nevada County viticulture. Allan Haley is a lawyer. He became enchanted with the locale when he returned to the mainland after running a wine distribution business called Bacchus Imports in Hawaii. It isn't hard to understand his interest in the place. It is shared by all the residents and most of the visitors.

Nevada City has been known as the Queen of the Northern Mines for almost 140 years. The town uses gas lamps for street lights. Easy to do when you don't have many streets. It is the only municipality in California with an open liquor law; you can stroll through town sipping a glass of wine and it will be perfectly legal. The whole region abounds with well-educated refugees from various forms of urban distress. The Arts are highly thought of and handsomely supported. Foothill Theater Company has a following throughout northern California. Music In The Mountains brings international symphony performers every summer. Just below the snow line, Nevada City is only a half hour drive from several major ski slopes. The Nevada City Classic is a bicycle race with a national reputation.

There are a lot of reasons to live in this small county northwest of Lake Tahoe. Grape growing wasn't an obvious one though because there were not any local wineries to use the fruit. In 1982, Haley organized a limited partnerhip to remedy the problem. He convinced Tony Norskog to become the winemaker and opened for business. The winery buys grapes from 20 local growers and makes a list of different wines as long as your arm. The vineyards lie from 1,300 to 2,800 feet elevation, substantially higher than Sierra Foothills competitor Amador County. They grow Sauvignon Blanc, Chardonnay, Gewürztraminer, White Riesling, Cabernet Sauvignon, Cabernet Franc, Merlot, Petite Sirah, Pinot Noir, Charbono, Nebbiolo and Zinfandel. All the vineyards are within a 15 mile radius of Nevada City.

The community has taken to the idea very well. 45% of the winery's sales come from their tasting room, and 70% of them occur within 30 miles of the winery. Managing the business and winemaking chores does not, however, "knit up the ravelled sleeve of care." Norskog is no longer associated with the winery, and the current winemaker could not be more appropriately named. Ron Goodspeed. He has one assistant, an even temperment and no free time. Business affairs are handled by Sandra Woods. She worked for a big corporation in the Bay Area before moving to Nevada City 3 years ago. Both Sandra and Ron own vineyards.

Given the many separate lots of wine which must be fermented and stored, Ron's favorite pieces of equipment are floating head tanks. These stainless steel vessels allow him to adjust their size by moving the top up and down within the cylinder of the tank. If one batch of Chardonnay occupies 876 gallons and another one is only 640 gallons, Ron doesn't have to choose between a big air space and blending the two lots together. He can put one in oak and adjust the head of a stainless tank to fit the other. He can also take the head off completely to punch down a red wine while it is fermenting, and then put the head back to let the skins macerate without injecting a large volume of CO_2 as a protective blanket after fermentation stops. Even so, Ron tries to do as much barrel fermenting as possible. "Winemakers don't talk about it much," Ron explains, "but every winery has decisions dictated to them by the amount of tank space they have available at a given time. The only downside I can see for floating head tanks is that you have to check each gasket before you go home."

A CALIFORNIA TABLE WINE

NEVADA CITY
W·I·N·E·R·Y
Zinfandel
NEVADA COUNTY 1986

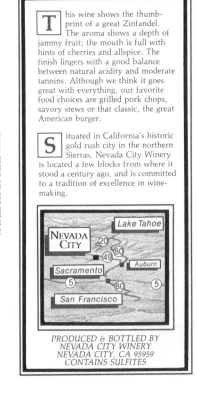

This wine shows the thumbprint of a great Zinfandel. The aroma shows a depth of jammy fruit; the mouth is full with hints of cherries and allspice. The finish lingers with a good balance between natural acidity and moderate tannins. Although we think it goes great with everything, our favorite food choices are grilled pork chops, savory stews or that classic, the great American burger.

Situated in California's historic gold rush city in the northern Sierras, Nevada City Winery is located a few blocks from where it stood a century ago, and is committed to a tradition of excellence in winemaking.

PRODUCED & BOTTLED BY
NEVADA CITY WINERY
NEVADA CITY, CA 95959
CONTAINS SULFITES

1986 Chardonnay	475 cases
Nevada County	750 ml
1986 Zinfandel	112 cases
Nevada County	750 ml
1984 Petite Sirah	400 cases
Nevada County	750 ml

Tell me about some of your favorite local vineyards.

"Lester Ranch is a Cabernet Sauvignon vineyard above 2,300 feet on the south fork of the Yuba River. We've been making it since '85. It does get frost damage, but the fruit is always good quality and it comes in with excellent balance. We are definitely cooler than Amador. We also have a lot of clay soils with low fertility.

"The Merlot from Indian Springs Vineyard should be impressive. It is at 1,800 feet. I think Boeger has shown that Merlot does well at these elevations. This year we had a problem with cluster set though. The vineyard usually comes in with low tonnage, but '88 looks like half a ton per acre. I like to give it extended maceration. That way the tannins don't focus right in the front of the wine. It is a good technique for spreading the tannins throughout the wine.

"To help differentiate the wines I generally take Zinfandel off the skins earlier. I'll press Zin at 3°Brix to get a lighter, more fruity style. We're looking at different barrels too. I love the nutmeg quality of Tronçais. New American barrels are hard to get a handle on. Sometimes the wine seems to change daily in them."

Ron Goodspeed

The city of Nevada City   CL

CL

NEWLAN VINEYARDS & WINERY

Cabernet Sauvignon was winemaker and grape grower Bruce Newlan's favorite wine, and the reason he got into the business in the first place. "As a home winemaker I was making so much Cabernet, that I thought it would make sense to go professional," he says.

In 1967 he found the kind of land he thought would be ideal for the grape: rocky, alluvial soil on the old flood plain of Dry Creek south of Yountville. The conventional wisdom of that time held that Cabernet should be planted in the warmer region around Rutherford. Rutherford is separated from the cooler southern part of Napa Valley by a set of hills spanning the valley just north of Yountville. Newlan cleared off the walnut trees on his chosen site and planted Cabernet. Over the next few years he built a strong reputation as he sold his Cabernet grapes to premium Napa Valley wineries. Meanwhile conventional wisdom began shifting in Newlan's direction as the public started to demand more elegant wines and winemakers began looking for cooler climate grapes.

During 1981 Bruce bought out his partners in an earlier winemaking venture called Alatera. There had been some disagreement on what the term "working," as in "working partners," actually meant. He became the sole proprietor of Newlan Vineyards and Winery. He specializes in full bodied, but supple Cabernet Sauvignon. In 1986 a prestigious wine tasting society evaluated 20 Napa Valley Cabernets from the 1980 vintage including all of the expensive "reserve" wines put out by the most famous producers. The Cabernet Bruce Newlan made in 1980 and eventually released under his own label for $10/bottle finished in first place.

Newlan has also made spectacular botrytized Rieslings and a series of highly acclaimed Chardonnays. His '81 LH JR had 31% residual sugar. His '82 won Best of Show at a prestigious international competition in London. But Bruce's current passion is Pinot Noir. He has been experimenting with small lots of selected Pinot Noir clones and has isolated the one he likes best for his particular style of wine. The vines produce less and have small berries with intense flavor. The canes grow horizontally and have a yellowish cast to them. Newlan has been able to trace the source of these vines back through 4 different vineyards. He thinks the original cuttings were imported from Romanee-Conti by Paul Masson. Bruce got his budwood from Joe Swan. Whatever the vine's origin, Wine Spectator rated Newlan '85 one of the 5 best Pinot Noirs they reviewed from the vintage. That was

Bruce's regular wine. He also made a few barrels of '85 Pinot Noir from John Gantner's 100-year-old vines on Spring Mountain

Bruce Newlan got his technical background in the Navy as Electronics Officer aboard the carrier Essex and the cruiser Pittsburg. He recently retired from the Reserve as a full Captain. In the early '60s he worked at Lockheed as a Missile Systems Engineer. His family heritage, however, is deeply rooted in the land. Both his grandfather and his wife Jonette's grandfather were farmers. His father, an accountant, owned farms. As a young man, Bruce spent summers helping to prune and harvest in relatives' San Joaquin Valley vineyards. In person, Bruce might be described as unassumingly competent. He looks more at home on a tractor than in high society tastings. He does not volunteer sophisticated opinions nor speak in technical jargon. When he is asked sophisticated questions, however, the depth of his understanding emerges, and it becomes clear that he follows the burgeoning science of wine more closely than many of his media-darling competitors.

The Newlans have four grown sons, all of whom have helped in the vineyard and winery over the years. Two of them now work there full-time.

NEWLAN
VINEYARDS & WINERY

ESTATE BOTTLED

1985
Napa Valley

PINOT NOIR

TABLE WINE

1984 Cabernet Sauvignon   1,500 cases
Estate   750 ml

Gradually sloping alluvial soils on west side of Napa Vly south of Yountville. 18-yr-old, dry-farmed vines picked early Oct at 23.3°Brix, .92 acid. No SO₂ at crusher. Frmtd at 80°F with Pasteur Red, 21 days on skins. Aged 24 mos in small Nevers and American oak barrels, new to 3-yrs-old with medium toast. Btld Feb '87 at 13.4 alc, .85 acid, 3.40 pH.

1986 Chardonnay   1,200 cases
Estate   750 ml

10-20 yr old vines picked at 23.2°Brix, .82 acid. 8 hr skin soak. Frmtd with Pasteur White yeast, 50% in stnls and 50% in French oak. 50% on lees 10 mos, partial M-L. Aged 10 mos in new to 3-yr-old French oak barrels with heavy toast. Btld Jun '87 at 13.5 alc, .72 acid, 3.4 pH.

1985 Pinot Noir   585 cases
Estate   750 ml

16-yr-old vines picked at 23.9°Brix, .90 acid. No SO₂ at the crusher. Frmtd with Pasteur Red to 80°F, 20% whole berries, 14 days on skins, portion punched down. Aged 2 yrs in new to 3-yr-old Taransaud barrels with medium toast. Btld Dec '87 at 13.5 alc, .78 acid, 3.42 pH.

1986 LH J. Riesling   225 cases
Estate, bunch selected   375 ml

Hand sorted botrytized bunches picked at 45°Brix, 1.1 acid. Overnight skin soak, settled after pressing. Frmtd cold with Auslese yeast. Btld Feb '87 at 11.7 alc, .98 acid, 3.3 pH, 20% rs.

Tell me about your Pinot Noir clonal research?

"It was sort of a horseback experiment. I started in 1975 by tasting a lot of Pinot Noir wines to decide what I liked. Then I went to the vineyards that had grown grapes for the wines I liked best and got them to give me budwood. I talked to Francis Mahoney a lot at Carneros Creek because he was doing similar studies in a more official capacity. I also asked U.C. Davis for clones they called 'horizontal growers.' The group they call 'vertical growers' or PNGB generally produce more tonnage with lighter color and a simple, but distinctly fruity, nose. That PNGB clone, incidentally, was about the only one you could get from nurseries back in the '70s. They go into a lot of sparkling wine.

"I ended up grafting 5 clones in my vineyard. I had one called M58, another called H7V16 from Davis, the Louis Martini clone, a PNGB and one from Joe Swan. For the first couple of years I made 10-15 gallons of each. Then I started altering time on the skins and adding different amounts of stems. The results usually involved intensity of aroma and complexity. I also concluded that vintage conditions and soil made as much or more difference than the clone. Nevertheless I liked the Joe Swan clone best. Word of mouth traced it back through Paul Masson to Romanee Conti in France. It was more perfumed than the others and lighter in color. In 1982 it came in with the highest sugar and the highest acid of all five candidates. Of course, all the '82s were superior to all the '83s. That particular lot of '82 wine was recently awarded Best Pinot Noir in a big international competition in London.

"I ended up budding 4 acres to the Swan clone. I left the H7V16 clones in, and Etude has made some prize winning wine from them. I also left a little PNGB for blending with the other two. It brings up the fruit in the nose."

Bruce Newlan

JR

OLD CREEK RANCH

Most people think of California as a long rectangle running north and south. It is surprising to learn that Santa Barbara on the Pacific coast actually lies further east than Lake Tahoe in the Sierra Nevada mountains. The granite upthrust of the Sierras runs south until it is sheared off by the North American tectonic plate and big pieces of it (Pt. Reyes) are moved northwest by the Pacific plate. The southern end of these mountains are called the Tehachapis. They separate Los Angeles from the Central Valley. Malibu is a strip of highway where the Tehachapis confront the Pacific Ocean. Between Malibu and Santa Barbara lies a marvelously fertile watershed where the Ventura River drains out of the mountains in an extraordinarily salubrious climate. Historically this region has been a fruit and vegetable garden for America's second largest megalopolis. Today, as urban encroachment cannibalizes this rich agricultural district, Old Creek Ranch represents the area's heritage. Le Mer, a bed-n-breakfast inn near Ojai, runs a horse-drawn carriage out to the ranch as an example of this ambience.

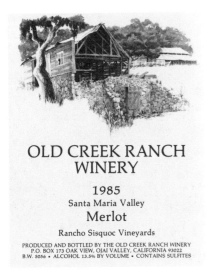

OLD CREEK RANCH
WINERY

1985
Santa Maria Valley
Merlot

Rancho Sisquoc Vineyards

PRODUCED AND BOTTLED BY THE OLD CREEK RANCH WINERY
P.O. BOX 173 OAK VIEW, OJAI VALLEY, CALIFORNIA 93022
B.W. 5056 • ALCOHOL 13.5% BY VOLUME • CONTAINS SULFITES

For 80 years the Rivas family ran an entirely self-sufficient farm on the property. They left in 1940 to move to the Salinas Valley. During the last half of their tenure at Old Creek, they grew black grapes and made jug wine for local restaurants. The ruins of this original winery include a basket press dated 1891 and a J.C. Penney crusher-stemmer which was powered by a belt attached to the back wheel of a Model A car. In 1976 Mike and Carmel Maitland bought the 850-acre, hillside ranch. Mike had just retired as a Vice President of MCA Records. The Maitlands donated 500 acres to the Boy Scouts, and Carmel began to operate an organic U-pick orchard to go along with her horses and 100 head of cattle.

Chuck Branham teaches Biology at Buena High School in Ventura. He went to college with the Maitland's daughter. Chuck became a winemaker in 1979 as an outgrowth of his teaching career. "In class you talk about the real world, but you're not part of it," he explains. "Winemaking let me apply science in a more tangible way. The experience makes me a better teacher." Chuck's younger brother Gary had gone to U.C. Davis, and worked at Chappellet and Stony Hill before becoming assistant winemaker at Sutter Home. Using Gary's advice, Chuck and another Biology teacher he knew from college began buying grapes at Rancho Sisquoc and Bien Nacido vineyards to make small batches in their garage. "In 1981 our egos got the better of our judgement," Chuck says. They teamed up with the Maitlands to bond a winery at Old Creek Ranch. 350 cases were made the first year. 5 acres of vineyard were planted in 1983.

Mike Maitland died in February, 1988, and Chuck's winemaking partner left the group to pursue a research sabatical in Costa Rica. Mrs. Maitland now handles sales and financial affairs for the winery. "Just call me the Bank of

Carmel," she chortles. Old Creek sells 70% of their current 1,200 case production right at the winery. Chuck makes the wine and finds autumn a busy time of year as crush coincides with the beginning of school and his daughter's soccer season. "I didn't know anything about business when we started," he says, "and the only thing I've learned is that you never get to sleep in September."

The vineyard at Old Creek rises from 325 feet to 550 feet elevation up the slope of a mountain which defines the southern boundary of the Ojai Valley. It is 8 miles from the coast, in the coolest agricultural section of Ventura County. 4 acres of Sauvignon Blanc and 1 of Chenin Blanc are grown due to a recommendation by Dr. Amand Kasimatis of U.C. Davis. Branham would like to try some Cabernet and Chardonnay too. "Water is the major issue," he points out. "We'll think about it when the drought ends."

Old Creek has made Gold Medal winning Merlots from Rancho Sisquoc grapes, but Branham is unsure how the variety would fare in their Estate vineyard. "We'll try some," he says, "but Merlot doesn't grow well everywhere. I've bought grapes in 3 different locations at exactly the same numbers and had 2 of them turn out stemmy and vegetal. Sisquoc is up on a bench where it gets sun and a breeze. They've said they'll sell me what I want, and I intend to keep going back." Chuck buys Chardonnay from Bien Nacido Vyd at the mouth of a canyon on the eastern edge of the Santa Maria Plain in northern Santa Barbara County. Tepusquet Vyd is further up the canyon and Rancho Sisquoc is 8 miles further than Bien Nacido. Branham says, "each additional mile inland translates into ripeness a day earlier." He ought to know. He has been driving his truck to these vineyards for 10 years to pick up grapes each September. It's a hectic month.

1985 Merlot 180 cases
Rancho Sisquoc Vyd 750 ml

10-yr-old vines on top of a bench picked mid-Sept over 22°Brix, .8 acid, 3.3 pH. Transport in lug boxes, crush in 3 ton/hr crusher-stemmer. Frmtd with Pasteur Red yeast in plastic lined half ton bins at low temperature in 20'x30' room air-conditioned to 60°F. Punch down 2x/day, inoculate for M-L at 7°Brix, press off skins at 1°Brix. Chill to 60°Brix in a tank and rack off lees in 30 days. Age 18-24 mos in combination French and American oak coopered by Nadalie. "I like the effect of barrels, but I'm not a fan of a lot of new oak flavor." Sterile filtered.

1986 Sauvignon Blanc 200 cases
Estate 750 ml

12% Sémillon. Picked end of August at just over 21.5°Brix, just under 3.3 pH, .85 acid. "When the acid starts to fall it can plummet in just a few days." No skin soak, no SO_2 at crusher, whole clusters put directly into press. Pressing stopped as soon as the pH of the juice coming out increases more than 0.25. Juice settled and chilled, then racked and inoculated with Pasteur White, then moved into barrels to frmt at 60°F. No M-L, SO_2 added after frmt, off gross lees immediately after light bentonite fining. Uses some 130-gal puncheons: "I like the wine from them, but you can't move or stack them so they always seem to be in the way."

1987 J. Riesling 200 cases
Rancho Sisquoc 750 ml

Picked early Sept at .95 acid, 3.05 pH. Frmtd in 600-gal stnls dairy tank. SO_2, bentonite and 25°F temperature drop used to stop frmt with 1-2% rs. Bottled in January. "I'd like to put half in neutral puncheons for a month to round off flavor."

Do you use yeast nutrients?

"I've read how yeast needs lipoproteins to reproduce. At the end of fermentation the yeast cells may generate H_2S as part of the process of autolyzing themselves if there aren't enough nutrients available. So I often put in yeast hulls around the second day to help build up a large population early. If you don't do it at the beginning, you may not get a big enough population and the yeast will have trouble reproducing at the end. So it is not a good idea to wait until you notice a problem. It is better to take precautions. Urea was considered a yeast nutrient 15 years ago, but nobody uses it now after the controversy about urethane in some wines.

"If you get burned once, you always use nutrients. However, there is a downside. Botrytis infected grapes are particularly deficient in nutrients. My problem is that I don't like to use yeast hulls in Chenin Blanc and Riesling. Once you get a big population rolling, it is hard to stop the fermentation and leave a little residual sugar.

"I don't think anybody knows exactly what is happening. It probably depends in part on the genetics of the yeast you have. Alcohol conversion rates and natural production of SO_2 may be part of the same process. The ripeness of the grapes seems to also play a role. In my opinion grapes from Edna Valley have to be completely ripe, or else have nutrients added, to avoid getting H_2S in the wine. Of course, free sulphur on the grapes may be the culprit, but *every* grower claims to stop spraying sulphur prior to veraison."

Chuck Branham

RL

RL

PACHECO RANCH WINERY

Juan Pacheco came to California with De Anza through what is now New Mexico before the Declaration of Independence was signed. Juan's son Ignacio was a soldier at the Presidio, San Francisco's oldest building. Mariano Vallejo, Comandante de Alta California, gave Ignacio Pacheco 6,666 acres of land bordering San Pablo Bay in 1843. Today the Rowland family lives on the second oldest Spanish land grant in California continuously occupied by the recipient's family. Most of the original property is now the town of Novato, although there are still 100 acres left on the ranch.

In 1878 the handsome Italianate house that

still stands today was built for Maria Duarte Pacheco. She also owned the Bull Tail Ranch which was sold in the mid 1980's to George Lucas. Maria's son married one of the Tanforan girls from San Mateo and then married her sister when his first wife died. The Pachecos bred fine horses to race with their relatives on the Peninsula. They also grew grapes on the ranch to make wine for everyday consumption. Today the racing tack has been moved out of the old carriage house to make room for a small commercial winery, and vines flourish again.

Part of the original property was taken to form Hamilton Air Force Base in the 1930's. Air Force temperature records going back fifty years place the property among California's coolest grape-growing regions. It is protected, however, by Big Rock Ridge, second highest point in Marin County, and it never gets frost or even much rain. The soil is mostly clay and relatively deep. Only Cabernet Sauvignon and Cabernet Franc are planted: 5 acres in 1970, 4 acres in 1973 and 3 acres in 1979. All the grapes look SE over San Pablo Bay, less than one mile away. Prior to the 1977 vintage, grapes went to Cuvaison.

Pacheco Ranch began picking at slightly lower sugar levels in '84, and the '85 and '86 wines will include about 10% Cabernet Franc in the blend. An interesting feature about their vineyard is the fact that everything gets picked in one day. They use six professional pickers and about 70 of their friends. The friends start calling in September demanding to participate. The pros start at the bottom of the hill and all the friends start at the top. Everyone usually ends up meeting in about the middle. They pick into lug boxes which go directly to the crusher/stemmer. No berry is off the vine for more than a half hour before it is crushed and in the fermenter.

There are 10 acres of land up the hill from the Rowland's house which have the potential to be planted. They are on a 20% slope, but they are fairly well cleared. Top soil is not very deep. There is a spring on the property up pretty high, so all they have to do is pipe the water to the new vineyard site and create some storage. This new project has the potential to double their acreage, and they are considering getting into Merlot and Cabernet Franc in a big way.

In the past Pacheco Ranch used one-third American oak and the rest French. Now it is all French. They rotate new barrels in each year. They ferment in stainless steel tanks, and then settle in 800 gallon oak uprights before finishing the wine in small barrels. The uprights can also be used for aging wines without imparting oak flavors too rapidly.

Frances Rowland lives in the 1878 house. Frances' son Herb is an attorney who lives in another house on the property with his wife, Debbie, and their young children, Cassandra and Herb III. The Rowlands manage the vineyard side of the operation. Frances' daughter Ann is married to Jamie Meves, winemaker at the Pat Paulsen vineyard south of Cloverdale. Ann and Jamie live in Geyserville with their four-year-old son Patrick.

1984 Cabernet Sauvignon	750 cases
Estate	750 ml

Grown on the gentle eastern slopes of northern Marin County across from Hamilton AFB. Picked into lug boxes and crushed immediately in early Oct at 24°Brix. Frmtd in closed stnls for 7 days, settled, inoculated for M-L. Aged 20 mos in small barrels, 70% Limosin, 30% American. Polish filtration, btld June '86 at 123 alc, .675 acid, 3.59 pH.

How's your Bordeaux blend shaping up?

"We didn't plant the new area because the water situation has been so desparate. After two years of drought, the water table is very low and we are not absolutely sure we could keep the new vines going if it didn't rain this winter. What we would really need is a reservoir.

"Assuming normal rainfall this winter, we will probably go ahead with the project next spring. We are real pleased with the Cabernet Franc we have been harvesting. It is in a place by the barn that gets a lot of afternoon sun. Given our harvest situation, I think we would end up making the wine as a field blend. That means the Cabernet Franc would normally be half a degree Brix sweeter than the Cabernet Sauvignon. Those vines are young, but I think the Cabernet Franc will always be a little less intense than our Cabernet Sauvignon. It has a nice cherry note which will enhance the blend. We don't have any Merlot now, but we'll certainly put some in the new field. I suspect our ultimate percentage will be 85% Cabernet Sauvignon with the remainder split between Merlot and Cabernet Franc.

"We might also go to longer in oak when the blend is in place. We used to be 50/50 American and French oak. Now we're 100% French. We like 25% new wood and I don't think there is any worry about overpowering the wine with oak. The small amount of Cabernet Franc will be balanced by the Merlot."

Debbie Rowland

CS

PAGE MILL WINERY

Dick Stark spent twenty years as a successful marketing executive in the electronics industry of Silicon Valley. He always promised himself that when he turned 45 he would quit and do somethin' he really wanted to do. In 1976 he reached the magic number, so he and his sons dug a 1,400 foot cellar under their house in the Los Altos Hills and started a winery. Dick does most of the work, from winemaking to sales. He has also found time to climb mountains in Nepal on two separate occasions.

Quarters at Page Mill Winery are cramped, even for the Starks' limited production of 3,000 cases per year. Many operations spill out into the driveway. Dick uses a "Mickey Mouse" Italian crusher-stemmer and a small hydraulic basket press for grape processing. They do not have a must pump, but they do have "an honest to God" Schenk filter. Bottling is done by one of the mobile bottling companies and requires only two days for Page Mill's entire production each year.

The house and winery are next door to the two acre Garbett Vineyard which was planted to Chardonnay in 1979. Elizabeth Garbett is one of the gardeners at the Filoli Estate (formerly owned by the heirs to the Matson Shipping Line, now a garden showpiece managed by the Mid-Peninsula Open Space District). An acre of land in Los Altos Hills currently sells for $300,000, but Elizabeth and her husband have lived on their property for 30 years. Their site is in a valley where cold air settles when it comes over a ridge from the Pacific. Stark measured high and low temperatures daily for a year to discover the site falls into U.C. Davis Region 1. The temperature on the hills 300 feet above Garbett Vineyard will often be 10°F warmer at night and during the end of the growing season. Garbett's soil is quite thin, especially at the upper end. Drip irrigation has to be managed carefully. Elizabeth has gotten as much as 6.4 tons from the 2 acres, but she now prunes and cluster thins more severely to hold it under 5 tons. She does all the work too. The vineyard covers 150 feet of elevation, so different portions are picked as much as 10 days apart. Sugar levels are always low and the wine has definite citrus notes.

Stark buys Chardonnay grapes every year from the Keene Dimick Vineyard in southern Napa Valley as well. Dimick reserves an area of the vineyard for him and calls it, logically enough, "Dick's Block." Stark keeps coming back because he feels these grapes give him good acid in the wine and low pH. "With no malo-lactic, I can get crisp Chardonnay complimented by a little French oak," he observes. "I'm not aiming for a big, fat, buttery, rich wine." Both Dimick and Garbett Chardonnays are made in exactly the same way.

Page Mill red wines all receive a special maceration technique that Dick says he learned from George Vierra when George was at Mondavi prior to starting Vichon Winery. "I've been doing it since 1980," says Stark. "Leaving the skins with the wine after fermentation extracts soft tannins while harsh tannins are re-absorbed. You have to be careful to avoid oxidation, but that long skin contact gives me elegant wines that hold their fruit and age well."

In fact, a violet or berry nose is the distinguishing characteristic of Page Mill Cabernets. They have all come from Volker Eisele's vineyard in Chiles Valley east of Napa. Stark thinks it has something to do with the three clones of vines in the vineyard. "There is a pre-certification clone with virus that has a strong berry nose. We usually make those grapes about half of the blend. There is also a clone originally from the See Vineyard which is darker and has lots of flavor but not much nose. Finally, there is a clone originally from the Fay Vineyard which is also dark and which has a completely unique character." In Cabernet, Stark wants elegance, not heavy body. He looks for strong fruit with low alcohol and not much tannin. European tasters frequently comment that his Cabernet seems to be more of a French style than what they expect to see from California.

Much of the winery's sales occur at tastings in the Starks' home held several nights per week in May and November. They invite 35 people each night from their mailing list to a sit-down tasting and comparison. Here, Dick can devote "concentrated personal time" to a discussion of the different wines and vineyards. He feels it is a big advantage to have the same wine in front of everyone in order to spark conversation and provide an enjoyable social context for his product.

Page Mill Winery

1984

Napa Valley

Cabernet Sauvignon

Volker Eisele Vineyard

Produced and bottled by Page Mill Winery
Los Altos Hills, California
Alcohol 12.6% by volume

This is produced from the Volker Eisele Vineyard, once again in true form. Volker's vineyard has a special microclimate located in Chiles Valley, 1,000 feet above the floor of the Napa Valley. The balance of rich fruitiness and good acid is typical of this vineyard.

The wine was carefully made with minimum cellar treatment to preserve the intense varietal character of these grapes.

This Cabernet is like a Bordeaux in its elegant balance of aroma and flavor. It is easily drinkable now and will age nicely for 5–8 years.

530 cases were bottled in May, 1986.

Dick Stark

1985 Chardonnay — 600 cases
Keene Dimick Vyd — 750 ml

Vyd on west side of Napa Vly near Redwood Road. Grapes from selected block 100 ft above vly floor, little irrigation and 13-yr-old vines. Picked 5 Sept at 22.8°Brix. No skin soak, basket press. Frmtd in 60-gal medium toast French oak with Prise de Mousse yeast at 75°F for 10 days, no M-L. On lees 6 mos. Bentonite fining, sterile filter, btld April '86 at 13.5 alc, .82 acid, 3.35 pH.

1984 Cabernet Sauvignon — 350 cases
Volker Eisele Vyd — 750 ml

Vyd 1,000 ft above Chiles Vly floor on hillside. Dry-farmed with 3 different clones. Each clone frmtd separately. Picked 20 Sept at avg 21.7°Brix, .9 acid, 3.3 pH. Champagne yeast in 2-ton open frmtrs, punched down 3x/day. Dry in 10 days then covered with CO_2 blanket 2x/day as skins sink over next 8-10 days. Basket press. Aged in 60-gal fire coopered American oak and 20% French oak. Btld June '86 at 12.5 alc, .6 acid, 3.6 pH.

1987 Sauvignon Blanc — 300 cases
French Camp Vyd — 750 ml

Vyd 20 mi SE of Paso Robles.

1987 Chardonnay — 300 cases
Garbett Vyd — 750 ml

Cool Los Altos Hills vyd planted in 1979. 5 tons picked from 2 acres on 1 Sept at 21.7°Brix, .9 acid. No skin soak, basket press. Barrel Frmt with Prise de Mousse, no M-L. On lees 6 mos, aged in French oak with medium toast. Sterile filter, btld May '88 at 12.7 alc, .75 acid.

I hear you're making Pinot Noir.

"I swore I wouldn't do it, but I am. I load my small boxes up and drive down to Bien Nacido. I'm doing 350 cases in '88. That's one truck load. People kept saying our style was perfect for Pinot Noir. I liked the wines being made from Bien Nacido by Austin, Calera, Wild Horse and Byron. So I'm in the game. It is a good cold climate area. I only made 50 cases in 1985. Wine Spectator rated it at 87 points, so I guess there is no pulling out now.

"I did a different clone each year in '85 through '87. Bien Nacido has clones they call 103, 104 and Gamay Beaujolais. I decided I liked a blend of 103 and 104 the best. They seem to co-operate with each other. One is light and the other dark. I don't think there is much to tell them apart in aroma intensity, but the fruit character is different. Those two clones are in a block right next to each other, so the difference is not due to microclimate. I make them separately, then blend. The Gamay Beaujolais clone has a nice smell, but it is simple."

Dick Stark

CL

Garbett Vyd at Page Mill Frwy Exit   CL

QUPÉ

Qupé (pronounced kew-PAY) is the Chumash Indian name for the prolific California state flower, the Golden Poppy. The Chumash tribe made its home along California's southern Central Coast in what are now San Luis Obispo and Santa Barbara Counties. This viticultural region is blessed with a dry growing season and temperatures moderated by cool ocean breezes.

Bob Lindquist attended U.C. Irvine until 1975 studying Social Sciences. He went to work for a small advertising firm setting up window displays in retail stores. One client, The Wine Shoppe in Orange County, offered to pay for the service in wine. Bob was quickly transformed into an avid

wine collector with daydreams of a career in the wine business. He worked the crush at Fortino Winery west of Gilroy and then took a full-time job at San Martin. Eventually he was promoted to sales manager of their tasting room in Camarillo. In 1982 Bob leased tank space from Zaca Mesa, took a part-time job there as a cellar worker and bonded his own winery.

Bob's passion is grapes from France's Rhone Valley. He feels Syrah makes red wine on a par with Bordeaux and Burgundy. "The fruit came from Persia to the Rhone Valley between 1300 and 1400 AD," Bob recites. "Petite Sirah in France is a less well regarded varietal called the Duriff. The true Syrah clone was propagated at UC Davis in the '60s from Rhone Valley cuttings. Syrah gives Qupé a special niche in the marketplace and I feel that the evolution of the American wine drinkers' sophistication will soon rank Syrah as a dominant red varietal."

Bob leases property from Valley Oaks Vineyard in Los Olivos. He grafted half an acre to

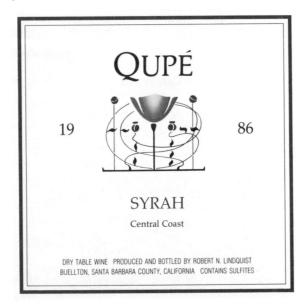

Syrah in '85 to test the effect of cool climate on those grapes. Other than Bonny Doon, most of the Syrah in California right now is grown in the Estrella Valley east of Paso Robles, at Phelps Vineyards halfway up the Napa Valley, or at McDowell Valley on the inland side of the mountains in Mendocino. All those areas are significantly hotter than Los Olivos. Bob also grafted a quarter acre to Mourvdre, a red grape well known for the wines of Bandol on France's Mediterranean coast. In 1986 Bob got some Marsanne and Roussanne budwood. Marsanne makes up a big percentage of the northern Rhone white wines with Roussanne blended in to provide a flowery, aromatic component. In 1987 Bob added some Viognier from Ritchie Creek to his collection.

Lindquist makes all of the wines, but his location is a moving target. He hopes to settle in the building planned for Bien Nacido's property just over the San Luis Obispo County line along with Jim Clendenen and Adam Tolmach of Au Bon Climat. Clendenen and Lindquist share a separate label of their own called Vita Nova. There are different winemaking philosophies applied to the individual labels, but the most important distinquishing feature is where the grapes come from. Each label represents a set of arrangements to procure grapes.

Vita Nova has made a Chardonnay in a rich, full blown style. It may become an important item for Lindquist and Clendenen. They certainly do plan to keep using Los Vinedos fruit. However, the impetus behind the partnership is Claret. Clendenen makes Burgundian wines with Tolmach as Au Bon Climat. Lindquist makes Rhone wines as Qupé. Clendenen and Lindquist make traditional Bordeaux blends as Vita Nova. Their '86 Cabernet Franc was released to significant critical acclaim. But like the majority of wines these young men have made in their lives, there is never much of it.

QUPÉ

1986 Syrah	500 cases
Central Coast	750 ml

Famous Syrah grape from the Rhone Vly planted on gently sloping river plain east of Paso Robles. Picked early Sept. No SO₂ at crusher, whole berries with all stems. Frmtd 10 days in stnls, punched down 2x/day, Assmanhausen yeast. Aged on lees 7 mos in Francois Freres Tronçais oak barrels. Egg white fining. Btld Feb '88. 12.5 alc, 3.35 pH.

1987 Chardonnay	2,000 cases
Sierra Madre Vyd	750 ml

Picked in sandy loam vyd on rolling hills in Santa Maria Vly from vines planted on their own roots in early '70s, 22.7°Brix. No SO₂ at the crusher. Frmtd in French oak barrels at 65°F with Pasteur Champagne yeast for 8 days. 7 mos on lees and complete M-L in Francois Freres Tronçais oak barrels with heavy toast, 1 and 2 yrs old. Bentonite fined, pad filtered. Btld June '88 at 13.1 alc, 3.2 pH, .78 acid.

VITA NOVA

1987 Chardonnay	600 cases
	750 ml

80% Rancho Vinedo 14-yr-old vines across the street from Bien Nacido, 20% Los Alamos. Picked at 22.5°Brix, no acid adjustment, french massage. Entirely barrel fermented in 60% new Francois Freres Tronçais oak. 100% M-L with MCW, 10 mos on lees. Btld at 3.38 pH.

1986 Reserve	200 cases
	750 ml

66% Merlot from Rancho Sisquoc, 33% Cabernet Sauvignon from Los Alamos. Extended maceration 20-25 days. 20 mos in Taransaud barrels (wood air dried 3 yrs) 50% new. Egg white fine. Antique green bottle, 6 btl lay-down box. Also 1987 blend 33% Cabernet Franc, 33% Cabernet Sauvignon, 33% Merlot.

Is it hard to graft vines?

"It is very specialized work. I hire an Armenian fellow from Visalia who grafts grapes and fruit trees all over the state. He charges $1 per vine. With two assistants he can do 2 acres, or about 1,100 vines, in one long day. He considers healthy growth in 90% of the vines to be a failure. He averages over 95%. I can describe how it works, but knowing the technique and actually doing it are two different things.

" 'Cuttings' are 20-30" long pieces of canes freshly pruned while the vine is dormant. They will have 4-6 buds and a stem at one end to indicate the direction of growth away from the trunk. You want big pieces of uniform size. I store cuttings in plastic bags in my refrigerator until early February. The vines to be grafted are cut off about knee high one day ahead of the event. The tops make great BBQ wood. On the day of the grafting, 'cuttings' are sliced into 'scions' 5-6" long with two buds. Dried out wood is eliminated at this time. The cut is made with a very sharp knife at an acute angle to expose a lot of surface. Corresponding slits are cut into the sides of the trunk about an inch below the top. A scion is inserted into each slit with an attempt to line up as much cambium layer (just below the bark) as possible. One assistant wraps the graft with bio-degradable tape, and the second assistant paints everything with a sealant. It is important to repaint the sealer a few days later to make sure cracks don't let moisture and bacteria get into any of the cuts. Six weeks later, you select the strongest of the two grafts on each vine and cut the other one off."

Bob Lindquist

Bob Lindquist (R)   RL

95

RAVENSWOOD

Joel Peterson started young. By the age of ten he was tasting wines on what he calls, half jokingly, "a semi-professional basis." His father, a chemist for Shell Development, headed The San Francisco Wine Sampling Club, which held extensive tastings of new imports twice a week. Tastings were held in the basement of the Peterson home, and young Joel frequently joined in. Before he reached his teens, he had a working knowledge of Europe's finest vineyards and vintages. Joel inherited his father's interest in both science and wine. He embarked on a career in immunology and at the same time wrote about wine and consulted for restaurants in the Bay Area.

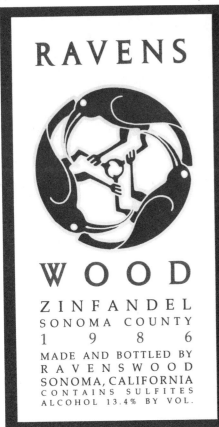

In the early 1970's, he moved to Sonoma County and apprenticed himself to the legendary Joe Swan. After working at several other wineries, he started Ravenswood in 1976. His first crush totalled under 500 cases. In 1981, he moved the winery to its present location just south of the town of Sonoma. Joel works at a nearby hospital as a medical technologist, taking unpopular shifts like graveyard and weekends to give him time for winemaking. Although he now has a full-time assistant at the winery, Ravenswood still produces less than 10,000 cases a year.

The winery buys Zinfandel grapes from three old, dry-farmed vineyards. Dickerson Vineyard, on Bale Lane in Napa, is 75-years-old. It is owned by the president of the Medical Friends of Wine in San Francisco. Joel makes wine for Dr. Dickerson's own Press Oak label too. Press Oak bottles less than 200 cases each of Zinfandel and Ruby Cabernet each year. The Ruby Cabernet is made from one of the oldest plantings (40 years) of that varietal in the world. Ravenswood's Old Hill Zinfandel comes from a vineyard across the street from Olive Hill near Glen Ellen in the Sonoma Valley. Those grapes are 90-years-old and described by Peterson as "peppery." The third Zinfandel vineyard is 85-years-old and on a bench half way up the east side of the Dry Creek Valley north of Healdsburg.

Ravenswood wines are fermented on the wild yeast, even Chardonnay. Peterson thinks wild yeast is the best thing that comes with grapes. He likes the good combination of fermentations, and the improved complexity of the finished wine. All his wines take 3 days in the vat before fermentation begins, but he wants that skin contact anyway. "People claim wild yeast causes stuck fermentations, off odors and high volatile acidity," he says. "I've had more stuck fermentations with pure strain cultures. My single abnormal

fermentation with wild yeast occurred when a vineyardist sprayed benolate captan to stop a severe botrytis infection. The only effect the fungicide had on the wild yeast was to slow the fermentation down. It finished just fine. All wines go through stinky phases in the fermenter, and most of those smells blow off. You have to monitor for H_2S and aldehydes in any wine, no matter what yeast you use." Wild yeast does give Joel conversions of sugar into alcohol which are higher than most wineries report.

Ravenswood red wines are punched down several times a day in open-top redwood fermenters. Racking is done with nitrogen pressure, not pumps, to minimize agitation. Joel works for maximum extract from the grapes in order to get rich, full bodied reds with good aging potential. He says that a winemaker can remove a component such as excess tannin after fermentation, but "if the flavor isn't in the wine to begin with, there's no way to add it. This whole 'food wine' craze has gone too far," he continues. "Wineries have started making wallflowers. I like big, spicy, rich wines and I'm out to produce as much as a red wine can give you."

In the past Ravenswood has gotten Cabernet Sauvignon from the Millryck Vineyard in southern Sonoma Valley. Merlot has come from a 14-year-old Knights Valley vineyard. In '86 a red wine was inaugurated from a Sonoma Mountain property called Pickberry Vineyards. No kidding. The wine is about 40% Cabernet Sauvignon, 40% Cabernet Franc and 20% Merlot.

The Ravenswood label was designed by the well known Berkeley artist and printer, David Lance Goines. Those who observe closely will notice that the fine print reads "made and bottled" instead of "produced and bottled." Rest assured though, the wine was fermented, aged and bottled entirely at Ravenswood. The word "produced" simply wouldn't fit into the layout.

1986 Merlot	1,200 cases
Knights Valley	750 ml

'85 got such rave reviews from Parker it sold out in 2 weeks.

1987 Chardonnay	800 cases
Sangiacomo Vyd	750 ml

Barrel frmtd with wild yeast. Etched glass bottle.

1987 Zinfandel	1,500 cases
Sonoma	750 ml

Very old vyd near Cloverdale. Frmtd on wild yeast.

Comment on wine writers.

"Having been one, I can sympathize with their position more than most winemakers. Generally, I think their goal should be consistency. That is hard when they use a 'one man, one wine, one day' approach. Their attitude in that situation will fluctuate along with the warmth of the relationship with their wife. I think it is more advisable to have groups do the tasting, such as several of the wine newsletters use.

"Commentary about food and wine is even tougher because they both affect each other so much. A recent article in the newspaper questioned the role of Cabernet with food. When I read something like that, I'm startled. I suspect the writer belongs to the 'no such thing as bad publicity' school. I personally would rather see some accuracy. I do understand that half-truths have creative appeal, but I don't like them.

"Fair judgings have similar problems. You can often predict what will win based on who the judges are. Seems like restaurateurs and midwesterners are always biased toward early drinkability. The judging panel at the Sonoma Harvest Fair rotates each year. One year our big, gutsy style will clean up. The next we'll get shut out. Our '85 Cab took a Silver this year. Same wine got nothing last year. Our single vineyard Zins got 3 medals last year including Sweepstakes. This year the subsequent vintages got nothing but a sniffling little bronze, and I think they are better wines."

Joel Peterson

RG

RICHARDSON VINEYARDS

Dennis Richardson, son of a career Navy man, was educated at Cornell University in upstate New York, where he studied Engineering as well as International Political Systems. He readily admits, however, to having majored in "demonstrations and waterfalls" during those years.

At 6'4", Dennis is much closer than most of us to the rim of the basketball hoop fixed to the wall above the entrance to his winery. He kept shooting (and making) baskets as he described his first homemade wines in 1974, the success of these early efforts, and his eventual decision to go professional (as a winemaker at least) in 1979.

Dennis and his wife, Carolyn, met at Cornell and soon trekked to Southern California where they experienced "one long season during a two year stay, all the while recovering from the serious poverty of being students." Thereafter, Dennis and Carrie decided they would go to wherever they wanted to live and then figure out what to do for a living. Following three months of crisscrossing the US and Canada, they settled in the Sonoma Valley. Carrie found work as a Medical Technologist, and Dennis, answering a blind ad, got a job at Inglenook's tasting room. Three months later he switched to Sebastiani's Sonoma Valley tasting room, where he remained for five years, advancing to Assistant Manager. During the years at Sebastiani, Dennis' interest in wine intensified, and he decided to convert his home wine-making hobby into a profession.

In 1979, after a thorough search for grape-growing property in Mendocino, the Sierra Foothills, and other Northern California areas, Dennis and Carrie purchased 10 acres, literally in their own backyard. Their vineyard is just south of the city of Sonoma on the border of the city of Sonoma on the border of the Carneros region. Here they built a small winery and over the years boosted their annual production to 2,000 cases.

Carrie is still employed as a Medical Technologist and does all the winery lab work. The Richardsons have two children, Jeremy and Angela. Winemaking duties are shared with Dennis' working partners, Al Wighton and Bob Weisheit (another former Sebastiani employee). Local winemaker Victor McWilliams also helps during the crush.

RICHARDSON

SONOMA VALLEY
ZINFANDEL

red table wine
CONTAINS SULFITES
made & bottled by RICHARDSON VINEYARDS, SONOMA, CA, U.S.A.

VINEYARDS

1986 Pinot Noir	400 cases
Carneros	750 ml

Grapes from Sangiacomo Vyd. Gold medal American Wine Competition.

1986 Merlot	180 cases
Carneros	750 ml

Grapes from Gregory Vyd.

How does your winery approach marketing?

"Marketing and sales are necessary evils in this business. Winemaking is not just a pastoral trip to the vineyard, watching balloons rising in the morning air. The fun of this business, though, is still making that tub of freshly-picked grapes into wine."

Why winemaking for a profession?

"I never really gave much thought to what 'career' I should pursue. I became a winemaker more because it was something I wanted to do and couldn't leave untried. If I had failed on my own, I'd certainly be a valuable employee for someone else in this business. I suppose it's my pursuit of the American dream, and I approach it one day at a time."

Dennis Richardson

JR

JR

RITCHIE CREEK VINEYARDS

When Dr. Richard (Pete) Minor first came to the Napa Valley in the mid '60s there were a couple of dozen wineries in the area. Now there are a couple hundred in the Valley alone, and more than six hundred located in various parts of California. Is he nervous about all the new competition? Not at all. "I love it!," says Pete, "I'm a dedicated consumer and I think the boom in new wineries is great. As far as I'm concerned, the more the merrier. Unless, of course, we had trouble selling what we've made." That's not too likely, given Ritchie Creek Vineyards' small size and the fine reputation the wines have earned. Total production averages 1,000 cases a year, divided more or less equally between Chardonnay and Cabernet. The Chardonnay has

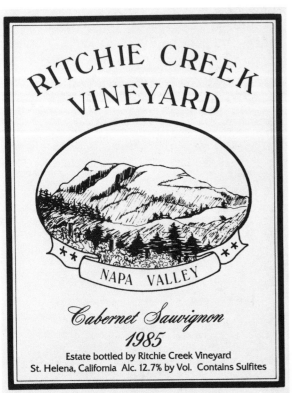

a ripe, fruity aroma, and a tendency to drive newsletter writers wild about six weeks after the wine has been completely sold out.

When the shyly affable Minor bought his forty acres of Spring Mountain in 1966, it cost a mere $500 per acre. The vineyards are located 2,000 feet up a steep, slightly north-facing hillside. Because of the lack of water, Minor has never been able to install any kind of frost protection. In some vintages the crop has been cut back severely by frost trapped in the surrounding trees. Minor also has to battle the Western Tanager. "The males," he says, "are quite pretty, with red heads and yellow wings, but they're voracious. We had to net the entire vineyard until one of our neighbors put in 250 acres of vines which offered the birds a bigger selection." At the time Pete planted his Cabernet vineyard, each vine had to be watered by hand. He was barely able to cover them all in a two-week cycle. "I was young and vigorous then," he says, remembering the effort. He has since installed a drip irrigation system which rarely gets used. "The less I water, the more I like it," he chortles, without explaining whether "it" means his wine or life in general.

4 acres of Cabernet were planted in 1967 and 4 acres of Chardonnay were added in 1980. Thin topsoil helps to keep yields low. Virus in the Cabernet vines (an old pre-certification clone) moderates the sugar level and contributes to the unique spiciness of the wine. Minor compares the flavors in his Cabernet to those from Diamond Creek or pre-1971 Mayacamas. He usually picks Cabernet in early October. About 10% of his red grapes are Merlot which come in 10 days earlier than the Cabernet. The Cabernet is fermented in 600 gallon vats on the skins for about a week, until the wine is dry. It is aged in Nevers oak barrels for approximately twenty months. The fermentation/storage room is cut

into the hillside to keep temperatures cool. Chardonnay is partially fermented in stainless, then transferred to 60 gallon French barrels to finish up.

Minor first tasted wine made from Viognier grapes in France around 1977. He started at the top with the world's most famous example. Chateau Grillet is France's smallest vineyard with its own Appellation Contrôlée. Getting budwood was difficult in the U.S., but by 1980 Pete had 500 vines, or about an acre, planted on AxR$_1$. The vines are not very vigorous, and they have rather scraggly clusters. "You'll understand how feeble these vines are," he says, "when I tell you I'm still watering them after 7 years." In '86 he got about a ton and a half of fruit. It was only enough to make 89 cases. The grapes mature late in the season, but they are not very susceptible to bunch rot. He cold ferments to retain the aroma, and then ages for a short time in his oldest Chardonnay barrels. He bottles in special antique clear glass and finishes the package with a pastel blue capsule. The wine takes 6 months in the bottle to develop its characteristically beguiling scent. Ritchie Creek doesn't have much, but Minor was the first American winery to get Viognier on the market.

A fourth generation Bay Area native, Minor attended Stanford and the College of Physicians and Surgeons before starting a dental practice in Berkeley. From '68 to '72 he built a house on the Spring Mountain property out of rocks removed from the vineyard. In '74 he moved his dental practice to St. Helena. His wife Maggie is a well known artist who has several wine labels to her credit. They have two children, aged 8 and 3. Pete retired from dentistry in 1985 and now works full time in the vineyard and wine cellar.

1987 Chardonnay   400 cases
Estate   750 ml

Picked early Sept at 23°Brix, .76 acid, 3.3 pH from 7-yr-old vines producing 2 t/a. UC Davis clone planted on AxR rootstock. Short skin
soak, frmtd in stnls with Champagne yeast at 55°F for 10 days, then
transferred at 11°Brix to 60 gal Nadalie Limousin oak barrels with
medium toast. 2 mos on lees, no M-L. Bentonite fining, DE filter,
btld June '88.

1985 Cabernet Sauvignon   400 cases
Estate   750 ml

Picked early Oct at 22.8°Brix, .74 acid and 3.45 pH from 17 to 21-yr-
old vines, pre-certification clone with significant virus. 10% Merlot
picked late Sept. Frmtd 1 wk in open stnls at 87°F with Champagne
yeast. Punched down 3x/day. Aged 60 gal Nevers oak barrels. Egg
white fined, btld June '87.

1987 Viognier   112 cases
Estate   750 ml

Picked late Sept at 22.6°Brix, .74 acid, 3.15 pH from 7-yr-old vines.
No skin soak, cold frmt, 5 mos in older Limosin oak barrels. Sterile
filtered, btld May '88 in clear, punted French bottles.

Are you glad you have virus in your Cabernet?

"The most interesting thing would be to have my old clone heat treated and see what the difference turned out to be. I get horribly low tonnage. Nobody ever asks me for budwood. I'm delighted with the flavor of the wine, however. It may be climate, or soil, or production, or it could be genetics. I've always suspected the flavor was a function of the old clone, and not a function of the low tonnage. If I could have this flavor and higher tonnage by getting rid of the virus, that would be my choice. In fact, I'd be happy to prune for modest crop size. I don't thank the virus for doing that. On the other hand, maybe the virus does play a role in the flavor I like so much.

"My Viognier has virus too. That was why Davis was so slow in making it available. They had trouble heat treating it. Both my Cabernet and my Viognier ripen very late. I've picked Cabernet in November, and the Viognier is almost as late. Their scraggly, low weight clusters are an advantage though. They can sit through several rains without getting bunch rot.

"I haven't seen any indication that the virus moves through the vineyard. Some vines have it worse than others, but it doesn't seem contagious. There isn't much effect early in the season. You first notice the vines slowing down when the sugar gets to about 18°Brix."

Pete Minor

Pete Minor (L) and friends crush Chardonnay   RG

J. ROCHIOLI VINEYARDS

In the late '30s Joe Rochioli followed many Italian immigrants before him to the fertile banks of the Russian River in northern Sonoma County. He managed farmlands for the well known Wohler Ranch and eventually bought 120 acres for himself. He started with string beans and then sold hops to the property next door, which is now Hop Kiln Winery. For a man of his ethnic origin it was almost an obligation to plant Zinfandel and Petite Sirah on the hillside above his river bottom property. His son Joe went to Cal Poly to study animal husbandry, then returned to farm the family property. In 1958 he took the initiative to plant some of the first Sauvignon Blanc and Cabernet Sauvignon vines in the area. Joe Sr. died in 1966. Today 30-yr-old Sauvignon Blanc vines, planted on the sandy soils near the river, bear only 2-3 tons per acre. The quality of their fruit more than offsets this 60% drop in productivity from their more robust youth. They represent an investment of time which money can not replace.

Tom Rochioli, like many third generation Italian-Americans, grew up working in the vineyards and drinking wine every night with the evening meal. Tom left to attend Sacramento State where he got a B.A. in Finance and Accounting. He then went to work for Bank of America, but found himself managing loans to wineries. As he says, "It just seemed logical to get myself back on the other side of the desk." Tom rejoined his father on the farm in 1982. Joe had been selling grapes to prestigious Napa wineries for decades. Together, they decided to start a winery to better represent their grape growing business. Today they crush about 20% of their grapes and make 3,500 cases of wine. Tom and Theresa were married on the 10th of March 1985 and opened the tasting room at the winery the following week.

About 40 acres of the Rochioli property is sandy river bottom land. Another third of the property is on a south facing hillside. Tom and his father plan to put some Cabernet Sauvignon, Cabernet Franc and Merlot on that hillside. the last third is on a bench above the river. This bench hosts Pinot Noir grapes which are particularly well suited to the cool climate of western Sonoma County. In 1986 these grapes produced the best Pinot Noir at the State Fair, and in 1987 they produced the State Fair Sweepstakes Award winner. Tom says he has noticed at least 2 clones of Pinot Noir in their "field." One hardly makes it to the top wire before it wants to lay over on its side. The other one has rounder leaves, more vigorous growth and 50% more production if pruned the same way. One vineyard is the common denominator in Pinot Noirs by Williams & Selyem, Gary Farrell (Russian River) and Rochioli (top rated Pinot Noir by Wine Spectator's panel in 1988). It has both clones interplanted. All those grapes are picked from it on the same day using alternate rows.

Asked about his father's Sauvignon Blanc vines, Tom points out they are old, but still have to be held back. The vines are hedged in June and then again in August. They pull leaves off the east side of the vines to let afternoon sun penetrate the canopy. "If you don't get sun into the middle of the vine, leaves there die and potassium is absorbed from those leaves into the berries," Tom explains. "That gives you protein instability in the finished wine. By opening the vine up, we lower potassium levels in the juice and keep pH way down. I usually pick between 22° and 22.4°Brix. At 22° the wine has more of that aggressive Sancerre character which purists love. At 22.4° it is softer and more popular."

Given his winery's limited production, Tom does not have to aim for the mass American palate, but it's an interesting artistic question. Rochioli's '85 won Best Sauvignon Blanc at the State Fair. (Quite an accomplishment when added to the success other wineries have had using his Pinot Noir grapes.) That same Rochioli '85 Sauvignon Blanc was simultaneously singled out for vicious abuse by a national wine newsletter whose rather excitable author found it "commercially unacceptable." Obviously, the wine has some very distinctive characteristics.

After sixty years of grape growing excellence, we are proud to offer the first releases of Estate Bottled wines from J. Rochioli Vineyards. Located just south of Healdsburg on Westside Road, our vineyards were one of the first varietal plantings in Sonoma County. These vines have supplied high quality fruit to some of the most reputable wineries in Sonoma and Napa Counties.

At J. Rochioli Vineyards, our commitment to quality has resulted in wines of distinct character and style. Only small lots of selected varietals are produced each year.

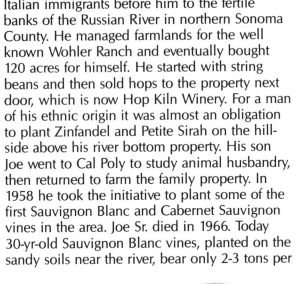

ESTATE BOTTLED

J. ROCHIOLI
VINEYARDS & WINERY

1985

RUSSIAN RIVER VALLEY

Sauvignon Blanc

SONOMA COUNTY

GROWN, PRODUCED & BOTTLED BY ROCHIOLI VINEYARDS
HEALDSBURG, CALIFORNIA   ALCOHOL 12.2% BY VOLUME

From vines that are now 27 years old, this dry Sauvignon Blanc offers herbal and slightly grassy aromas combined with a light hint of French oak. A fine balance of complex flavors and crisp acidity will compliment a variety of light fowl and seafood dishes.

Harvest Date:
September 25, 1985
Sugar at Harvest:
22.0° Brix
Titratable Acidity at Bottling:
76 gm/100 ml
Bottling Date:
April 11, 1986
Cases Produced:
716
Please Enjoy!

1987 Chardonnay — 1,155 cases
Estate — 750 ml

70% picked early Sept from 17-yr-old hillside vyd on red clay with 8'x10' spacing, 3.5 t/a, 23.2°Brix, .85 acid. "The beef of the wine." 30% picked late Sept from 15-yr-old Yolo loam vyd on 8'x12' spacing at 23.4°Brix with 4.5 t/a. "Rich, tropical fruit." No skin soak, no acid adjustment, 80% barrel frmtd with Montrachet yeast, 10% M-L. Stnls portion frmtd with Chanson. On lees until 1 mo before btlg. Francois Freres Allier barrels with med toast, 40% new. Bentonite fining, sterile filter, btld May '88 at 13.6 alc, .78 acid, 3.22 pH.

1987 Pinot Noir — 475 cases
Estate — 750 ml

3 t/a picked 20 Sept at 23.8°Brix, .95 acid, 3.3 pH from 17-yr-old vines on Yolo loam soil. 25% whole clusters. Frmtd in open outdoor tanks 9 days with Montrachet and Assmanhausen yeast at 85º89°F. Punched down 4x/day, inoculated with MCW, M-L complete in 1 mo. Polish filter, btld Jan '89 at 13.4 alc, .68 acid, 3.42 pH.

1988 Gewürztraminer — 380 cases
— 750 ml

50% from McElroy Vyd 2 miles west of Estate, 50% from Louis Martini's Los Venidos del Rio Vyd next door to Estate. Picked at 21.5°Brix, .8 acid, 3.5 pH. Frmtd in stnls with Epernay 2 yeast at 52°F. 1.5% rs.

1987 Sauvignon Blanc — 868 cases
Estate — 750 ml

'85 won Best SB at State Fair. Picked 13 Sept at 22.8°Brix, .9 acid. No skin soak. Settled 2 days, frmtd 3 wks at 55°F with Prise de mousse yeast. 20% frmtd in barrel. Aged 4 mo in small French oak. Bentonite fined, cold stabilized, sterile filtered, btld Feb 88 at 12.8 alc, 3.24 pH, .78 acid.

How important is clonal selection?

"In Chardonnay and Sauvignon Blanc the old clones tend to be low producers. I think it is more important in Pinot Noir. We are isolating clones from our own field, but when you move the vine it isn't going to act exactly the same. Going from deep soil to a hillside will cause some change. We've done that. We selected our Pinot Fin clone for its small clusters, low vigor, small leaves and tiny berries. Some of the Davis clones can get 7-8 tons per acre, but they are very light. Our skin to pulp ratio gives us an advantage. We planted the select clone from our proven vineyard 3 years ago on our hillside. We are already getting intense color. I expect a cherry/strawberry nose from a young field, but the color is a bonus. We are going to do 8 more acres with the budwood we've isolated.

"I'll be looking for others from Oregon. They have some great vineyards there, and I'd like to make some selections. We'll plant on AxR_1 because it has worked well for us. Farmers are conservative. I've read about a new nematode resistant rootstock called '33 something.' It would be nice because nematodes are the vector which will spread virus. And we do have virus in our Pinot Noir. But I think we'll stick with the proven rootstock and try a few buffer rows of vines between the old field and the new. Nematodes can travel on a dirty boot or a truck tire, so who knows.

"Planting on the vine's own roots is a hot topic, but it is just too risky. You spend $1,200 fumigating an acre and you don't want to take chances."

Tom Rochioli

Joe (L) and Tom Rochioli

RB

ROSE FAMILY

There is probably no connection, but Bill Rose grew up in Orange County and didn't drink or even like wine until he was 26 years old. At that point a friend gave him a glass of La Tâche. Within weeks Bill had taken up The Task and was working at Mondavi for the crush. He enrolled in Chemistry classes at Sonoma State and became a tour guide at Sebastiani. Bill and Ronnette were married in 1971. During the early '70s they became immersed in wine through the comraderie of the group who worked at Sebastiani. This group included Richard Paul Hinckle, now a free-lance wine writer, and Dennis Richardson (see page 98). After-hours they tasted many of the world's great wines.

Later Bill worked at Dry Creek Winery. Two graduate students in Enology come from France to work the crush each year at Dry Creek. Bill and Ronette made friends with them, in part because Bill had learned to speak French in college. The Rose's took a trip to France and spent 4 months touring famous areas. At the cellars of Marcel Gitton in the Loire, they were scheduled for a tasting from 11 a.m. to 12 one day. Marcel invited them into his caves to sample from the barrels. Testing Bill, Marcel asked if he could distinquish which barrels were made from separate vineyards. Apparently Bill passed because Marcel started bringing out wines from his library. They went back as far as '53. At 7 p.m. they repaired to Marcel's house where Mme. Gitton excoriated her husband for ignoring a dinner party they were hosting. As the Roses left, they saw Marcel headed back to the caves with a group of his dinner guests.

At Dry Creek Winery, Bill was able to get hands-on experience in practically all winery functions. He had also been making wine at home for several years. In 1981 he decided to "go pro." Sitting around with friends discussing a possible name for the venture, he pointed out that due to the gender of his offspring the winery would need to call itself Rose & Daughters Wine Company sometime early in the twenty-first century. After a few more glasses of wine, they decided Rose Family Winery would be easier to fit on a label. Bill began making Zinfandel from 20-year-old vines grown by Martinelli and Pinot Noir from Cameron Vineyard. Both places were near his home in Forestville on the Santa Rosa Plain. He rented space at Toyon Winery to make the wine. When Toyon went out of business in 1985, he moved to space on River Road in the middle of Martinelli's Gewürztraminer vineyard.

Bill's hobby is Tae Kwon Do karate. He took it up in 1983 as a way to get exercise. He only needs to pass the test on one more form to get his black belt. Ironically, with the pressures of the '88 crush and a mechanical failure in his television set, Bill didn't even get to observe the demonstration competition in Tae Kwon Do from the Olympics in Korea where the sport was born. Such are the rigors of autumn in the wine business.

ROSE FAMILY WINERY

1987
Russian River Valley

Chardonnay

(Cameron Vineyards)

PRODUCED & BOTTLED BY ROSE FAMILY WINERY, WINDSOR, CA
TABLE WINE   •   CONTAINS SULFITES

A full bodied, well balanced wine with abundant Chardonnay fruit accented with toasty oak flavors. Cameron Vineyards is located in the western Russian River area, a cooler region, well suited for the Chardonnay grape. The juice was separated at harvest, part was barrel fermented for complexity, body and oak; part was cold fermented for maximum fruit extraction. Fermentation was followed by ten months of aging in European oak cooperage.

The winery is located 2½ miles west of Hwy. 101 on River Road Exit just north of Santa Rosa. Visitors welcome. For further information call (707) 575-3160.

Bill & Ronnette Rose

| 1987 Chardonnay | 900 cases |
| Wes Cameron Vyd | 750 ml |

Picked at 23°Brix. Partially barrel-fermented in French oak with light toast. No M-L, 10 mos in 1 to 2-yr-old barrels. Sterile filter.

How much does varietal aroma differ between vyds?

"I think it differs a lot in Pinot Noir, but not as much in Chardonnay. Some vineyards give very good varietal character in Pinot Noir consistently. Others only do it 1 year out of 4. I can't explain why. In grapes like Chardonnay and Sauvignon Blanc the intensity may vary from year to year, but overall they are much more consistent. I don't like Pinot Noir as a sipping wine because you really have to look for complexity in it.

"As a winemaker, I have to like Chardonnay though. It is a very forgiving grape. If it has no flaws coming out of the fermentor, I assume I'm in business. The apple-like varietal smell is a foundation. I want to apply a buttery edge. Things like banana smells may result from ripeness, and oxidation can result from handling, but those characteristics are obvious. They really have very little to do with selecting vineyards.

"I never feel confident about a vineyard until I get some experience making that wine. My sampling technique has never really revealed much useful information. I chew on a few berries to see how much flavor comes out, but I suspect those results have a lot to do with the size of the berry I grab."

Bill Rose

RG

ROSENBLUM CELLARS

Amiable is a good word to describe Kent Rosenblum. Called at work, he often comes on the speaker phone to calmly chat while he "finishes up a client." He's a veterinarian, and the "client" is usually a cat undergoing surgery. Kent knew his winemaking activities would produce emergencies just like his vet practice. He didn't want to make wine in the country and commute to his office in Alameda. So, Rosenblum Cellars was launched in 1978 in one of the "liveliest" parts of West Oakland, across the street from a railroad station. Grapes were crushed in the former Dead End Bar of the 1880's. "Neat spot," Dr. Rosenblum avers. "We were between a soul food place and brothel. What with the girls, and the Cadillacs driving up, our neighbors saw nothing strange about a bunch of people crushing grapes in the middle of the night. We were just part of the action."

The winery quickly outgrew its 600 sq. ft. quarters. In 1982 they moved to a former Shell Oil research facility in Emeryville. Sale of that property required another move in 1987. Rosenblum Cellars now occupies a former Southern Pacific repair barn in Alameda. With heavy concrete walls, 40' ceilings and 12,000 sq. ft. of space, they think they've got it made. "Moving barrels between the floors of our last building got old fast," Dr. Rosenblum admits. "We changed locations during the crush which meant we couldn't make whites in '87. Transporting full tanks of cold fermenting wine would have been a little too chancey."

The reds are fermented in 4' x 4' plastic bins. Total storage is approximately 15,000 gallons and Rosenblum is now able to produce 6,000 cases per year of which 80% are red. "When we started out, we had this old crusher that didn't quite crush all the berries," Rosenblum reports. "Then we got this new Zambelli which gets them all, but we discovered we didn't like the results quite as much. So now we add back whole berries which seems to give the wines more fruit. It's our high-tech secret."

Rosenblum Cellars is a general partnership that includes Kent, his brother Roger (a computer consultant) and three other families they knew from a shared ski cabin. Everyone pitches in at every stage of winemaking, from picking grapes to bottling the wine. In 1980, they bought the 30 acre Lone Oak Vineyard on Eastside Road in the Russian River Valley. The winery also buys grapes from a number of old, hillside vineyards.

One Zinfandel comes from the Cullinan Vineyard in Sonoma. Tom Morrison near Lytton Springs is selling them Zinfandel again as well. They had used his grapes in '81 with spectacular results. He subsequently pulled out the original 80-year-old vines, but used budwood from the old clone to replant. Kent also found some 100-year-old vines just below the east slope of Mt. Diablo in Antioch. Jim Dragon had been selling those grapes to home winemakers in Canada.

Hendy Vineyard in southern Napa grew the '84 Zinfandel which Rosenblum used to win the Sweepstakes Award at the 1987 San Francisco Exposition. Those grapes came in with extraordinary acid. Kent fermented the wine in a stainless tank at cooler temperature than normal and didn't punch down as he would have in the small open bins. He didn't want too much tannin with all that acid. Finally, the low pH stopped malolactic before completion so he filtered it. In '85 and '86 Hendry sold all his grapes to Beringer for White Zin, but Rosenblum got them back in the picture for '87.

Small vineyards at the north end of Napa Valley produce the Petite Sirah. In '87 it came from Bob Barbras' vineyard near Calistoga. He has 80-year-old vines on a gravel bench near the river. When he doesn't sell to Rosenblum, the grapes are washed into the sea of Gallo via the Napa Co-op. Cabernet comes from Holbrook-Mitchell Vineyard (formerly partners in Alatera) near Yountville in Napa. All these grapes are harvested at 23-25°Brix to produce the hearty style that is Rosenblum's trademark. A reserve Cabernet is made from McGilvray Vineyard in Bennett Valley near Santa Rosa. This reserve Cabernet from a cooler climate area is picked at lower sugar and requires longer aging.

Despite moving, Rosenblum crushed 105 tons in '87, up from 65 tons in '86. Typically, their red wines are among the first to be released in any particular vintage. They also sell out quickly. The explanation for this situation is a well developed audience of collectors who buy the wines to lay down. The wines' track record for improvement in the cellar is remarkable, but it is only recognized by a small coterie of cultists. Little opportunity exists for casual consumers to stumble upon older vintages at any price.

Rosenblum Cellars

1985
NAPA VALLEY
MERLOT
ALCOHOL 13.7% BY VOLUME

PRODUCED AND BOTTLED BY ROSENBLUM
CELLARS B.W. 5139 EMERYVILLE, CALIF.

1985 Merlot
Napa Valley

Vineyard:	Holbrook Mitchell Vineyard, Yountville
Harvested:	September 1985
Sugar at harvest:	24.2° Brix
Total acid:	0.79 gm/cl.
pH:	3.26
Aging:	French Nevers oak

This wine exhibits ripe cherry and olive scents in the bouquet with soft, mouthfilling fruit and oak flavors.

CONTAINS SULFITES

1987 Cabernet Sauvignon   600 cases
Holbrook-Mitchell Vyd, Napa

Hillside vyd on the westside bench near Rutherford. 18-yr-old, dry-farmed vines picked mid-Oct at 23.9°Brix. Frmtd with Champagne yeast 16 days on the skins. Aged 20 mos in new to 3-yr-old Nevers and Limosin oak barrels. To be btld unfiltered July '89 at 13.8 alc, .64 acid.

1987 Zinfandel   1,500 cases
Sonoma   750 ml

52% from 75-yr-old, dry farmed, head pruned Cullinan Vyd at Fifth and Denmark in Sonoma. 48% from Morriston Vyd in Dry Creek. Picked at avg 23.4°Brix. Frmtd 14 days at 92°F with Champagne yeast. Aged 9 mos in Nevers and American oak barrels. Egg white fined, btld Oct '88 at 13.4 alc, .68 acid, 3.32 pH. Also small lots of '87 Hendry and '87 Dragon Zins.

1987 Petite Sirah   750 cases
Napa   750 ml

75-yr-old vines in the Barbras and St. George Vyds west of St Helena on a sloping hill with gravel soil. Head pruned, low production. 12 days on skins. Picked 25 Aug at 24.2°Brix. 12 days on skins. Btld at 3.41 pH, .72 acid.

1987 Gewürztraminer   400 cases
Sparkling   750 ml

Still wine made by Ventana Vyds won a Gold medal at Intervin competition in Montreal. Sparkled with UCD 595 yeast, en tirage 8 mos, 0.3% rs.

Are you still bucketing into the press?

"We try not to use a must pump on red wine after fermentation because the piston, or the impeller, or the screws are going to chew up seeds and stems. Our volume increased this year. The physical strain of bucketing by hand from the fermenters into the press was killing us. We got an idea about lifting the fermenter with the fork lift, and then dumping skins and must into the press through a system of chutes. The first time we tried it was pretty scary. We've never dropped one, but we've annointed a few walls. The liquid just doesn't come out from under the cap the same way twice. The fork lift rotates the bin sideways. So the idea is to tilt the forks forward, then rotate the bin so the liquid comes out of a corner. You just have to get the angle right."

What are you using for malo-lactic now?

"Terry Leighton has packaged the old 4440 strain of M-L bacteria in a freeze dried form that UPS delivers to your door in dry ice. The package insert calls it a cross between Leuconostoc and Pediococcus (which multiplies quickly) bred for cold tolerance. You mix it up with the medium that's enclosed and use it the next day. Seems to work great. As long as you can time your order properly, it should be a winner."

Kent Rosenblum

CL

CHANNING RUDD CELLARS

Channing Rudd has a legitimate claim to being the most persistent of California's tiny wineries. "No one has maintained my level of non-existence over 12 vintages," he claims. Channing has made about 800 cases of wine commercially every year since 1977. He started in an old Victorian home in Alameda. His early specialty was big-bodied reds, particular Zinfandel and Petite Sirah. He liked the flavor. Joe Swan and David Bruce were his heros in the middle '70s. His paying job was art design, but he always wanted to complement that expression with land and a vineyard of his own.

Money was the limiting factor. He looked all over Napa and Sonoma, and finally decided to take the plunge in Lake County. At $900 an acre he could get a healthy chunk of real estate. It was undeveloped, but Channing had always been athletic (17' pole vault, Olympic diving hopeful in '68, Sports Illustrated Award in '65), and he enjoyed working outdoors. The place he

found was 3 miles from the Napa County line and 2 miles from Sonoma County. In fact, it had been part of Napa County until 1871. His 60 acre parcel runs from the 1,240 foot elevation up to 1,750 feet. It is on the north side of Mt. St. Helena. Because of the elevation it is 10°F cooler than Middleton and the low lying areas of Lake County. The climate is much like St. Helena in Napa Valley, i.e. U.C. Davis Region 2. The soil is called Konocti gravel loam, and it is loaded with tufa (compressed volcanic ash). Historically many Austrian, Swiss and German farmers had settled here because of the springs emanating from the mountain and the absence of frost on the hillside.

Clearing the land to plant grapes was very difficult work. It did not become easier when he decided to move to the vineyard in December, 1982. There was no electricity and no phone. Sale of the Victorian in Alameda made the transition all the more hectic when a buyer showed up the first day it was offered, paid cash and gave Channing 45 days to move his winery out. That is how a winery became the first building on the new property. It took Rudd 18 solid days to transport 130 barrels in a rental truck to 3 overseas cargo containers he had bermed in the hillside next to a spring on the property. "Rained the whole time," he says shaking his head.

His plans for rapid expansion of the vineyard and facilities got a whiplash over the next few years. Jerry Harris, the owner of Pacific Fresh Seafood, had taken a liking to Channing's wine. Jerry was buying 100 cases of it a year. They became friends and Jerry decided to invest in the project. Channing made elaborate plans. Then one night in 1986 he was taken up short by a news report on television. His investor had been kidnapped. Harris's body was found in Nevada shortly thereafter, rumored to be the victim of a mob killing. "Strange," says Channing.

"He was the nicest damn guy."

Today Rudd has rebounded from that reversal. He has 3 acres of Merlot, 2 of Cabernet Sauvignon, 2 of Chardonnay and a half acre each of Malbec and Cabernet Franc. 1988 will be his first Estate vintage. He has continued to make wine from grapes bought at top Napa vineyards, although he has not made Zinfandel nor Petite Sirah since 1980. His graphic design business is flourishing, and that is helping out on the vineyard expense. He lives in Middleton with his wife and two children. Within a short time we will know whether vineyards on a hillside up out of the river clay in Lake County have as much potential in the glass as they appear to have on paper.

1985 Cabernet Sauvignon   120 cases
Napa   750 ml

17% Cabernet Franc from the Moorehead Vyd. Remainder Cabernet Sauvignon from Bella Oaks. Picked at 23.5° to 23.8°Brix. On skins 20 days with CO_2 cap after end of frmt, punched down 4x/day, basket press 135 gal/ton.

What do you think of the state of wine labels today?

"The most obvious thing about labels is their need to get people's attention. It isn't enough to look elegant and tasteful. Many things are being done with die cuts, four color printing, embossments and foil which are obviously designer specials. Some I like. The Veronica diRosa watercolor on Belvedere's label comes to mind. Some, however, lack an awareness of design.

"I've been an artist ever since I could pick up a pencil. I've worked in many different situations from big agencies to free lance to art director at Paul Masson. They all have certain advantages. Big agencies tend to put you in a certain category. Eventually you lose the artistic touch. You get burned out. Working on your own you have to be a jack of all trades. Free-lancers tailor things more to the clients wishes. Therefore you may not notice a specific style as much in the work they do on wine labels.

"I enjoy the work I'm doing now for Cuvaison because I can tie it all together. I don't have any trouble working with Manfred Esser because I'm used to that German personality. I was trained by Germans. I grew up with tyrants. I married two of them."

Channing Rudd

The rigors of turning raw land into vineyard

SALAMANDRE WINE CELLARS

The salamander on Wells Shoemaker's label can be explained many ways. It is a common symbol in the Cognac region of France and even adorned the coat of arms for Francois I four hundred years ago. A more insightful story, however, involves a two acre marsh near Wells' home in Aptos. An endangered species of salamander lives there, prompting one of those emotive confrontations between developers and environmentalists that are so beloved by local newspapers. Dr. Shoemaker may have mellowed since his days as a Stanford student in the late '60s, but he still enjoys a gentle poke at his more conservative neighbors.

Wells chose to practice pediatrics in Watsonville for three reasons: he wanted to use his Spanish language skills; he wanted to dive for abalone; and he wanted to make a difference in society. He has started an intensive care nursery,

serves as medical advisor to the Lactation Center at the community hospital, and in 1985 wrote a book called *Little Ills and Bitter Pills.* He and his wife Sandy have three children.

Dr. Shoemaker is superbly qualified to comment on health issues facing the wine industry. He is emphatic that Fetal Alcohol Syndrome is a real phenomenon. However, he points out that it has only occurred when the mother chronically consumed high volumes of alcohol (cheap or distilled in virtually every documented case) or engaged in binge drinking. "Researchers have looked long and hard for any indication of harm caused by modest consumption of wine during pregnancy," he explains. "There is no indication that it occurs. I tell parents that pregnancy lasts 18 months. For the first 9 months I suggest they put their alcohol dollars into a fine bottle of wine each month and lay it away. Then, during the second 9 months, they should reward themselves each month with a very special meal. The amount of alcohol a baby can get from breast milk is too small to be measured."

Shoemaker grew up on the eastern seaboard. Wine was not a part of his childhood because his mother strongly campaigned against such notions. The embryonic development of Salamandre Cellars began when Wells was making cabinets to pay bills during his pediatrics residency. A close friend worked at Ridge Vineyards. Culls from the bottling line enabled Wells to discern early that

not all wines are made equal. With limited financial resources, he discovered that a small amount of good wine is preferable to a large amount of mediocre wine.

In 1977, Shoemaker and a group of medical friends began making wine as amateurs. They were encouraged by Ken Burnap and Jeff Baker (now the winemaker at Carmenet). Shoemaker's "compulsive dishwashing, tolerant wife and superior water pressure" earned him the lead role. Terrel West, manager at Arroyo Seco Vineyards, indulged this motley crew by allowing them to show up with their children and pick grapes before the mechanical harvesters entered the fray. They had a lot of fun, and won several Best of Division awards for home wine at the Santa Cruz County Fair. In fact, one Chardonnay scored higher (19.3 out of 20) than any wine in the history of the competition. Shoemaker availed himself of every winemaking class he could find. He thinks those hours may be approaching the number he spent in medical school. In 1985 he dug a cellar under his house in a densely wooded canyon and bonded the winery. "I drove more nails than bargains," he says.

Salamandre's history includes many different wines. "I annually violate a perennial promise not to make tiny lots," Shoemaker complains. "It has something to do with having to pick the grapes ourselves. Hopefully this tendency will decrease as my age increases. Small batches of wine are like the premature babies I deal with every day. There is very little margin for error." The winery does not own a fork lift, so all the barrels and equipment must be moved by hand. They also bottle the wine themselves because the road leading to the winery is not big enough for any of the mobile bottling lines to drive in. They make about 800 cases a year and would have to move to bigger quarters if they wanted to make much more.

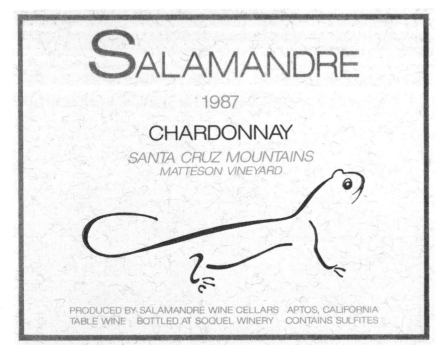

SALAMANDRE

1987

CHARDONNAY

SANTA CRUZ MOUNTAINS
MATTESON VINEYARD

PRODUCED BY SALAMANDRE WINE CELLARS   APTOS, CALIFORNIA
TABLE WINE   BOTTLED AT SOQUEL WINERY   CONTAINS SULFITES

1986 Chardonnay	120 cases
Matteson Vyd	750 ml

Grapes from 7-yr-old vines on steeply terraced, sandy soil near Corralitos above Watsonville. Mike Matteson has been Shoemaker's partner in pediatrics for 12 yrs. Picked 4 Oct at 23.1°Brix, 1.1 acid and 3.15 pH. Stemmed and crushed as the grapes came off the vine. No SO_2, 8 hrs skin soak. Frmtd 6 wks in barrel with Chanson yeast. Racked of gross lees, but left on fine lees til spring. No M-L. Aged in small Limousin cooperage 1/3 new. Btld May '87.

Are low pH Chardonnays unique?

"Certainly not. That is how the Chardonnays from northern France, like Chablis, have been for ever and ever. They are tightly structured, and nobody ever drinks them the year after the grapes were picked. They need time. My '79 is just wonderful now. California is used to the Dolly Parton style of Chardonnay because they are easier to sell. They jump out of the glass right away. But they're not that great with a meal, and they don't age well at all.

"Santa Cruz mountains are ideal for the low pH style of wine I want to make. I can avoid SO_2 because the pH of the wine protects it against spoilage and oxidation. You have to do the work in the vineyard to get small berries and intense flavor, but those two factors go together. If you only had small berries without the low pH, you would have more phenolics to oxidize and the risk of bitterness. We know we are going to get low pH because of the climate. So we thin the crop and pull off leaves. We only want 2 leaves between the clusters and the sun.

"As my low pH wines develop in the bottle, they take on a lush and slippery mouth feel. It isn't there in the first year or two. I know this sounds like winespeak, but the flavor elements come together. I think it is like an All-Star base-ball team. You've got oak over there, and sur lie flavor over here, and Chardonnay varietal fruit in the corner. They are all present, but they don't turn any double plays. It takes a while for them to develop teamwork."

Wells Shoemaker

RB

SANTA CRUZ MOUNTAIN VINEYARDS

With his father a "boomer" in the construction business, Ken Burnap attended eleven schools in as many cities before he graduated from high school. Ken ran his own construction contracting business for many years. During this time of travel and hard work, he developed a love for good food and wine that left him aghast at the prices restaurants charged for "portion controlled, heat-and-serve food with standard wines and Hollandaise sauce out of a #12 Rykoff can." As "therapy," and with an accomplished chef for a partner, Ken opened the Hobbit Restaurant in the city of Orange in Southern California. The restaurant prospered, but in the back of Ken's mind was the nagging desire to chuck it all and try to make great Pinot Noir. In 1974 he bought the Jarvis Vineyard from David Bruce.

The property was originally planted in 1863 by John Jarvis. The Jarvis brothers at one time owned 1,000 acres of vines in the Santa Cruz mountains, which they used as a real estate lure for snow-bound Easterners. Their vineyards and Santa Cruz Wine Company label went under at the end of the last century when San Francisco merchants Kohler and Froehling dominated the market and manipulated wine prices. The Jarvis

Vineyard, however, remained in production as the home ranch. It was replanted in 1916, and Zinfandel was grown all through Prohibition. David Bruce acquired the property in the early 1960's and enhanced his emerging reputation with 1966 and 1968 Zinfandels from the vineyard. The Zinfandel vines were replaced with Pinot Noir in 1969 and 1970.

When Burnap bought the property there were no roads or buildings on it. He built a 900 sq. ft. concrete block garage for winemaking operations. In 1977, the concrete block building was converted to case storage when Ken completed the 4,000 sq. ft. winery and house on four levels built into the steep hillside.

Grapes are cut from the vines with shears and run through the crusher within twenty minutes of picking. All winery operations are gravity flow. The crushing pad is on the roof, fermenters are on the second level down, the press on the third and the barrels on the bottom. Barrels are racked from the top of the stack to the bottom and then fork-lifted to an upper level for further racking and transfer to the bottling tank. Bottling is also done by gravity, using a 14-spout filler with vacuum corker and nitrogen sparge. Foils and labels are applied one year later, so that any problem bottles can be culled.

Because Jarvis Vineyard has been in continuous use for 120 years, Burnap has always felt certain that he had a dominant, naturally selected yeast in the bloom of the grapes and in the soil. He has been using this wild yeast for all of his wines since 1974. The yeast is a slow fermenter. It often takes 18 days to finish the

fermentation, but has no trouble tolerating alcohol nor the lower pHs that Ken has been getting in the last few years as he began picking at lower sugars. Lees and pomace are distributed back into Jarvis Vineyard.

Burnap feels vineyard sites from the summit of the mountains to the ocean require very careful positioning. If they are too low, grapes will never get ripe. At Bonny Doon one can be within a couple of miles of the ocean as the crow flies because altitudes go up quickly. But at Aptos and Corralitos, one has to come inland 5 miles or more to reach the 400 foot elevation that he thinks is necessary. Fog does more than block out sun. The moisture can be very detrimental to Chardonnay by encouraging bunch rot and mildew. He prefers southwest facing slopes which are not surrounded by trees or ridges because he wants to see constant air flow. The beneficial effect of moisture in fog is to reduce stress in dry farmed vines at the end of the growing season. Property which has been logged for redwood trees is not particularly good for vineyards. The acidity of the soil is too high to cope with. You can introduce lime rock, but you need a lot of it. Even so, there are thousands of acres in the Santa Cruz mountains which would be ideal for future vineyards if they were not in demand for houses. The problem is the cost of farming in the mountains. Everything is too expensive for somebody who just wants to sell grapes. "I pay a premium every year for the grapes I buy," he says. "This situation means there is never much fluctuation in price from year to year. Just a gentle and persistent upward trend."

SANTA CRUZ MOUNTAINS — *Chardonnay* — 1986 VINTAGE TABLE WINE

PRODUCED AND BOTTLED BY:

Santa Cruz Mountain Vineyard

2300 JARVIS ROAD, SANTA CRUZ, CA 95065   K.D. BURNAP, PROPRIETOR

This wine was produced from Chardonnay grapes grown on the Hyde and Treasure Island vineyards at Vanumanutagi Ranch. Yes indeed, there is also a Jekyll and Kidnapped vineyard on this ranch that was formerly owned by Mrs. Robert Louis Stevenson.

After Robert Louis Stevenson's death in Samoa, his widow returned to the United States and Vanumanutagi Ranch. It was she who gave it this Samoan name which means "veil of the singing birds."

This wine is 12½% alcohol by volume and contains a sulfiting agent.

1985 Pinot Noir   400 cases
Jarvis Vyd   750 ml

Picked 29 Aug from Estate vyd at 1,400 ft elevation on steep hillside,
thin Hugo loam soil with sandstone/limestone deposits, 15-yr-old
dry-farmed vines, some virus. Entire vyd netted against birds. Severe
cane pruning produced only 0.5 t/a at 23°Brix, .86 acid, 3.2 pH. No
SO_2, 10% whole clusters. Frmtd 8 days with natural yeast, 54-90°F
in open stnls, hand punched 2-8x/day. Natural M-L finished in summer. Aged in new 60 gal Tronçais and Allier oak barrels from Francois Freres with light toast. Egg white fined, btld Aug '87. 12.8 alc,
.68 acid, 3.3 pH.

1985 Merlot   1,400 cases
                               750 ml

Picked 18 Sept at Ceres Ranch in rolling hills west of Templeton at
23.2°Brix, .70 acid. Frmtd 7 days on skins with SCMV yeast.

1983 Cabernet Sauvignon   2,000 cases
Bates Ranch   750 ml

Picked 8 Nov in steep vyd on Santa Clara side of the Santa Cruz
mtns behind Mt Madonna, 3-6 ft soils, Hugo loam, 14-yr-old vines
on AxR rootstock, dry-farmed. 22.1°Brix, .86 acid, 3.1 pH. On skins
10 days in open stnls. SCMV yeast. Aged in French and American
oak 2-3 yrs old. Egg white fining. Btld Sept '85 at 12.4 alc, 3.2 pH.

1987 Chardonnay   950 cases
Vanumanutagi Vyd   750 ml

Vyd in SE end of Santa Cruz Mtns, 1 mile from Bates Ranch. Picked
at 22.5°Brix, .80 acid, 3.2 pH. 10 hr skin soak, barrel frmtd in Vosges
oak, complete m-l, 8 mos on lees. Btld Aug '88, 13.1 alc.

What is the downside of wild yeast?

"The only other winery I know to be using it
is Paul Draper at Ridge. I haven't spoken to him
about it in a couple of years. At the time, he was
not having any trouble. He had Leo McCloskey
working with him then, so they probably monitored everything closely. They wouldn't have
had any problem introducing a pure strain if
one of the wild ones got stuck.

"My own yeast needs to be investigated. I
think there are at least 3 players. One starts right
away. A second one carries it down to a few
Brix. Then the alcohol tolerant dude kicks in.
I've had it ferment must bone dry at 18.2% alcohol. It has done it in the 16s a couple of times
and in the 14s several times. The complexity of
the wine is doubtlessly helped. I suppose there
is a risk of volatility if you had some vagrant
strain, but mine is as dominant as the one making Sourdough bread in San Francisco.

"My malo-lactics always go spontaneously too.
They never even start until the barrels warm up
in the spring."

Is there a story about Vanumanugati Vyd?

"It was supposedly owned by the widow of
Robert Louis Stevenson. I have Chardonnay from
Treasure Island Vyd. I will release Chardonnay
from Hyde Vyd later. Yes, there is a Kidnapped
Vyd and a Jekel Vyd. Jekel and Hyde Vyds are
right next to each other. One is deep rich soil.
The other is inhospitable rocks. Two years ago I
made a barrel of Chardonnay from each one.
Both wines were okay, so I blended them together. The result was horrible. Lesson: Don't
blend like that when the moon is full."

Ken Burnap

CL

SARAH'S VINEYARD

Marilyn Otterman is one, perhaps both, of the best interviews in the wine industry. You really had to be there. Marilyn holds certain opinions and "Sarah," her alter ego, has very definite opinions of her own. They don't always agree, and things sometimes get a little hectic with both opinions coming from one mouth, but it is always good fun. The winery makes consistently great wine, even though they appear to use mirrors to do so.

The grapes and micro-organisms involved in the winemaking process talk to Sarah. All the time. Marilyn maintains a personal relationship with the wines, which she always refers to in the female gender. The '84 Ventana Chardonnay, for instance, "is 5'9" and very aggressive. Show her off at elegant functions." The '84 Estate by comparison "is more adaptable. She's not as tall and has Greek eyes. She's the type you marry to be with every day." Got the picture? There's more. Marilyn says the '85 Ventana is "for men who like boobs and hips." While the '85 Estate "comes out of the bottle slowly. She stands back and waits for maturity on your part." Buying these wines is like asking the Homecoming Queen for a date. You expect to be quizzed about your prospects.

Then there is the intrigue. Marilyn makes a mystery red blend called Sarah's Affair. "But I don't do it every year," she points out coyly.

Marilyn and John Otterman bought 10 acres in 1977 and moved north from Los Angeles to open Sarah's Vineyard. They planted 7 acres of Chardonnay on the property. John and Marilyn met while she was working in John Daumé's home-winemaking store. John is a good-natured businessman who keeps the equipment running at the winery and handles the mundane aspects of sales when he is not commuting to his manufacturing business in Whittier. Details like price bore Sarah. Marilyn and Sarah make the wine. You know, two hands make light work.

The winery is compact and scrupulously clean. There are fresh flowers, candlelight and music in the private tasting room. Invited guests receive elegant balloon glasses, bread and cheese. And, of course, they get a generous slice of Sarah's charm. "The winery is Sarah's doll house," says Marilyn enthusiastically. "It even looks like a doll house, with cute little baby tanks." Sarah's label is probably the most expensive in the business. It is made with a die sculpted by an engraver from Smith & Wesson. It is printed by Jeffries Bank Note Company on paper normally reserved for wedding invitations. The bottles are wrapped in tissue paper and shipped in a wooden box. One day Sarah hopes to offer a Chardonnay in a hand-blown bottle.

Sarah is clear about the role of different barrels, half of which are bought new each year. "Sirugue oak is like silk chiffon," Marilyn says caressing the air with her hands. "It exposes the bones of the body so you can see the structure. It's the opposite of a flannel nightgown. Seguin-Moreau adds a little lemon kiss. Francois Freres is the perfect eraser. It covers up all your mistakes. Like oregano, it makes everything taste good."

Sarah likes to draw an anology between yeast

and a teacher. Different kids, like different grapes, interpret the teacher in individual ways. The variations are obvious when the wine is young. Sarah chooses Chanson yeast for its delicacy. It reminds her of a powder puff. Sarah also goes without SO_2 as long as possible to let wild yeast operate before the pure strain culture takes over. "Malo-lactic in Chardonnay is like sexuality in a loud bar," Sarah opines. "It competes for attention, much the way a sun tan and a bikini do. I prefer more of a finishing school refinement and an air of mystery. I never worry about my Estate Chardonnay. She's always a perfect Lady, relying on good bone structure to attract attention. Ventana, however, is a shameless crowd pleaser. She has to be restrained. I've started to pick her early in order to get a grip on the reins."

Sarah's Vineyard presently makes about 3,000 cases a year. Typically, Marilyn is simultaneously revealing and vague when asked about Sarah's future. "She is going to make very balanced wines, more balanced than every before," she hoots. "I predict extreme balance!" Grinning, she adds, "Sarah is also going to listen better, have more patience and," Marilyn concludes, "become more spontaneous."

Not likely.

1987 Chardonnay	400 cases
Ventana Vyd	750 ml

No SO$_2$ at crusher, no skin soak. Frmtd in stnls at 48°F with Chanson yeast. No time on lees, portion goes through M-L. 6 mos in new and 1-yr-old Sirugue barrels. Bentonite fining, sterile filter. Btld June '88.

1987 Chardonnay	
Estate	750 ml

7-yr-old vines, made like Ventana, but aged in Francois Freres and Seguin-Moreau barrels.

1986 Merlot	150 cases
Radike Vyd	750 ml

35-yr-old vines on westside near Paso Robles. Aged 15 mos in French oak.

What's new?

"Sarah is moving into red wines. Sarah likes them more than she used to. They add balance to the dining experience. Sarah is becoming more aware of the potential for red wines in Hecker Pass. In '87 she did a red wine from several different grapes grown here nearby. It is fragrant, and ethereal, and not on the skins very long. The grapes come in at different times. They include a Grenache, but it has to be picked at 24°Brix. They are made separately, then blended. Winemaking is really just listening and allowing the refinement and dimensions of the wine to occur.

"Then there is our old Burgundy bottle with the monogram blown into the glass of the neck. It is the most beautiful bottle I've ever seen. They have 3" punts and weigh a ton. We have to ship the wine as individual bottles in wooden cases because they don't fit anything else. We are also having to redo the label. If I had my druthers we wouldn't put any label on at all.

"I've put the warning sign up in our winery, but I sure think it is barbarian. I don't want people to take care of me. People just seem to cease being responsible. We are building walls around ourselves and turning into robots. All these actions seem aimed at making it so people don't see, or feel, or smell any more. I think it is going to continue. I'll just say, 'That's it!' No tasting, no visits. Sarah will cease to exist."

Marilyn Otterman

KF

SEA RIDGE WINERY

Dan Wickham grew up in Michigan. His first vintage was in 1955. At age eight his winemaking debut came as quite a surprise to his tee-total parents. Dan did undergraduate work at the University of Miami and received a Doctorate in Zoology from U.C. Berkeley. He works at UC's Marine Biology Research Station in Bodega Bay. Connoisseurs of West Coast cuisine will surely wish him success, as his area of expertise happens to be the Dungeness crab. He has taken considerable heat from California's Fish & Game Dept for suggesting that fishing pressure might be responsible for the depressed state of crab populations around San Francisco. They want to blame water temperature or pollution. Wickham questions this position, saying *"Cancer magister is one of the dominate creatures on the ocean floor. It is particularly hardy and seems to take nasty chemicals in stride. The only demonstrated killer appears to be a worm that eats crab eggs."* Wickham reports there was a good settlement of baby crabs from Mendocino north in '84. They take about 4 years to grow to maturity, so he is looking forward to crab, sourdough bread and Chardonnay real soon.

Tim Schmidt grew up in Santa Rosa, where his father raised apples. Tim has an MA from the University of Canterbury in New Zealand. Schmidt and Wickham met at the Bodega Bay research facility, while Tim was employed as a Chemist studying marine pollution. After deciding to start a winery, they began looking for property along the coast near historic Ft. Ross. Conventional grape growing wisdom at that time would have placed this region beyond the borders of Lunacy for a vineyard. But Dan and Tim were using Burgundy as a model. They knew that northern France was much colder than California's "acceptable" areas. When they discovered that sheep rancher Mick Bohan had some Cabernet grapes which ripened to 24°Brix in 1978, they bought 40 acres next door for $1,000 an acre.

Coastal ridges in that region are built of limestone that originally precipitated from sea water. They are on "Merced Cap" soil, with broken shale going down 50 feet. Tim, Dan and one carpenter did all the construction on the winery over a 3 month period without electricity. The 3,000 sq. ft. building with 20' ceilings is cut into a north-facing hillside and passively cooled. The property was logged over in 1910, but only perfectly straight trees that could be hand split were utilized. As Dan and Tim cleared the land they sold 150 redwood stumps for burls, and cut 20,000 board feet of lumber from 70 year old redwood logs left by the early loggers. Besides providing siding and decking for the winery, this windfall paid for developing and planting the vineyard.

Dan's access to oceanographic weather studies showed him that the cold thermoclime from the ocean only goes up to 500 feet. Fogs and winds are blocked by a 1,500 foot ridge between the vineyard and the sea. Sea Ridge Winery is on the second ridge back and has a fairly mild climate. Heat waves are not a problem, and the temperature stays at about 75°F all summer long. Frost presents little danger although it does occasionally snow. Winter rainfall is as high as anywhere in California; in 1982 nearby Cazadero got 140 inches.

Tim and Dan have planted 8 acres of Pinot Noir on AxR$_1$ rootstock. They think the clone, from Summa Vineyard near Bodega Bay, is the Pinot Fin: small clusters with a pine cone shape plus very small berries that are elliptical rather than round. They'd like to plant 7 more acres of vines. Dan says experimental vineyards near Beaune, France, have 80 different clones of Pinot Noir. "Oregon State University brings the most successful ones over here," he continues, "and I'd like to plant two or three acres of each. Oregon is way ahead of California in clonal selection experiments."

Sea Ridge Chardonnays are always put through malo-lactic fermentation because the cool climate grapes have so much acid. "We got involved in some 1980 research," says Wickham, "when the Penn State strain proved too passive for our juice. The resulting 4440 strain was great, but the company making it folded. Now we use the MCW strain Merry Edwards isolated from an old milking shed at Matanzas Creek."

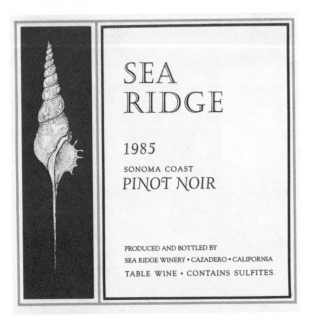

SEA RIDGE

1985

SONOMA COAST
PINOT NOIR

PRODUCED AND BOTTLED BY
SEA RIDGE WINERY · CAZADERO · CALIFORNIA
TABLE WINE · CONTAINS SULFITES

1985 Chardonnay   800 cases
Mill Station Vyd   750 ml

Cool, large vyd in hills west of Sebastopol , 10-yrs-old, on marine deposit, Gold Ridge, sandstone soils. No skin soak, no SO_2 at crusher. Barrel frmtd at 65°F with Pasteur Champagne yeast. M-L during alc frmt. Aged 1 yr in French oak barrels with light toast, 1/3 new. Bentonite fining, polish filtration, btld July '86.

1985 Pinot Noir   800 cases
Sonoma Coast   750 ml

10% whole berries, frmtd in 2,000-gal open redwood tanks, punched down 2x/day. On skins 18 days with Champagne yeast at 80-85°F. Bladder press, settled, aged in Center of France 60-gal barrels with light toast. Egg white fined, polish filter, btld May '87.

1985 Sauvignon Blanc   350 cases
Scalabrini Vyd   750 ml

Cool vyd on the Sonoma coast behind Sea Ranch.

1984 LH Zinfandel   180 cases
Occidental   750 ml

Same grapes that made the legendary LH Zins of Ridge Vyds ten years ago. Picked at 33°Brix and 1.65 acid° 16 alc, 2% rs.

Do you stay on the lees much?

"As a general matter I will do our first racking in January or February each year, after the wines have completed malo-lactic. Chardonnay is different than Pinot Noir. We settle Chardonnay before fermentation, but it still has some grape solids in the fermentation lees. Pinot Noir is fermented in a big tank, then pressed, then settled before going into small barrels. It is going to have fewer lees in the barrel naturally.

"H_2S is the major risk in staying on the lees. Some yeast may have more propensity to produce it than others, but I suspect the growers' sulphur regimen is the chief culprit. Grapes from Mill Station Vineyard have never given us a problem. We specify in our contract that no sulphur can be applied within 45 days of harvest, but occasionally a grower will freak in wet conditions and try to sneak something past you.

"I like the complexity and mouth feel from yeast autolysis. How long you stay on the lees probably has to do with how much you like that 'bread dough' smell. I don't think the yeast stops producing it after some limited number of months. Look how much there is in Bollinger RD Champagne after being on the yeast for 10 years. I wouldn't want to overdo it in a simple, citrus scented Chardonnay or a barrel with light toast. I'd want more autolysis as a balancing element in the most complex wines with the boldest oak statements."

Dan Wickham

Dan Wickham   RG

SILVER MOUNTAIN VINEYARD

Standing in Silver Mountain's young vineyard at the 2,000 foot elevation, you can see Los Gatos in a valley to the northeast and Monterey Bay 8 miles to the west. It's too high for much summer fog, but winemaker Jerry O'Brien has seen 80-mph winds off the Bay, and his vineyard averages 60-80" of rain each winter. "There are only a couple of inches of topsoil here," Jerry observes, "then sandstone. Rain drains away pretty fast." In 1985 a big fire in the Santa Cruz mountains came within a mile of O'Brien's property and all of his neighbors had to be evacuated.

O'Brien grew up in Inglewood near Los Angeles and joined the Air Force in 1960. As a counter-insurgency officer, he flew assault transports and prop-driven fighters in Viet Nam. He became interested in wine because base officers' clubs had good selections. His interest grew when he

SILVER MOUNTAIN
VINEYARDS

1984

Chardonnay
Ventana Vineyards Monterey

PRODUCED AND BOTTLED BY SILVER MOUNTAIN VINEYARDS
ALC 13% BY VOL • BOX 1695, LOS GATOS, CA • 353-2278

was posted to Argentina and Chile. He left active service in 1968, selling real estate for awhile, then commodities futures.

In 1973 he purchased 17 acres and built a house on Skyland Ridge, in an area once known for grape growing. He found ruins of old wineries nearby and discovered his land was once a vineyard. "Volunteer Verdelho kept springing up," he says. "You know Verdelho— early Thompsons with seeds." In 1981, O'Brien planted 9 acres of Chardonnay on their own roots with cuttings from Mt. Eden/Martin Ray. He has no irrigation and has developed a rapacious following among the local deer population. As a result he dropped the '87 crop to encourage more root development.

"My ex-wife was quite a whiz in the catering business," Jerry says. "We moved up here thinking Burgundy. Then I did apprenticeships with Joe Swan and Chalone. Pinot Noir is too damned temperamental." O'Brien decided to limit his Estate wine to Chardonnay. 75% of present production is Chardonnay with the balance of his 2,000 cases per year in Zinfandel. Since 1983 the Zinfandel grapes have come from the old Chauvet vineyard in Glen Ellen.

The current Chardonnays come from Ventana Vineyards. O'Brien's primary concern is the average harvest date. "I want grapes which are on the vine a long time," he says. "I might be able to accomplish the same thing in Edna Valley or in Anderson Valley if I could only find growers who pick by hand rather than using mechanical harvesters." The other reason O'Brien goes to Ventana is that Doug Meador will field crush for him using a Demoissey crusher/stemmer. It is a top-of-the-line piece of equipment. Meador picks different sections of vineyard to balance the sugar/acid numbers just the way O'Brien wants them. Then all Jerry has to do is bring the must up to Silver Mountain

for fermentation. "I also like that fruity aroma his grapes get," O'Brien explains. "I'm fermenting 20% of the must in stainless now at 55°F instead of in barrels so I can retain a strong fruit nose. I compliment that by leaving the barrel fermented portion on the lees a little longer."

Silver Mountain's 1,200 sq. ft. winery was built new in 1980. It has air-conditioning, but O'Brien says he never needs it. He owns a Zambelli crusher with plastic rollers, and has a 1,200-gallon stainless "ex-milk tank" for fermentations. They lift 40-pound lug boxes 9 feet in the air on to a sorting board where several people remove foreign matter. It takes 45 minutes for a ton of grapes. They punch down by hand, and then move skins from the fermenter into the press in buckets. Jerry and full-time property manager Victor Balderas need 8 hours to press 5 tons of grapes in their single-basket press. Pomace is taken out of the press with pitchforks and shovels.

Barrels are filled on the ground and then lifted onto the racks with a manual forklift. When they are emptied, all the barrels have to be brought back down to the ground in order to be cleaned. Silver Mountain rents filters and bottles with a 4-spout gravity filler. They are quite proud of a new corker they acquired in 1986. They can bottle with two people. One person takes empty bottles out of the cases, purges them with nitrogen gas and fills them with wine. The second person corks and stacks boxes on a pallet. The corking machine is the most automatic part. When a plate is stepped on, the machine pulls a vacuum in the bottle and inserts the cork. They can do 56 cases in 3 hours. Later, one person spins on the foil capsules. He then runs a label through the glue machine and smooths it onto the bottle with a soft cloth to press out any air bubbles. It takes an hour to label 5 cases.

1984 Chardonnay	1,400 cases
Ventana Vyds	750 ml

Field crushed from 14-yr-old Ventana vines on 23 Sept at 23.1°Brix, .92 acid. No skin soak, no SO_2 at crusher. Barrel frmtd at 78°F with Champagne yeast. Complete M-L by Jan. 6 mos on lees. Aged 1 yr in Limosin oak barrels, 2 to 3-yrs-old with medium toast. Btld 12 Oct '85 at 13.5 alc, .78 acid, 3.33 pH.

1983 Zinfandel	800 cases
Sonoma	750 ml

Grapes from 30-yr-old Chavet Vyd north of Sonoma on eastside of valley, and Polson Vyd on the west side of upper Dry Creek Vly. Picked 30 Sept. 3 wks on skins with CO_2 cap. Frmtd in open redwood tank with Montrachet yeast to 88°F. 20 mos in 60% French oak and 40% American. No fining, no filtering. Btld May '85 at 12.8 alc, .68 acid.

What is your view of the discount store scene in CA?

"I think discounters do a bigger percentage of the wine business in California than they do elsewhere, but it isn't a strictly California situation. I get ads in the mail from discounters in New York and Washington DC that I've never even heard of. I think discounters are around all the metropolitan areas. The are just not as big a factor in other states. I bet discounters sell 80% of the jug wine in California and 50% of the premium wine. Supermarkets do another 15% of the jug wine and 20% of the premium wine. That leaves about 30% of the premium stuff and 5% of the jugs for full-service stores.

"In California there are consumers who won't shop at traditional full-boat stores. From my point of view, a traditional store is much more valuable because my wine is not well known. I'm better known in the industry than by the public. I want a merchant who can educate the consumer about quality. Personal service is important to my product. I want a merchant who can match certain wine characteristics to his particular customers' taste.

"Most of my experience with discounters is limited to one store that bought a huge amount of wine from me. They passed the volume discount along to their customers and put a big recommendation sign on the display. All the store employees told customers it was a great deal. As a result, the wine sold quickly. I don't know if there was any demand for repeat sales because I stopped selling to them with the discounted price.

"I do know that full-service stores will not buy my wines if they hear the local discounter carries them, no matter what price the discounter has them listed. In the future, I expect we'll see discounters offering more service and traditional merchants offering more discounts."

Jerry O'Brien

Jerry O'Brien (L) and Victor Balderas

CL

SKY VINEYARDS

If pie-in-the-sky refers to an impossible dream, one might expect Sky Vineyards to be a sumptuous estate built by a gentleman farmer using gains ill gotten in another field. The truth is that Sky Vineyards doesn't even have electricity, and probably never will. The property is at the top of the Mayacamas mountain range between Napa and Sonoma, but the trade-off for the spectacular view is that turning on a light in the evening involves more than flipping a switch. For TV they have to park a Toyota truck on top of the ridge and run a line from the generator.

Lore Olds grew up as the son of an architect in Berkeley, but was enchanted by the farming life when he visited his grandmother in Missouri. The aesthetics of wine appealed to him as much as its agricultural connection. So after college at Humboldt State in the late '60s, he jumped at a chance to serve as caretaker for Hillcrest Vineyards in Roseburg, Oregon. He returned to work for several vineyards in Sonoma Valley and then apprenticed at Beaulieu and Mayacamas. Unique California wines were his interest so he

1985 NAPA VALLEY ZINFANDEL
ESTATE GROWN AND BOTTLED BY SKY VINEYARDS NAPA CALIFORNIA
TABLE WINE   CONTAINS SULFITES

studied vineyards that produced top Zinfandel. He concluded that high elevations with good air drainage and a reddish, volcanic soil were the conditions best suited to distinctive flavor. Sky Vineyards was planted in 1973 and the winery bonded in 1979. Lore carves the art work for the labels himself.

Linn Briner grew up in Massilon, Ohio. She took a degree in Food Technology at Ohio State where an advisor found her a scholarship to study wine. Given a petite physique, and the fact that wine ranked substantially behind football in her neighbors' esteem, she decided a move to California would be a good idea. She ran the lab at Phelps Winery and then married Lore after meeting him at an Enologists' conference in Las Vegas. When asked why she would want to live in a place as remote as Sky Vineyards, she says, "I think it has something to do with my father refusing to take me fishing with him when I was a child. He eventually took me to Alaska, but it was too little and too late."

The grapes from Sky's 12 acre vineyard have been used in several top wines including a recent '84 Late Harvest Zinfandel from Mayacamas and the '83 Calafia Zinfandel. There is always a noticeable pepper note in the nose. Linn and Lore are not sure what causes it. Grown at over 2,000 feet elevation and dry-farmed, the head pruned vines usually produce under a ton per acre. The pH is always low. Winemaking may have some influence on the "spice" quality as well. By hand picking the grapes, culling out substandard bunches and not allowing any stems in the fermentor, they ultimately get more concentrated fruit.

Harvesting is weekend work accomplished by friends, and it often takes a month to complete. Pressing without electricity requires muscle power applied to an old half-ton basket press. In winter, only vehicles with 4-wheel-drive can

negotiate the road to the winery. Until 1987 there wasn't even a phone to call for help. Not everything is primitive though. Aging is done exclusively in French oak barrels, 10% of which are bought new each year.

Linn points out that they have some unexpected advantages too. The biggest problem most mountain vineyards have is water. Sky enjoys a good well and there are springs on the property. "The vineyard is fenced to keep the deer out," she says, "and the rabbits only eat a little bit. It is surprising that we don't get more bird damage because a lot of the other mountain vineyards have to net their grapes. We have different trees than Mayacamas does, mostly scrub pine. Maybe that has some effect on the birds." Could be, Linn, or maybe they go some place they can watch TV while they eat. Maybe their little noses bleed at Sky Vineyard's altitude.

1985 Zinfandel	800 cases
Estate	750 ml

Head pruned, dry-farmed vyd at 2,000-2,200 ft elevation with well drained, volcanic soil at top of a canyon. 11-yr-old vines give 1.5 t/a. Month long harvest in Sept. Frmtd with Montrachet yeast, 7-10 days on the skins in 1-ton lots in plastic frmtg bins, punch down 2-3x/day. M-L finishes in summer. Aged 1 yr in French oak barrels, 10% new. Filtered, btld Mar '87 at 13.2 alc, .78 acid, 3.28 pH.

How was your crop size in '88?

"Fine. We pulled in a massive 2 tons per acre, which is normal for us. All our neighbors were crying about their short crop on Cabernet, but I figure it evens out. They get twice as much money, they deserve to get a short crop every now and again.

"I used to long prune the vines we have in a lower section by the house because the cold air can settle there. I don't think I'm going to do that any more. They set a bigger crop to start with because the soil is deeper. Big vines like that tend to slap the pickers around in the heat of harvest. It's like wrestling with a gorilla. When I long prune them, they don't ripen until a month after everything else.

"The rest of our vineyard looks like hell, but the fruit comes in just great. We're not trying to grow a big, strong American vineyard; we're trying to grow fruit. Our pickers are trained to leave the second crop behind and check every bunch from the bottom. When they haul one of those heavy buckets up the hill only to have Linn give them a stern eye and pour half the clusters on the ground, they learn quickly too. My dad touches every bunch before it goes in the crusher. I think the whole year is aimed at that moment the cluster is cut from the vine. It's the vine's climax. You ought to take the time to do it right, and it ought to be a pleasure.

"Leaving 6-8 tons of second crop behind can make you feel bad at times. I've made small batches from the second crop though, and it is just not as good wine."

Lore Olds

RB

P & M STAIGER VINEYARDS

Paul Staiger grew up in Portland and became a dedicated wine fanatic during 1959 while studying in France. He returned to graduate from Northwestern and went on to study at the University of Chicago in the interdisciplinary Committee for Social Thought. "Didn't learn much about wine from Saul Bellow," he remarks, "but I sure had an interesting time." He moved to Berkeley as a PhD candidate but became caught up in the Free Speech Movement. He ended up with a Master of Fine Arts in Painting and began teaching at San Jose State, "where I've been ever since," he concludes.

Paul and his wife, M. (pronounced Em), had been making wine at home for a couple of years when Paul's paintings started to sell very well in New York. "Paintings paid for everything up here," Paul says of their winery and hillside vineyards. The Staigers were drawn to the Santa Cruz Mountains because of the proximity to San Jose and because they had tasted fine wines from the old Vine Hill and Hallcrest vineyards. They researched federal records to find properties that had been vineyards in the past and even set out thermometers to compare microclimates. In 1973 they bought a south-facing hill on the old Locatelli ranch that had been planted to Zinfandel from 1900 until Prohibition.

The Staigers planted 5 acres of grapes on a fairly steep slope running from 1,000 to 1,150 feet of elevation. The altitude is critical to grape quality, they feel, because the cool marine inversion layer (read "fog") comes up to about 900 feet in the fall. Half the vineyard is Chardonnay, planted on a southwest slope. The rest is 80% Cabernet Sauvignon and 20% Merlot in drier, shale soil with a direct southern exposure. Paul thinks the Merlot is an "early Inglenook clone." He knows the Cabernet came from David Bruce and believes it originated in the Davis Experimental Station at Oakville. It must be an early ripening clone. In 1986 the Staigers picked Chardonnay on September 28, then Cabernet and Merlot on October 2. The vineyard looks out on Monterey Bay, but gets its cool breeze from the San Mateo coast to the Northwest. "On paper," Paul says, "we look warmer than we really are, because we do get a high temperature peak for about ten minutes every afternoon."

M. doesn't think rain is a particularly big factor in determining crop size in their vineyard. "Grapes need about 15" a year," she explains. "We average 55-60" a year and get 30" in a dry year. We don't irrigate though, so maybe late rains do play some role." She suspects that wind has more impact, especially when it comes up strong during pollination.

They dug holes in 3 sections of the property. Top soil ranges from 5' to 15' deep. A foot of humous is mixed with weathered marine sandstone, then followed by large chunks of sandstone. After this top soil, the sandstone is more compact with a few fractures in it. The Staigers can stand at the top of their vineyard and trace areas with different soil depths by looking at the vigor of the vines. Numbers at harvest are not dramatically different though, even in vines of varied age. When the vineyard was young and production was small, the ripening curve was fairly steep. Now everything ripens more gradually. The Cabernet vines on shallow soil are still increasing in size and production, but they continue to lag behind the rest of the vineyard.

Paul and M. handle all of the vineyard operations. "We're thinking about putting our initials on individual vines to see who does a better job," they laugh. The vineyard is mowed in March and tilled with an Italian walking tractor in June. The entire vineyard has to be covered with netting by August because birds are a severe problem. Picking is done into 5-gallon buckets because the vineyard is too steep in most places for a truck.

The winery was completed September 19th, 1973, just in time for the crush. The house was built on top of the winery the following winter and spring. Crush starts at 8:30 in the morning while the berries are still cool. They crush on the deck of the house and drop everything through a chute to the fermenters in the cellar below. They currently produce about 500 cases a year.

1986 P AND M STAIGER

SANTA CRUZ MOUNTAINS

CHARDONNAY

PICKED SEPT. 28, AT 23.1° BRIX, T.A. .87

ALC. 13.5% BY VOL.   CONTAINS SULFITES

ESTATE GROWN AND BOTTLED BY P AND M STAIGER

BOULDER CREEK, CALIFORNIA

1986 Chardonnay	200 cases
Estate	750 ml

11-yr-old Wente clone grapes on a 20 degree slope with SW aspect. No skin soak, basket press, 24 hr settle. Frmtd with Pasteur Champagne yeast up to 65°F in food grade tanks with ice bath. No M-L. Aged 6 mos in Mercier Limousin oak. On fine lees 1 mo, no fining, .45 μ filtration. Rotated through 50 gal stnls when not in barrel. Btld Sept '87 at 13.5 alc, .79 acid, 3.29 pH.

1985 Cabernet Sauvignon	200 cases
Estate	750 ml

11-yr-old vines planted on a south facing slope to an early ripening clone called #34 by David Bruce who procured the budwood from the U.C. Davis research station at Oakville. Frmtd 1 wk with Pasteur Red yeast. 2 yrs in oak previously used for Chardonnay plus 30% new French barrels. No fining, no filtration. Btld at 13.3 alc, .78 acid.

What was the '88 vintage like for you?

"The canopy in the Chardonnay was not nearly as developed as it normally would be. The Chardonnay ripened 3 weeks faster than usual and showed a significant amount of sunburn because the heat at harvest was quite high. In fact the whole season was hot. I was particularly surprised by how fast the sugar went up in the Chardonnay. On September 1st a field sample came in at 21.6°Brix. Four days later on September 5th a sample from the same place came in at 23.8°Brix. Now, the whole vineyard didn't crush that high, but it is still extraordinary for grapes to go up half a degree Brix each day during harvest.

"Cabernet had a lot of shatter. We were off 50% in Cabernet. The pickers said our Chardonnay looked more normal than any they had been picking in the Santa Cruz area, but it was still off 25%. The Cabernet was a little under 23°Brix, but we picked because the leaf quality was looking shaky, and I figured the fruit might start to dehydrate. If we don't get some rain by November, I'm going to reactivate our drip system. I'll have to truck the water in. The Chardonnay canopy was sparse but at least it looks healthy. The Cabernet is browning awfully early, and I think it is getting too much water stress.

"My acid levels in the '88 wines are up. The Chardonnay came in at 1.1 acid. I won't know what the relative proportion of malic might be until the portion that goes through malo-lactic is done. Usually malic is the one that respires in the heat."

Paul Staiger

CL

STELTZNER VINEYARDS

In contrast to many of his neighbors, Dick Steltzner is a farmer. The buildings at his place exude an air of agricultural competence rather than designer chic. Dick and Kristin Steltzner have four children (aged 4 to 15), and their varied industries lend the scene a note of joyful disarray.

Steltzner likes to say that the Stag's Leap area of Napa Valley is "the Margaux of California... if the wine is made right." He is refering to the way Cabernets can show a clear berry fruit and soft style. "If done wrong," he continues, "the wines will show high pH characteristics and turn out tannic and flabby." It is a challenge to himself because Steltzner Vineyards occupies 100 acres right at the base of the dramatic cliff that gives the region its name. Rocky soil washed down from that cliff gives Dick excellent drainage and the mountains behind his property trap cool air curling up the east side of the valley from San Pablo Bay. The rocks in his vineyard retain heat, which Dick feels is beneficial for Cabernet at this chilly end the valley. "Further south," he says, "it gets downright cold with more river-bottom soils. I think there is a pronounced herbal note in wines made from those vineyards."

Dick was raised in Oakland, but his parents came from old California farming families. He studied pottery and became well known for his craftsmanship before moving to Napa in 1960. Over the next couple of years, he used his sunny disposition and quick wit to horsetrade several vineyards. He also developed quite a reputation as a vineyard manager. He put in Diamond Creek Vineyards, as well as part of Spring Mountain's. He also managed Clos du Val's vineyards for a time.

Steltzner acquired his Stag's Leap District property in 1968 and planted 46 acres to Cabernet Sauvignon. First Spring Mountain, then Clos du Val bought his grapes. The 1974 Phelps Insignia was made entirely from Steltzner grapes. Dick still sells to Lakespring and Cakebread, among others. Three acres of Cabernet Franc and one of Merlot have been planted recently. The Cabernet Franc is a clone acquired from the School of Viticulture at Montpellier in France. That gives it a different pedigree than much of the Cabernet Franc being planted in California. Dick is also looking at rootstocks like 420A and 3309 from France which were hybridized with quality rather than yield as the primary consideration. "I'd even like to experiment with some controlled irrigation," he says, "to see what happens when we approximate summer rain conditions in Bordeaux."

The first Cabernet bearing Steltzner's label was produced in 1977. For several years the wines were made at nearby facilities, but in 1983 an old prune shed on the property, which pre-dated Prohibition, was converted to a winery. The shed had been urethaned on the outside to store berries, and Dick decided to put his money into equipment rather than worry about the look of the building. He put stainless steel tanks up outside and bought a Bucher press along with a Demoissey crusher.

Steltzner offered his '85 Cabernet to Winewright's members during the fall of '87 (12 months before its release). His "futures" price was about half what the wine cost when it was finally released on the market officially. Dick wanted to get knowledgeable consumers on his team. "We are going to have extraordinary quality coming up in the next couple of years," he says. "I think the best endorsement is word of mouth. Therefore, I'm trying to get the wine in the hands of collectors BEFORE it sells out." Most "futures" aim to generate cash flow. Steltzner's interest was more sophisticated. He wanted influential people to have a stake in his wine. "Hopefully, they'll mention it to their friends as a savvy investment," he explains. "My interests and theirs will be moving in the same direction. We both want to see our investment appreciate."

In addition to his own Estate vineyard, Steltzner is a partner with Markham Winery in the Oak Knoll Vineyard near Yountville. Oak Knoll grows Markham's best wine every year. Ever the prudent farmer, however, Steltzner chooses not to be entirely bound by grape expectations. He also grows 18 acres of blackberries and Kiwi fruit on his Silverado Trail ranch.

Steltzner

1985 ESTATE BOTTLED NAPA VALLEY CABERNET SAUVIGNON

GROWN, PRODUCED & BOTTLED BY STELTZNER VINEYARDS, NAPA, CALIFORNIA USA. CONTAINS SULFITES. TABLE WINE.

1985 Cabernet Sauvignon	4,200 cases
Estate Vyd	750 ml

Essentially dry-farmed grapes planted in 1968 on AxR₁ rootstock. Soil is decomposed rock washed down from Stag's Leap. 4 t/a picked 29 Sept, 11 Oct and 18 Oct with .72 acid, 3.39 pH. 15 days on skins in stnls. Pumped over and frmtd with Epernay II yeast. Settled 2 wks, spontaneous M-L. Portion aged in 180-gal Yugoslavian puncheons, remainder in French 60-gal barrels. No fining, polish filter. Btld Mar '88 at 13.2 alc, 2462 ppm total phenols.

How's the Stag's Leap Vit appellation going?

"As of 15 September, we are entering our fourth year of non-determination. The original application was smaller than the one presently being debated. Once a boundary is proposed, anyone near the boundary may apply for inclusion. Qualification for inclusion is based, unfortunately, on minimum evidence. Sometimes it seems like the wind blowing across Napa qualifies people in the city inclusion. I suspect that a hot air balloon launched in Carneros which lands in my vineyard would be considered prima facie evidence to reopen the application process.

"General Services employees of BATF handle the original application and determine a boundary. Then they pass the paperwork to political administrators who must decide whether or not they can live with the outside pressure to which General Services employees are not subject. This decision may require some unspecified number of trips to the Napa Valley during months when Washington, DC is particularly uncomfortable. Deadlines for the submission of evidence are set, but they may be changed whenever new (earth shaking) material comes to light.

"As we speak, the proposed boundary is the Napa River to the west and Yountville Cross Road to the north. These are in dispute. Even so, they represent a much larger area than originally intended. The first application used ridgetops as boundaries. Those require snakebite kits to investigate. Government officials prefer to use roads large enough to drive in an air-conditioned car as boundaries."

Dick Steltzner

STORTZ/SUNRISE VINEYARDS

Soon after he arrived in California in the 1870's, Vincenzo Picchetti began working for the Jesuits at Villa Maria on the inland side of the Santa Cruz Mountains overlooking the northern Santa Clara Valley. The church helped Vincenzo obtain some property high in the foothills. In the 1880's the Picchetti brothers dug a road several miles into the hills and established the first winery on Montebello Ridge. Soon others joined them. Jimsomare Vineyard was established by Pierre Klein, and Pirrone Winery was built at the top of the hill on property now owned by Ridge Vineyards.

The Picchettis were virtually self-sufficient, with 500 acres of vines, pears and apricots along with pigs, chickens and cattle. San Francisco wine merchants would drive wagons fitted with redwood tanks through the hills to the winery to purchase wine in bulk for their blends. The Picchettis lived on the ranch, making wine and grappa until 1975, when the property was sold to the Mid-Peninsula Open Space District.

Ron Stortz has an accounting practice in San Jose. Ron and his wife, Rolayne, helped home winemakers Keith Hohlfeldt and Gene Lokey create Sunrise winery in 1976. The operation was originally housed in the old Locatelli Winery on the Empire Grade north of Santa Cruz. In 1978, a fire started in the house above the winery and fell through onto barrels in the cellar. All winery stock was destroyed, including inventory, equipment and records. The winery was rebuilt, but Gene Lokey had left, and in 1983 Keith Hohlfeldt took a job as winemaker for David Bruce.

Ron and Rolayne had been talking with the Mid-Peninsula Open Space District about the Picchetti Winery since 1981. In 1984 they negotiated a 25 year lease on the 6 acres of buildings and on 3 acres of 80-year-old Zinfandel vines. The property is on the National Registry of Historical Sites, and the Stortzs are charged with renovating it according to Federal and State standards. They have put all new plumbing and electrical fixtures into the 1885 house where they now live with their two children. They have replaced aluminum windows with wooden replicas of the originals, and they milled siding to match the original house. The 2,600 sq. ft. underground aging cellar has been restored and put back into use as the winery. The upstairs portion of the building is used as a tasting room and banquet hall because it gets a little warm during the summer for modern standards of wine production. Air conditioning is not considered historically accurate. The fermentation building is about to be restored as the lab and winery office. Ron has moved his accounting practice into an old wash house and summer kitchen on the property. He chooses to ignore any remarks about what he might be "cooking" out in the office.

Rolayne has had help from consultants, but since 1985 she and Ron have done most of the physical work themselves. Rolayne says barrel fermentations aren't too bad once you get the barrels set up. They hand stack them two-high using barrel chocks. Then she can move them with an ingenious device from the original winery. She burned sulphur wicks for a few years, but now uses SO_2 and citric acid to freshen barrels between wines. Muscle work is concentrated in brief periods. Arata Vineyard grapes go into their crusher from lug boxes. That means lifting 40 pounds overhead all afternoon. They own the lug boxes and ask the grower to use them because it reduces juicing. Most growers would refuse. It causes more work at the vineyard end than using half ton bins would.

In 1987 Rolayne began experimenting with avoiding SO_2 until after malo-lactic fermentation, and eschewing acid adjustments. "I need to pick for lower pH in the vineyard, but it's not like announcing I've become a vegetarian," she continues. "The minute those babies complete M-L, they get a dose of sulphite."

In 1986 a movie was filmed on the ranch. Ron and Rolayne had hoped the movie makers would help with restoration work on the property. "Everything they built turned out to be temporary and fake," Rolayne says shaking her head. The historic ranch is open to visitors from 11-3 on Fridays and weekends. Private parties can be scheduled in the evenings.

SUNRISE

PRODUCED AND BOTTLED ON MONTE BELLO RIDGE
BY SUNRISE WINERY, CUPERTINO, CALIFORNIA

1985

Santa Clara County
PETITE SIRAH

Alcohol 12.5% by volume • contains sulfites

1986 Pinot Blanc	360 cases
Santa Clara County	750 ml

Grapes from 20-yr-old vines in San Ysidro Vyd picked 20 Sept at 22.0°Brix, .99 acid. Barrel frmtd, aged in French oak, induced M-L. Btld Aug '87 at 12.65 alc, 3.4 pH.

1983 Cabernet Sauvignon	360 cases
Arata Vyd	750 ml

18-yr-old vines from the inland side of the Santa Cruz mountains 800' above Saratoga. Unfiltered.

1986 Pinot Noir	180 cases
Dutton Vyd	750 ml

Tell me about San Ysidro Vineyard.

"It is up against the foothills on the south-eastern edge of Santa Clara Valley. Fog comes through the hills by San Juan Bautista and then curls up to San Ysidro. I drive down there a lot during harvest, and it is always 10°F cooler than at our house.

"I want to try making a botrytized Sémillon from San Ysidro grapes. '88 may be my last chance because their vineyard manager says they don't sell as well as his other varieties, and he may graft them to Chardonnay. There is a lot of botrytis in that part of the vineyard. It was first introduced by San Martin. They can also encourage it by turning on the sprinklers. I'd want to get the grapes between 32° and 34°Brix and try a barrel-fermentation. That might require a November harvest. It is always chancey because heavy rain can wipe you out. I was thinking about doing it in '87, but it rained in mid-October before the grapes sugared up. They all rotted.

"I've been getting PN now four years from San Ysidro, and I'm real happy with it. There is a little bit of elevation in a certain plot back by an old Indian trail. The vines are older there with less tonnage. I think I'll be able to pay a little premium to say which rows I want, get them thinned and stop irrigation a little earlier. The fruit is wonderful already, so extra attention may only be gilding the lily. I'm hoping San Ysidro will get appellation approval in time for me to vineyard designate the '87 wine."

Rolayne Stortz

CL

Rolayne gathering eggs to fine red wines.　CL

STORYBOOK MOUNTAIN VINEYARDS

The combination of history and wine comes naturally to Jerry Seps. His father was a Southern California wine wholesaler. At age 21 Jerry was already Sommelier at the Ahwanhee Hotel in Yosemite Valley. He went on to a career in teaching and was a professor in the History Department at Stanford University for many years. In 1976 he decided to make a switch. "I figured it would take me ten years to establish a good wine property," he says. His estimate was accurate. In 1986 Storybook Mountain won more Gold Medals than any Zinfandel in memory.

Dr. Seps and his Franconian born wife Sigrid

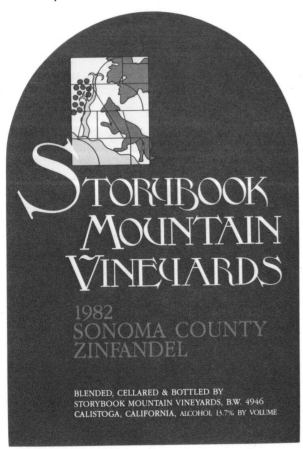

STORYBOOK MOUNTAIN VINEYARDS

1982
SONOMA COUNTY
ZINFANDEL

BLENDED, CELLARED & BOTTLED BY
STORYBOOK MOUNTAIN VINEYARDS, B.W. 4946
CALISTOGA, CALIFORNIA, ALCOHOL 13.7% BY VOLUME

searched for years before buying one of Napa Valley's ghost wineries. The property had originally been owned by brothers Jacob and Adam Grimm, whose winemaking roots dated back to 1542 in Germany. The Grimms dug caves into the mountainside in 1888 and created the second largest winery in the northern half of 19th century Napa Valley. At the suggestion of fellow immigrant Jacob Schramm of Schrammsberg, they grew Zinfandel to make a very popular Claret. The winery flourished, and a hidden road behind the mountain with an entrance to the cellars even indicates a brisk Prohibition business. It finally closed in the 1940's with the vineyards abandoned about ten years later. In 1964 a forest fire destroyed the old winery buildings.

The Grimms of Napa were not the famous storytellers who saved folk tales like *Billy Goat Gruff* and *The Fox and The Grapes,* but after acquiring the 90 acre property in 1978, Seps decided to remember them with an allusion on the label and in the name of the winery. Consultant Andre Tchelistcheff and Al Brounstein of Diamond Creek Vineyards both recommended devoting the entire vineyard to Zinfandel. The winery is the northernmost in Napa Valley. 36 acres are planted on steep terraces rising from 400 to 1,200 feet elevation where they receive some ocean breeze over the top of the ridge. Vines face southeast and thus get full sun in the morning, but are shaded from direct rays in the heat of late afternoon. The red clay soil with hillside drainage is classic for Zinfandel.

Jerry apprenticed with Joe Swan for a year and worked to bring back many of the original vines. Hopeless cases were replaced with AxR_1 rootstock and budded to the "Hand" clone which U.C. Davis developed for its ability to retain acid. This characteristic was amply demonstrated in 1980 when Seps harvested several lots at 26°Brix, but with more than 1.0

acid and a final pH of 3.2 in the wine. "Acid is an important component for the elegant, 'table wine' style of Zinfandel I want," Seps says. "It leaves a clean feeling after you swallow and contributes to the wines' longevity."

Continuity is important at Storybook Mountain. They regulate water and fertilizer in half row adjustments. The vineyard is only irrigated until color starts to show in the grapes around July. Then parts of clusters are removed to promote even maturation by matching size of crop to amount of canopy and size of trunk. Raspberries are planted in drainage ditches to host a species of wasp that preys on leaf hoppers. No pesticides. Weeds are removed by hand hoeing. No herbicides. The vineyard is picked several times. They harvest all the way from 22° to 23°Brix in order to bring different plots in with a consistent pH.

Jerry and Sigrid select their Reserve wine by tasting all of the barrels, 40 at a time, competitively. Substantial variation from barrel to barrel appears as the wine ages in small cooperage. "We must both agree," he explains, "which is not as easy as you might think." It is an open debate; no secret ballots. This first round reduces the field by half. Then they do two more elimination rounds. They look for intensity, which they define as "vertical aroma; it must penetrate up the nose and suffuse the sinuses." They also want length on the palate and cleanness.

Gouges made by picks in the volcanic rock of the walls are mute testimony to the backbreaking labor which hollowed out the 5,000 sq. ft. winery nearly a century ago. Ambient air temperature ranges from 54° to 58°F. Seps shares space with former Phelps winemaker Walter Schug. Storybook Mountain will eventually make 8,500 cases a year of estate grown Zinfandel.

1986 Zinfandel	4,000 cases
Estate	750 ml

Grapes from hillside vyd at northern end of Napa Vly. Second crop dropped in July. Frmtd in stnls 15-30 days at 70-75°F with Pasteur Red yeast. Must pumped over skins until dryness, then tank closed and CO_2 monitored. Settled in large oak ovals, then aged 1 yr in 60 gal French and American air dried, fire shaped barrels. Sterile filtered, btld May '88 at 13.5 alc, .7 acid, 3.35 pH.

1985 Zinfandel	900 cases
Reserve-Estate	

Small barrels selected for 6 additional months in 800 gal German ovals to marry different elements and provide additional maturation. No egg white fining necessary.

What are crushing and pressing like?

"Our normal crush period covers 6 weeks. Five days out of seven we are picking at dawn and crushing until dusk. We normally do 6-8 tons in a day. Everything is carried in 44-pound lug boxes. You sleep very well at night. The phrase 'oh, my aching back' represents this year well. We went 16 days in a row, and I felt it.

"Our Zambelli stemmer-crusher spreads all of the grapes out so I can see every single bunch and remove anything substandard. There are a lot of bunches in 100 tons of fruit. The Zambelli is primitive, but reliable. It only has one setting, one speed and only needs one paint job a year. It is also gentle. You can look at the stems as they come out of the drum and rarely find any broken ones.

"Our Willmes press is a pneumatic model which allows infinite pressure settings. The free run juice is always a little lighter in color and a little simpler than the press fractions. We stop pressing as soon as we start to notice any harshness. You don't want to go too far and break seeds up. I can't tell you the amount of pressure we use because all the dial markings are in German, but I know the spot on the dial that works for us. We usually get around 150 gallons per ton. I'm happy with this press. I had some experience with a Rota press once and didn't like the way it macerated the berries. It was basically a cement mixer."

Jerry Seps

RG

JR

SUMMIT LAKE

Howell Mountain Viticultural Area has a wonderful way of defining its boundary. They use the fog line. As you drive up the mountain east from St. Helena in Napa Valley toward Angwin, arrival in the BATF approved district is often announced with golden radiance as you burst from a moist, grey coccoon into clear, warm sunshine. The line falls at approximately 900 feet elevation. It is hard to reconcile this seemingly whimsical piece of label regulation with the U.S. Treasury department which promulgated it. Important vintners, such as Burgess Cellars, fall just below the fog line, and thus outside the district. But rest assured, the same department of government that brings you the Internal Revenue Service has not been infiltrated by middle-aged flower children. The unique feature of Howell Mountain is the consistent climate found above the inversion layer. They are 10°F cooler than the Valley on hot days, but warmer at night.

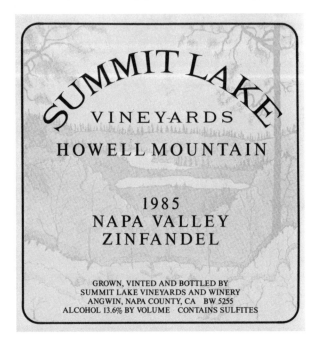

SUMMIT LAKE
VINEYARDS
HOWELL MOUNTAIN

1985
NAPA VALLEY
ZINFANDEL

GROWN, VINTED AND BOTTLED BY
SUMMIT LAKE VINEYARDS AND WINERY
ANGWIN, NAPA COUNTY, CA   BW 5255
ALCOHOL 13.6% BY VOLUME   CONTAINS SULFITES

Long before Howell Mountain became a chic name to drop in conjunction with Cabernet, and before wealthy winery owners from the Valley started buying property there, the region had a reputation for producing some of the most distinctively flavored Zinfandel in California. This reputation was an insiders' secret though, because there weren't any wineries on the mountain. Occasionally a winery from the Valley would use a vineyard designation, like Beatty Ranch, but most Howell Mountain Zinfandel grapes ended up as components in a blend. They were valuable components to be sure, because 25% Howell Mountain Zinfandel would give fabulous character to even the most ho-hum Zinfandels from the Valley floor. The identifying characteristic of Howell Mountain Zinfandels was, and still is, a forceful black pepper spiciness and chewy full-bodied structure.

Bob and Susan Brakesman came to Howell Mountain in 1970. At their young age, most people would have interpreted their lifestyle choices as faddish, or experimental. Bob had graduated from the engineering program at San Jose State, and decided to grow grapes after taking one look at 500 draftsmen sitting in a room when he interviewed for a job at General Electric. Four hours after their last college final, they left for 6 months in South America. Upon return, they picked Howell Mountain, even though the property was remote and undeveloped, because the land was cheap and they considered it a healthy place to raise kids. They took out a $40,000 mortgage and, without bothering to endure a marriage ceremony, began clearing oak and manzanita from their property. They embraced a frontier lifestyle. You can call it commitment, foresight or luck. Nearly 20 years later, they live in a beautifully compact house with 12 acres of extremely valuable vineyard and 3 children ranging in age from 9 to 16. Surely their more

peripatetic contemporaries envy the satisfaction Bob and Susan fashioned for themselves from the "new age" attitudes of the late '60s.

Bob worked at Freemark Abbey in the mid-'70s while planting the Summit Lake vineyard. There were 2 acres of old Zinfandel vines on the property which had survived from the historic Ferrazzi Winery. The Brakesmans planted an additional 6 acres of Zinfandel in their shallow, but well-drained, red soil. Later they added 2 acres of Chardonnay and 2 acres of Cabernet, bowing to the standard opinion that these varieties command more money for the same amount of work. Assured by local wisdom that frost danger passed on the 15th of May each year, they uncovered these bench-grafted vines on May 19th in 1975 only to lose the entire year's growth to a freak frost. "It was an omen," Bob says. "Zinfandel is traditional to our location, and we've begun feeling guilty since bonding our winery in 1985. Next year we will graft the Chardonnay over to our old clone of Zinfandel." Summit Lake produces 1,200 cases each year, and the Cabernet is blended into the Zinfandel for structure. Besides running his own winery, Bob works at The Compleat Winemaker in St. Helena.

It is somewhat ironic that "survivalists of the left" would thrive cheek-to-jowl with the religious community that surrounds Pacific Union College in Angwin. "We've had our differences," Susan allows. "Mainly over corporal punishment in the schools." However, neither side engages in the conspicuous consumption rampant in the Valley below. In the end, respect for honesty and consistency seem to outweigh disputes over lunchtime hot dogs. It seems both groups of long-term residents may be more comfortable with each other than with the arrivistas who began "discovering" Howell Mountain 3 years ago.

1985 Zinfandel	700 cases
Estate	750 ml

8% Cabernet Sauvignon. Picked mid-Aug at 24.6°Brix, .96 acid, 3.52 pH. Frmtd with Epernay 2 yeast, 8 days on skins, punched down 3x/day. 6 mos in large upright, then 2 yrs in Nevers and Limousin barrels 3 to 4-yrs-old. Btld at 13.8 alc.

What is the history on your old vines?

"The Ferrazzi Vineyard was planted in the 1920's. They had 30-40 acres at one time. The grapes traditionally went to Charles Krug Winery who paid a $5/ton premium for them. That is a healthy bonus in an era when grapes sold for $15/ton. Krug would also pay for the shipping; no small consentience when they had to be hauled by horse drawn wagons. Each load cost $2 to transport, and probably carried about 3 tons since it was a downhill run.

"We live in the original house built by the Farrazzis. We've talked to Mario Farrazzi a couple of times, but never gotten him to sit down and tell us what he remembers. He is about 65 now and lives in San Francisco. We have found papers in the attic dated 1896. The Park-Muscadine Vineyard is nearby. They have 30-40 acres of old vines which are largely a black mix. They send those grapes to Ridge.

"Our 2 acres of dry-farmed old vines are different than our younger blocks even when they produce the same yields. They have such an intense berry flavor, you can't mistake them. There is not much vigor in that section which means the canopy is sparse and the clusters get a lot of sunlight. You have to stay on top of them at harvest too. They can go from 22° to 26°Brix in just a couple of days. I don't think soil has much to do with the difference between those vines and our others. We have the red Aiken clay three feet deep throughout the whole property. On the southeast side of Howell Mountain (near La Jota) they have whiter, tufa-based volcanic soil."

Bob Brakesman

RG

ROBERT TALBOTT

The beauty of Carmel has inspired many people. It is Robert Talbott's home, and he can trace a relationship with the place back for half a century. Rob's father was an insurance banker living in Connecticut and riding the train into New York every day. He wore colorful bow ties made by his wife. Friends on the train kept asking where they could purchase these ties. Finally Mr. Talbott resolved to enter the neckwear business. He and his wife had honeymooned in Carmel and never forgotten the majestic scenery or the mild climate. In 1950 they packed up their family and moved west.

Stop me if this sounds like a "power of positive thinking" advertisement on a matchbook cover, but the tie company now employs 230 people in a 60,000 sq. ft. "workshop" near the Monterey airport. Four-n-hand ties currently out sell bow ties 20 to 1, and all of the company's

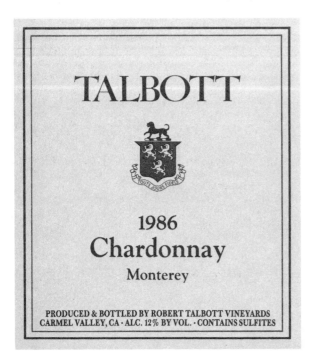

production has been on strict allocation since 1976. The materials are woven for Talbott, from their own designs, in England and Italy. Silk is the mainstay. Rob remembers being given wine with water at the dinner table as a child. His father began collecting Chateau Talbot in 1952 and moved on to Stony Hill Chardonnays by the early '70s. It is a long standing tradition for the Talbott family to approve fabrics in Italy, and then visit wine regions across France on their way to perform a similar task in Britain. Filthy work, but somebody has to do it.

The great equalizer occurred in 1983 when Rob decided to plant a vineyard at his home ranch, called the Diamond T, in Carmel Valley. The property is 10 miles from the ocean on a south-facing slope that drops from 1,000 feet to 600 feet elevation. The land is primarily Monterey shale with top soil ranging from 6" to 18" thick. It took them all summer to cross rip the vineyard to a depth of 30". In many places they had to use augurs and bring in top soil to fill the holes. They spent hours each day breaking up rocks with ten pound sledge hammers. The 24 acre vineyard is planted with 6'x8' spacing exclusively to Chardonnay. The vines are on a low-vigor, phylloxera resistant, Burgundian rootstock called SO_4. There is barely enough water from the Talbott family's deep well to drip irrigate the vines. When the first Estate wine is released in 1989, it will be a monument to struggle by both the planters and the vines.

It will also be a very interesting cool climate, low yield example of the grape variety. The vineyard is close enough to the coast to get some fog, but high enough to be above it most of the time. It is cool and they get wind, but not the type that would damage vines. There is just enough air flow to keep mildew and bunch rot from giving them much trouble. Frost runs down the hill and never settles in their vineyard. In

'87 the grapes ripened to 23.5°Brix with 3.1 pH and more than 1.0 acid. Too bad the land in Carmel Valley is so expensive. Habitually understated, Rob uses the phrase "lucky" to describe his purchase of the property for $500 an acre in 1961.

The Talbott's house and vineyard are near to a residentially zoned area. Since Monterey County is pretty tough on building permits, they thought it prudent to put the winery some place else. "The vineyard is also up a very steep 800' cliff," Rob explains. "We've dropped trucks and equipment into precarious situations there in the past." In 1983 they built a 5,000 sq. ft. winery out of cedar board and batten construction. It is near Jamesburg, on the road to Tassajara Hot Springs, some 25 miles from the coast and about half way to Arroyo Seco. A really beautiful spot. It is 1,800 feet high, surrounded by mountain maples that change color in winter. The property runs up to a 5,000 foot mountain that even gets snow. Californians notice things like that.

Talbott has a big commitment to Chardonnay and an understandable affection for Monterey County. They have long-term contracts for grapes from the northern end of Salinas Valley with no intention of dropping those vineyards when their Estate wine comes to market. Their winemaker, Sam Balderas, claims 1987 as his twenty-fifth harvest in California. His father helped plant Mt. Eden Vineyard for Martin Ray. Sam's formal training is in architecture, but his hands-on, barrel fermentation experience in the winery is extensive. He worked at Stony Ridge and did free-lance consulting just prior to joining Talbott. Actually, Sam's brother Rubin was the first Balderas to move in at the Diamond T. Rubin is the vineyard manager.

1986 Chardonnay	2,200 cases
Monterey	750 ml

Grapes from Sleepy Hollow Vyd and nearby River Road Vyd in Gonzales on a north-facing hillside. Hand sorted, no skin soak. Crushed in a Demoissey and pressed in a center-feed bladder model. Settled overnight. 100% barrel frmtd with a changing proprietary blend of 4 yeasts. Burgundian oak, new to 5-yrs-old from 5 different coopers. Partial M-L. On lees entire time in barrel. Btld Nov '87 at 12.4 alc, .85 acid, 3.2 pH. Btl aged 10 mos before release.

Tell me about dealing with writers.

"I haven't done a lot of it because we don't seek their attention. The only unsolicited bottles I've sent were to Parker and to A. Dias Blue. Parker sent me a check by return mail. It was a very refreshing experience. I probably talk to 20 writers a year on the phone. They are all wine writers; nobody from the fashion industry wants to interview me about wine. The writers I see are evenly divided among free-lancers and staff writers for newspapers and magazines. I would agree with the prevailing assumption that less than 10 writers dominate 80% of the readership in the U.S.

"I don't have much experience with writers who take an adversarial or investigative position. Most of them are writing about Monterey Chardonnays or the locale in general. The only critical article I can remember was written by a man from Napa who found our wine more acidic than those to which he was accustomed. I told him high acid was a style we preferred, not a style meant for everyone.

"The recent controversy over writers who accept wine and hospitality from wineries is a tough issue. I suppose there is a line which should be drawn, but I'm not sure where it should be. They need access to the product and the information. If their publications won't pay for it, they will have a hard time writing their articles. I'm not offended by writers who call asking me if they can taste the wine. I usually send it to them if it seems like they have a significant readership. I mean I bet I get 20 solicitations a day for charity donations, and I turn most of those down. If I went to lunch with a writer from a big newspaper, I would make an overture to pick up the check. If they insisted on paying, I'd be surprised, but I'd respect their position and let them do it."

Robert Talbott

CL

RB

133

TOBIAS

Out in the Santa Monica harbor one day, Pat Wheeler met a retired Yugoslavian fisherman. They both owned sailboats and had slips next to each other. Like most sailboat owners, they spent more time working on the boats than they did sailing. The fisherman had an entertaining annual ritual. Every September he made 3 barrels of wine. He would start drinking it around New Years. It would last until the next September, when he would fill the barrels up once more. Pat thought this rather sociable activity made good sense. He went to John Daumé's home winemaking store in 1974 and joined the Cellarmasters.

He found he could make better wine than he could afford to buy. Many of the strong flavored Zinfandels and Petite Sirahs that he enjoyed most were made from grapes grown near Paso Robles. So, in 1977, he moved there. Pat is a journeyman tool-and-die maker. He figured he had landed in clover when he found a job the first morning and a house that same afternoon. He took up residence with his wife on a 100 acre walnut and Zinfandel ranch owned in part by Peter Ueberoth. His favorite Zinfandel grapes came from the Casteel Vineyard nearby. Pat enrolled at Cal Poly to take science and Ag courses related to winemaking, worked for a manufacturer of grocery store shelving and made 6-8 barrels of wine each year with his neighbors in a pumphouse on the ranch. They would do the harvesting and crush work together, then split the wine up as it came out of the press. Pat's first commercial vintage was 1980. He named the winery after his son, born 2 years before.

Until 1984, everything seemed to be going Pat's way. He made Zinfandel from Benito Dusi's vineyard which had been planted in the 1920's near Templeton. He also made Zinfandel from the highly regarded vineyard farmed by John Radicke. Petite Sirah came from the Jones Ranch near San Miguel. All these wines were deep, dark and solidly structured with the character that comes from old vines. 1984, however, was a tough vintage. Frost took half the Dusi grapes, and all the Radike and Jones crop. The Pat's wife left him. "That was the only crush I had in '84," he summarizes.

Wheeler's 3 kids now split time with him and with their mother who lives in Cayucos on the coast. His ex-wife's interest in the winery was bought in 1985 by a former liquor store owner from San Diego named Doug Beckett. Pat had first met Doug at one of those social events typical of small wineries. 10 to 15 interested parties show up on a day when some large task, like bottling, picking or pressing, is to be performed. They eat and drink all day, then take home a few bottles as compensation. Doug had ideas, and a checkbook with something in it. Together, Wheeler and Beckett expanded production. They rented a tasting room for $125/month in the cellar underneath a 100-year-old stage coach stop in Cayucos. White Zinfandel and Sauvignon Blanc were bought in to service the tasting room clientele.

This partnership, like many similar ones among California's craftsmen winemakers, is ill-fated. Differences inevitably occur between creative desires and the financial imperatives of the traditional marketplace. Beckett and Wheeler are in the process of amicably splitting their assets, which ironically include the name Tobias. Wheeler will continue to act as a winemaking consultant for Beckett's marketing interests. Meanwhile, he continues to make big, gutsy Zinfandels from Benito Dusi's ancient vineyard for use sale under his own license. The name may change, but the source and the motivation remain the same.

1983

Tobias

PASO ROBLES
ZINFANDEL

DUSI RANCH

The grapes which produced this fine California Zinfandel were grown on the Benito Dusi ranch located between Paso Robles and Templeton. These hand-tended vines were planted by Benito's father in the 1920s, and have consistently produced some of the finest fruit from this old, established Zinfandel region. The grape must was fermented to dryness from an initial Brix sugar of 24.5°. Total acidity of the wine was tested at .78% by volume, at completion of the malolactic fermentation. This wine was made in a robust style and will gain considerably in complexity and suppleness over the next few years. It will throw a deposit with bottle age and should be decanted when serving. We hope that you and your friends have as much fun enjoying this wine as we had with our friends in making it.

PRODUCED AND BOTTLED BY TOBIAS VINEYARDS
PASO ROBLES, CALIFORNIA • B.W. # 4984

ALCOHOL 14.4% BY VOLUME

1984 Zinfandel	420 cases
B. Dusi Vyd	750 ml

60-yr-old vines picked at 23.2°Brix, 3.4 pH. Frmtd in individual bins, 10-12 days on the skins. Aged 3 years in neutral American oak. No fining, coarse filter, will throw sediment. 13.8 alc.

Are these heavy reds you make tannic?

"I believe there are two distinct types of tannin. One is smooth; the other is harsh. The smooth one comes out of the skins early; the harsh one reminds you of biting into seeds or stems. The question with many red wines is whether the bite comes from harsh tannin or from the greenness of a young wine. I think you need to extract a lot of flavor, and then let the wine harmonize in a barrel for an extended period. If you do it right, the result will be finesse throughout the entire flavor profile.

"To accomplish this flavor extraction, I want my reds to macerate for several days prior to the onset of fermentation. I crush, then take some juice to start my yeast culture, then add 20-40 ppm SO_2. It takes 2-3 days for the starter culture to get going vigorously. I'm not worried if the wild yeast begins the fermentation. My culture will take over when I add it on the third day. I use 4x4x4 bins as fermentors. Taller containers retain more heat, and I want to get up to 96°F at least once for total extraction. As soon as the fermentation begins to subside, I start tasting the must. The minute I perceive the rich tannins starting to take on a bitter edge, I press. This point is different with every batch of wine. I've been on the skins 5 days, and I've been on 23 days.

"I use 2 old-time basket presses. These guarantee the press fractions will only see gentle pressure. You can't exert enough force with a hand-ratchet basket press to get the last few gallons of wine, but I figure that is the cost of top quality."

Pat Wheeler

RL

TRIBAUT-DEVAVRY

Champagne is synonymous with celebration. It is taxed at 20 times the rate of still wine. Diamonds may be the only commodity with a comparably successful marketing history. The ubiquitous saucer-on-a-stem glass is an example of this marketing fervor. The original molds for those glasses were made from the breasts of Louis XVI's consort. In 1945 all the wine producing countries of the world, except the United States, signed an agreement at Madrid to not use "champagne" as a name for sparkling wines. Champagne is actually a geographic designation for a specific region in France. Its very colorful history is due in no small part to a location directly on the line of march taken by troops from northern Europe who wish to advance toward Paris. The region is fully planted and Champagne producers are simply unable to expand their volume. Pinot Noir grapes from these vineyards cost 5 times what they do in California. During the last 10 years, no fewer than 6 Champagne producers have begun planting grapes and making sparkling wine in California.

The family of Michel Tribaut traces their winemaking history back to 1650. Michel, who is 51-years-old, lives in the village of Romery,

population 400. Three-quarters of his vineyards were originally the garden at the Abbey of Hautvilliers. This landmark is famous as the site where a blind abbot named Dom Perignon "discovered" sparkling wine with his exclamation, "Come quick. There are stars in my glass." Although presumably he said it in French.

Michel has an 12-year-old son, and a long-term vision. In 1982 he was advised by an influencial friend from the fraternity of Champagne producers that establishment of a business in California would be an enduring legacy. Michel discovered that many businesses had jumped into the California wine industry during boom periods, only to abandon these interests during a subsequent bust period. Michel's view was more patient. He saw himself as a craftsman, and he expected success to be achieved gradually over several generations the way it had been in France.

He formed an association with Bertrand Devavry, another Champagne artisan, and they began a series of trips to California. They decided to forego the marketing advantages of Napa and Sonoma in favor of the natural acidity in grapes from Monterey. They set up pressing and fermentation operations at Smith & Hook Vineyard in the Salinas Valley. Both Michel and Bertrand reside in France where they have family wineries. Since they make as many as 10 trips a year from their home to California in order to actually process the wine, they decided to temporarily locate their aging and bottle handling facilities near an airport. Neither speaks English. All their equipment is French, and they are the only winery in California following rules established by France's Union of Champagne producers. These points explain, in part, why they bring all the workers they use with them from France. Experience may be another reason. Tribaut claims one of his riddlers can turn

10,000 bottles in an hour.

All the grapes are picked by hand. In France it is illegal to use machine harvested fruit to make Champagne. They press in a Vaslin Champagne press which does not have internal chains. There is minimal skin contact. 20 separate fermentation lots are used in the cuvée. They began sell vintage-dated Brut and Rosé which are about 75% Pinot Noir and 25% Chardonnay. However, they hold back some wine each year for future blending. A traditional non-vintage wine, blended each year for consistency, is scheduled for release at Christmas 1988. Afterward, a Tête de Cuvée and a Blanc de Blanc will be made available. Very few companies in France are still barrel fermenting base wines. Tribaut has started doing barrel fermentations for their Tête de Cuvée and the Blanc de Blanc. They currently leave the wine en tirage for 3 years. They have noticed, however, that wines made from Monterey grapes age more quickly than their French counterparts. So they may reduce time on the lees for their regular wines. In 1984 production was 6,500 cases. Michel figures 15,000 cases will be the break even point. Neither he nor Bertrand want to get much bigger than 20,000 cases. They say that would be the limit of what they could produce and still do the winemaking work themselves.

1984 Brut	6,000 cases
Sparkling	750 ml

Chardonnay and Pinot Noir grapes grown in the Salinas Vly. Crushed at Smith & Hook Vyds by Tribaut.

1984 Rosé	1,000 cases
Sparkling	750 ml

Pinot Noir grapes from Salinas Vly.

How do you see the wine & health issue in the U.S?

"Being a Frenchman, I am surprised by all the fuss. Big campaigns, like the warning label signs in retail stores, don't exist in France. My perception is that there are many more important health matters to occupy one's attention. Alcohol is not a significant danger. That Americans are talking about such issues reflects the newness of wine as a concept. As the wine industry is progressing successfully, new ideas come up and that always causes some degree of turmoil. I suspect concern will pass on to hard liquor in the low income area. Expensive wines will be seen in a different classification.

"Media and controversy need each other. The points being thrust forward are not real facts, so people in the wine industry react with rage. That alone gets media attention. I might recommend that winemakers ignore the whole media. If they did so, it would be much harder for antagonists to get press attention.

"Since I am not an American citizen, I don't think I should comment about what role an election year might play in this process. I will say that I suspect drunk driving to be more common in France than in America. But there is no ripple affect in France of the health issue concern in the U.S. France is paying more attention to cigarettes."

Marc Bossut, Marketing Director

Michel Tribaut   **RB**

VEGA VINEYARDS

Rancho de la Vega, or "Ranch of the Meadow," was founded in 1853. The rancho and 8,000 acres of sunny, oak-studded grasslands were part of the dowry of Micaela Cota for her marriage to Dr. Ramon de la Cuesta. The historic hacienda is still standing, with 3'-thick adobe walls surrounding thirteen rooms and a lovely courtyard. Some of the original grapevines planted by the Californios are still bearing fruit today.

Bill and Jeri Mosby grew up in Oregon and were married when Bill was in dental school. After his stint in the service, they decided they'd like to live in Southern California, "but not Los Angeles." They settled in Lompoc and bought their first ranch in the Santa Ynez Valley in 1962. In 1971 they planted White Riesling on the property they now call River Ranch. They purchased the Rancho de la Vega adobe in 1976 and began restoring the red Victorian carriage house for use as a winery. In 1977, a severe wind storm caused massive damage. Undaunted, they rebuilt the interior into an efficient winery while reconstructing the circa 1860 Victorian

1986
Santa Barbara County
Pinot Noir

PRODUCED AND BOTTLED BY VEGA VINEYARDS WINERY
BUELLTON, CALIFORNIA BW 4936
ALCOHOL 13.9% BY VOLUME   CONTAINS SULFITES

exterior. Vega Vineyards was bonded in 1979.

The Mosbys have four children. Rick, 36, works at the winery, and Gary, 32, is winemaker at Edna Valley Vineyards (part of Chalone, Inc). The family owns 34 acres of grapes. River View Vineyard, adjacent to the winery, includes 10 acres of Gewürztraminer and 8 acres of Chardonnay on decomposed shale soils. River Ranch Vineyard is 2.5 miles west, on the north side of the Santa Ynez River. It has 8 acres of Pinot Noir and the original 8 acres of Riesling, on alluvial soil washed down from the Purissima Hills. The climate is cool, due to ocean air flowing from the Pacific 25 miles to the west through the Santa Ynez River Valley and 10 miles to the south through Gaviota Pass.

When harvesting Gewürz grapes, they look for the very first indication of color change. Then they check pH. They never let the pH get above 3.2, and would pick at 2.9 if the sugar were pushing 21°Brix. On Riesling the market has convinced them to move toward botrytized styles because it is hard for average consumers to discriminate quality in semi-dry Riesling. Fog coming up the valley gives Vega reliable botrytis in Riesling every single year. Their Gewürz, however, is in a vineyard 2 miles further from the coast. Those grapes rarely get botrytis, so they do not make late harvest Gewürztraminer. In '87 Bill started using 30°Brix as his lowest sugar level for harvesting Riesling. If the acids are holding, he'll wait longer and watch the weather. Six pickers can finish that vineyard in a week. There are 6 acres of grapes. A normal harvest would yield 1,000 cases of wine. As the desiccation from botrytis goes up and sugar levels rise, production can drop as low as 250 cases.

Vega produces around 5,000 cases a year. Aromatic whites are fermented in jacketed stainless steel tanks at low temperatures, to preserve the delicate scents imparted from the cool growing conditions. Chardonnays are barrel-fermented, as one might expect, with Gary Mosby advising his father on winemaking techniques. Pinot Noir is transferred by gravity flow from fermentation tanks to barrels and pushed with nitrogen from one barrel to another during racking. Both Chardonnay and Pinot Noir got quality Medals and rave reviews for value during 1987. Vega uses a Demoissey crusher and a Howard batch press to handle grapes. All of the fruit is brought to the winery within minutes of picking.

Since 1981 the aromatic whites from Vega have assembled an extraordinary Show record. J. Riesling has won Gold Medals in several competitions every year. The Gewürztraminer has done similarly well every year except one, and that year Vega sold the wine off in bulk to maintain their high standards. Paul Jardine, an ex-Navy pilot who handles sales for Vega, says with a chuckle, "Wouldn't you just know that our unique, can't-miss grape variety would have a name nobody can pronounce. It sells very well in the tasting room because of the sugar/acid balance and the delicately fragrant style. I tell people the Riesling smells like Granny Smith apples and the Gewürz goes unbelievably well with any dish containing ginger."

1987 LH J. Riesling 1,000 cases
Estate-Special Selection 375 & 750 ml

Picked 9 Oct at 33°Brix, 1.1 acid. Overnight skin soak. Frmtd in stnls at 55°F with Epernay 2 yeast. Frmt stopped by chilling, SO_2 and bentonite. Sterile filter before btlg April '88 at 8.8 alc, .95 aicd, 13.5% rs.

1986 Gewürztraminer 1,200 cases
Estate 750 ml

0.9% rs, .9 acid, 11.4 alc. Picked 12 August.

1985 Pinot Noir 1,200 cases
750 ml

Grapes 50% from Vega Estate and 50% from Sierra Madre. Picked 28 Sept. 12.4 alc.

1986 Chardonnay 800 cases
Santa Maria Hills Vyd 750 ml

Picked early Sept at 23.5, .9 acid. Overnight skin soak, chill, frmt entirely in 4 to 6-yr-old mixed French barrels with Epernay 2 yeast. On lees until Feb, complete m-l. Btld June '88.

What's it like to filter botrytized wines?

"I've learned a lot about it in the last few years. I decided to stop banging my head against that wall of people who fail to distinquish between top quality dry Riesling and fragrant jug wine. The botrytis occurs every year in my Riesling plot, so I'll stop fighting it. I budded 4 of those 8 acres over to Pinot Noir, and I'll make Late Harvest J. Riesling from the rest. I thought the big expense was going to be lost tonnage from the dessication of the botrytized grapes. Turns out LH JR is twice as expensive as the regular to make because of the filtering expense.

"We are located right in the middle of a large diatomaceous earth deposit. My dental assistant's husband manages the Grefco plant in Lompoc which produces a real fine pink DE. I use that. My pre-filter is a serum cartridge made by Gelman. Each one cost $122. The Gelman salesman said he ought to give me the hardware because he was going to retire as soon as I got hooked on the filter units which need to be replaced regularly. He was right. Those long-chain polysaccharides clog the filters very quickly. The first time I ran a LH Riesling through the system, it clogged up after 25 cases. I've learned to slow down the flow and clean filters with pectic enzyme solution, but it is still hard. Using a 7-hole model instead of my original 3-hole unit has helped.

"The .45-micron sterile filter cartridge costs $200. When it clogs up, the whole filtration line has to be re-sterilized with 180°F water for half an hour. You can spend a lot of time on botrytized wines just getting ready to filter.

Bill Mosby

KF

WINDEMERE

Windemere is the name of a Scottish town destroyed long ago by English soldiers. It was the ancestral home of the clan MacGregor. Cathy MacGregor has a Masters in Food Chemistry from U.C. Davis, where she studied under Rose Marie Pangborn in the sensory evaluation subsection. Cathy's father is an aerospace engineer who developed a jet propulsion pump used to fly Mercury and Saturn rockets to the moon. Cathy grew up in Malibu. She went to college about the same time her dad decided to retire to San Luis Obispo. He had become interested in wine during the '60s, and thought he might like to grow grapes and start a winery. When he discovered how much work the vineyard entailed, he chose to leave the winery end to Cathy.

The first job Cathy took after college was in Chicago with Wrigley Gum. She trained people to perform as consistent taste panels for use in product development or quality control. "You start with standardized samples," she says. "The goal is to create a human laboratory instrument that will give reproduceable results. The hardest part is to get everyone to agree to the same intensity scale and vocabulary. About 10% of the

population have to be dropped because they are not sensitive enough, and 10% are eliminated for being hypersensitive. Some percentage of the remainder are always screened out because they can't be motivated to use a conventional set of descriptors." Her biggest project at Wrigley was bubblegum that wouldn't stick to your face. "I think they called it Hubba Bubba," she remembers. "I'm not sure because it originally came out in France with a different pronunciation."

Cathy's next job was in the Salinas Valley at Bruce Church, the nation's second biggest lettuce producer. "That's where I resolved to get into the wine industry," she says. "It's hard to take creative pride in a bag of shredded lettuce." She went back to U.C. Davis for a refresher course, then began working for La Crema Vinera. In 1983 she set up the lab at Grgich-Hills. While there, she isolated a strain of malo-lactic bacteria which captured her attention by succeeding in a barrel of very low pH Zinfandel. She maintains this culture today for use in a portion of each Windemere Chardonnay. Her own label was launched in 1985 with a custom crush at Lytton Springs Winery. She made 650 cases.

MacGregor Vineyard began selling Chardonnay grapes from its original 14 acres in 1977. It has since expanded to 80 acres. Several wineries have used MacGregor fruit to make clearly identifiable Chardonnays with which they have won a host of medals. The vineyard is located in Edna Valley on deep soil. There is a substantial amount of clay, but also a streak of limestone to provide good drainage. Cathy gets the grapes for her Windemere label from the oldest vines. They are the same clone found at Stony Hill Vineyard. There is a small knoll on the MacGregor property, but Cathy has chosen not to take grapes from the top of the hill. "I walk through the whole vineyard tasting berries," she explains. "I prefer the bottom portion of the slope."

Grapes are trucked to the J.W. Morris Winery in Healdsburg. Cathy is in charge of the lab there now. She barrel ferments in her own cooperage and seems perfectly happy with the size of her Windemere operation. "I might like to try a Cabernet from Napa some day," she says. "Otherwise, 900 cases of MacGregor Chardonnay will satisfy my creative needs. I still have time to tackle an occasional stained glass project." Married in August of 1988, it remains to be seen what effect domestic bliss will have Cathy's winemaking ambitions.

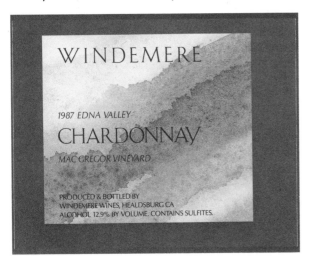

WINDEMERE

1987 EDNA VALLEY

CHARDONNAY

MAC GREGOR VINEYARD

PRODUCED & BOTTLED BY
WINDEMERE WINES, HEALDSBURG CA
ALCOHOL 12.9% BY VOLUME. CONTAINS SULFITES.

1987 Chardonnay	885 cases
MacGregor Vyd	750 ml

Grapes from 16-yr-old, drip irrigated vines planted on their own roots. Picked at 23°Brix, .9 acid. Transported at night in 2-ton gondolas. Overnight skin contact. 100% barrel frmt in French oak with med-heavy toast. 80% Limousin oak 1 to 3-yrs-old, 20% new Nevers. 50% put through M-L, no time on lees. 13.1 alc, .72 acid, 3.34 pH.

Do you find wine judgings unprofessional?

"They don't annoy me. They are usually not conducted in a clinical setting. People don't put as much effort into them as you would expect in the lab. I do find it interesting when two identical wines are entered in a contest. They rarely end up with even similar ratings. Eventually, I suspect the fairs will get caught. Then they will have to put more effort into 'training' judges. Training is not meant to make judges better tasters. It's purpose is description without personal variation. It involves reaching an agreement on phraseology. Then getting participants to apply the phraseology in a consistent manner. Training can be accomplished in 5 one-hour sessions. It can be tested simply by standard deviation.

"You will always find varied sensitivities to different stimuli. Bitterness is a good example. Humans show a wide differential in their ability to detect bitterness. One reason is that it affects the whole mouth. Sweetness or sourness tend to be more localized. Once you have profiled a person's sensitivities, you can balance panels accordingly. Smokers are not disqualified, by the way. Pangborn has done several studies which show that trained smokers are as perceptible as anyone else. The problem occurs in mixed groups. Non-smokers lose sensitivity when they are sitting with smokers. Smoking is an interference, but not to the people who have trained themselves to overcome it."

Cathy MacGregor

WINTERS

It is only a coincidence that the owner/wine-maker at Winters Winery in Winters, California is named David Storm. Really.

The town was settled by Theodore Winters, a wealthy horse breeder, in the late 1800s. It sits in the middle of a flood plain where El Rio de las Mil Puta descends from the mountains separating Napa Valley from the Central Valley. The River of a Thousand Whores used to flood frequently on its way to join the American River south of Sacramento. At least it did so until Monticello Dam was erected in 1958 creating Lake Berryessa. Attempting to disguise history, as well as the landscape, local cartographers changed the name of the waterbed to Putah Creek.

Nevertheless, alluvial soils of the region had been attracting fruit growers for nearly a century. Until WWII Winters was a railroad hub shipping the earliest apricots and peaches available in the U.S. There were 4 or 5 packing houses in town then. Now the crops have shifted toward almonds, walnuts, pistachios, citrus and kiwis. Tufts Ranch is the largest kiwi producer in the country, mainly supplying Asian markets. Not long ago they were shipping 10,000 tons of kiwis annually.

Winters is also quite close to the rice bowl of America. Cal-Oro is a genetically engineered rice developed in the area to mature in early October. Since the region is right in the middle of the Pacific Flyway, predation by waterfowl every autumn had limited its rice growing potential. Now the ducks arrive two weeks after the rice harvest and only have residual grain to work over.

David Storm is a sanitation engineering consultant of some renown in the wine industry. He writes a column for Practical Winery magazine. 43 different wineries presently engage his services to help them plan, design or improve their waste water drainage systems. He has been a serious home winemaker since 1961.

His winery is in a vintage brick masonry building he purchased in 1976. The building was constructed exactly 100 years earlier. It is two stories, with a cellar where he does barrel aging. The ceilings are 17 feet high. There is a theater being restored next door. His job, and his urban location, make David very conscientious about the way his winery operates. He can not spread out into the alley behind his building during crush because that would block egress from the local firestation at the height of the fire season.

So he crushes grapes right in the vineyard. "They don't even know they're off the bush 'til I've got 'em in the tank," he says with a wink. Juice and skins are brought back on a 10-ton truck in German fiberglass tanks (introduced to America by Walter Schug) and pumped into the winery. Pomace is sold to a hog farmer who claims to have the happiest hams in town. "I've demonstrated to the City that our winery puts out less waste water than the average residence," Storm allows.

The grape growing region that Winters Winery represents is only 35 miles from the center of Napa Valley. However, it is warm. Therefore, David favors the selection of grapes that will do well there. Gravelly hillsides have been best for him. His superstar is an 82-year-old Petite Sirah vineyard owned by Aida Naismith until her death at age 103 in 1988. If the name sounds familiar, Aida's husband Wellon was a cousin of James Naismith, the man who invented basketball in 1891. For a long time Aida was the only living person who had ever talked to James. Storm leases the vineyard and manages it himself.

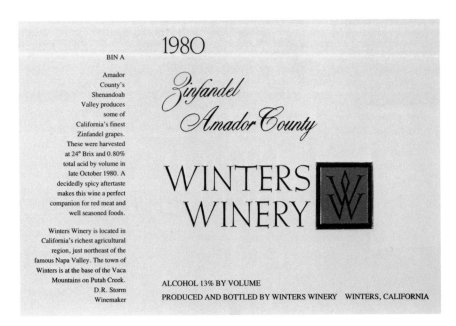

BIN A

Amador County's Shenandoah Valley produces some of California's finest Zinfandel grapes. These were harvested at 24° Brix and 0.80% total acid by volume in late October 1980. A decidedly spicy aftertaste makes this wine a perfect companion for red meat and well seasoned foods.

Winters Winery is located in California's richest agricultural region, just northeast of the famous Napa Valley. The town of Winters is at the base of the Vaca Mountains on Putah Creek.

D.R. Storm
Winemaker

1980

Zinfandel Amador County

WINTERS WINERY

ALCOHOL 13% BY VOLUME
PRODUCED AND BOTTLED BY WINTERS WINERY   WINTERS, CALIFORNIA

1985 Petite Sirah   800 cases
Aida Naismith Vyd   750 ml

Dry-farmed 82-yr-old vyd picked at 23°Brix. 6 days on the skins.
Aged in 50% American and 50% French barrels. Btld at .65 acid.

Is your consulting business booming now?

"Local governments are much more aware of waste water from wineries than before, but the whole planning process has gotten more complicated for any sort of construction. We saw this coming. The moratorium on new winery construction in Napa has been simmering for years. We helped design Gloria Ferrer and Domaine Carneros.

"Winery waste has no pathogens, nor much in the way of chemicals save a few sulphites. Basically it is water, juice, yeast and alcohol. The problem is that it is very high in dissolved oxygen demand. That means it takes oxygen out of the water. If you dump it into a stream, it is going to put a load on the fish and other aquatic life forms. Wineries generate 2-5 gallons of waste water for every case of finished wine.

"We do well at planning commission hearings these days by showing that wineries use less water than dairies. You know a cow drinks 30 gallons of water a day, and most dairies have several hundred head. Wineries are no bigger impact than the existing land use in many places."

David Storm

CL

WOLFSPIERRE

It is convenient to think great wines will be made by supremely competent, creative and energetic young superstars who own fabulous equipment and wonderful old vineyards in famous locations. Unfortunately, all these assets are rarely found in a singular package. Worldwide, the tendency is for one party with a large checkbook to cut some sort of deal with a second party containing the human talent. California's wine businesses are both exciting, and confusing, because there are so many different permutations of the necessary assets. These units are constantly breaking apart and recombining in a kaleidoscopic effort to produce great wine and find satisfaction.

The business I will now attempt to describe is a perfect example of magnificent wine assets spontaneously forming a unit which in turn generates excellent bottled product. My problem: What do you call this unit? It consists of a wine-maker with enviable credentials, and four vineyards with superb pedigrees. It is not a winery; they rent facilities. It is certainly not a brand name; the individual vineyards are the major feature on the labels. Ownership is not the cohesive force; the vineyards belong to different people and the winemaker is speculating on sale of the wine. The unifying factor is the design of the label and the fact that all the vineyards represent one fine viticultural appellation, Sonoma Mountain. In short, it is great wine produced by a shared idea.

The winemaker is Rod Berglund. He is best known for starting La Crema Vinera winery with a group of friends in 1979. No one in their group had deep pockets. For six years they made cool climate Chardonnays and Pinot Noirs in Petaluma. Their winery was a single bay of an industrial warehouse sublet from the printing company that occupied the rest of the building. They barely had running water. They practiced the traditional French techniques of minimal wine handling years before these became vogue in California. Rod says, "We tried to get the best grapes and manipulate them as little as possible. Winemaking is 95% sanitation and 5% wishing you'd done a better job." La Crema was bought out and expanded by an East Coast financier in 1985. In 1986 Rod married Joe Swan's daughter Lynn. Rod has worked at other wineries and helped Joe with the Swan wines since that time. Joe had hip replacement surgery in early '88.

Berglund's relationship with Steiner Vineyard goes back to 1976 when Rod made a Steiner Cabernet "in his bath tub." Steiner Vineyard's 22 acres of Cabernet are one of the better kept secrets in Sonoma County. The vineyard sits at 1,000 foot elevation on the western extreme of the Sonoma Mountain Viticultural Area. It is right at the fog line and very cool. Although the grapes flower at the same time as those in Sonoma Valley, they ripen 3 weeks later, often in early November. Clouds from the ocean drop a lot of water on Steiner Vineyard as they rise over Sonoma Mountain. The property is the source of a significant waterway running through Santa Rosa called Matanzas Creek. Sandra MacIver, owner of Matanzas Creek Winery, was once married to Dave Steiner.

Wolfspierre Vineyard is across the street from Steiner Vineyard. It is owned by Dennis Samson. Wolfspierre is an Alsatian family name on Samson's maternal side. In the 1860's the property was a vineyard and a resort. These early growers cross-cultivated the land resulting in severe erosion. Steiner Vineyard has much deeper soil than Wolfspierre. The 14 acres of Chardonnay growing at Wolfspierre produce small clusters of very tiny berries. The fruit averages about one-third the size of the Chardonnay clones approved through the U.C. Davis indexing system. Dennis Samson lives on the property with his wife Karen. If this group ever decides to build a winery facility of their own, it will likely go on the Wolfspierre site.

Berlin is a terraced 7 acre vineyard growing Sémillon and Sauvignon Blanc. Merry Edwards obtained the budwood for Steve Berlin's Sémillon from an old vineyard when she was working at Matanzas Creek. The Sauvignon Blanc budwood came from Ventana Vineyard. The mix of the two grapes fluctuates 60/40 one way or the other each year depending on bird damage. The Sauvignon Blanc ripens a week to 10 days earlier than the Sémillon.

Farina's Pinot Noir block only produces 7-8 tons per year. The vines have physical characteristics typical of a group of clones described as Pinot Fin, i.e. drooping canes, deeply lobed leaves and small clusters without shoulders.

1987

SONOMA MOUNTAIN

Chardonnay

A Table Wine produced and bottled by
Wolfspierre Vineyards, Geyserville, California • Contains Sulfites

1985

STEINER VINEYARD · SONOMA MOUNTAIN

Cabernet Sauvignon

A Table Wine cellared and bottled by
Wolfspierre Vineyards, Geyserville, California • Contains Sulfites

1986

BERLIN VINEYARD · SONOMA MOUNTAIN
53% Sauvignon Blanc · 47% Semillon

A Table Wine produced and bottled by
Wolfspierre Vineyards, Fulton, California • Contains Sulfites

1986

FARINA VINEYARD — SONOMA MOUNTAIN

Pinot Noir

A Table Wine cellared and bottled by
Wolfspierre Vineyards, Geyserville, California • Contains Sulfites

とはいえ

1987 Chardonnay   400 cases
Wolfspierre Vyd   750 ml

Picked late Sept in 2 lots; a large one at 21.8°Brix and a small one at 24°Brix. Combined 3.2 pH, .9 acid. 24 hr skin soak, settled cold, barrel frmtd with Montrachet, Prise de Mousse and Epernay 2 yeasts. Partial m-l, 30% new barrels of various French oaks and toast levels. 6 mos in barrel, on lees entire time. 3,000 gallons made, then 17 barrels selected for the blend. Sterile filter.

1985 Cabernet Sauvignon   400 cases
Steiner Vyd   750 ml

October harvest at 23°Brix, .82 acid. 2 weeks on skins, Pasteur Red yeast. Aged in Taransaud barrels 2 years being rotated through some new ones, then finished in used Ch. Latour barrels 6 mos. No filtration, decided against egg white fining after trials.

1987 Berlin Vyd   200 cases
     750 ml

Blend of Sémillon and Sauvignon Blanc. SB skin soaked, then frmtd with Epernay 2 in older French oak. Partial m-l in SB. Finished 2 mos in French oak. 13 alc, .75 acid.

Tell me about your label concept.

"We are not a brand name, nor are we really a winery yet. I mean, the wines have been made at various locations and are currently housed at Vinwood in Geyserville. That is a facility on the Gauer Ranch that rents out space and equipment. I see 15 different winemakers every time I go there.

"The important feature of our program is the vineyards. They are tied together by their location on Sonoma Mountain. When I started discussing this situation with the artist, we clearly saw that the similarity of design would reflect the commonality of Sonoma Mountain. Brand name would be inconsequential. Vineyard name would be more important than grape variety, just as it is on most European labels. The only task remaining was for the artist to try and capture the personalities of the vineyard owners in the typeface used for their vineyard names.

"Dennis Samson has been a longshoreman, and he has lived in a Zen commune on Sonoma Mountain. The Japanese brush strokes on that label have an aura that reminds me of him. He liked the typeface too. Dave Steiner is a strong, sturdy individual. He is not just a farmer; he is a researcher. He sits on the local planning commission and is constantly trying new things in his vineyard to improve it. Steve Berlin is a masonry contractor. He took a virtually unplantable piece of property and turned it into a textbook vineyard. Guido Farina is a restaurant owner. Overall, I think we've done a pretty good job of indicating something about the people and the wines in a simple piece of lettering."

Rod Berglund

Rod Berglund (L), Dave Steiner (C) and Dennis Samson   RG

145

WOLTERBEEK-WESTWOOD

Bert Urch is a 42-year-old research biochemist at U.C. Davis. Ever since he went to Holland to do post doctoral work, he has figured wine was a fine adjunct to his field. It allows him to use his scientific background. And it provides an alternative job if his career begins to plateau. "The early '70s were not a great time for bio-chemistry," he says. "I'm married to a lawyer for Yolo County, and I always want to be able to stay here. If my 'soft-money' position (dependent on grant writing fortunes) at U.C. Davis should falter, I'd like to have some choices. It would be nice to choose between a Nobel prize lab and a successful winery. I'm not sure age is on my side in this matter." Right now Urch works on a grant from the USDA in pig fertilization. His specialty is enzymes that release embryos.

Al and Teddie Wolterbeek came to El Dorado County with their 4 children in the early '70s from San Francisco. They were seeking something of an alternative lifestyle. Al was a carpenter. They have since retired and planted 8 acres of Sauvignon Blanc on their 20-acre property. It sits at 1,400 feet on a ridge in the Sierra Foothills. The property is rolling and all of it could be planted. The original plan was to sell the grapes. But the grape market of 1985 made them consider other alternatives. They were introduced to Bert through a friend at Boeger Winery where Bert was working as assistant winemaker. Bert's own label is called West-wood. He makes the Wolterbeek wine for Al and Teddie. The Wolterbeeks have constructed the winery where Bert makes wine for both labels. Wolterbeek Vineyard is a distinct departure from the warm climate characteristics that one expects in the Sierra Foothills. Cold air from the high mountains to the east washs over the vineyard every night. The grapes have remarkable acid levels even at 23°Brix. In their '87 Sauvignon Blanc, Bert decided to leave 2% residual sugar to balance out a 3.0 pH. In '88 he is planning to induce malo-lactic fermentation to soften the wine and make it drinkable earlier.

For his own label, Bert wants to do Chardonnay and Pinot Noir. He thinks high elevation vineyards in El Dorado County have potential for some extraordinary examples of these cool climate grapes. But he is not sure the public is ready for his discovery about the characteristics in these vineyards. "People remember romance and elegance from a visit to Napa," he says. "Often they remember a traffic jam from a visit up here." For this reason Bert buys grapes in Napa, and vineyard designates them, while he is waiting for the market to catch up with his perception of El Dorado. "I'm just an empirical scientist," he smiles. "I'm not trained to manipulate the marketplace, and I'm not very adept at it."

Don't worry Bert. If your theory on high elevation vineyards is true, Winewrights will get the word to places where it can do the most good.

WESTWOOD:

1986 Pinot Noir	300 cases
Haynes Vyd, Napa	750 ml
1986 Chardonnay	650 cases
El Dorado	750 ml

WOLTERBEEK:

1987 Sauvignon Blanc	400 cases
Estate	750 ml
1987 Cabernet Sauvignon	300 cases
Mansfield Vyd	750 ml

Does El Dorado have an image problem?

"El Dorado County has some of the highest elevation vineyards in the world. We are discovering very interesting characteristics about these grapes. Unfortunately, the market works at cross-purposes to the style of wine that El Dorado grapes could ideally produce. For instance, Amador is 1,200 feet lower than we are. Amador is to us as Calistoga is to Napa. Amador has this reputation for big, gutsy Zinfandels. We have vineyards that can't ripen Zinfandel.

"The image of our area lends itself to casual visitors who are looking for pleasant little wines at moderate prices. We do not attract deep pocket financiers the way Napa does. As a result successful wines from our region are approachable early. We can't afford to bottle age the wines for 5 years before release, and we can't sell them for the prices they would need to command if we tried to do so. Yet at the high elevations in El Dorado County, our grapes come in at extraordinarily low pH. Our fruit is ideal for long lived, barrel fermented, reserve-type wines. It is an opportunity, and a curse.

"U.C. Davis has a lot of influence on the winemaking practiced up here. Davis tends to promote stainless steel fermentations without malo-lactic and no lees contact. Chardonnay from a vineyard at 3,000 foot elevation is likely to smell like apple juice if it doesn't go through malo-lactic. Moreover, the alcohol conversion rate in a cool temperature fermentation is likely to be enormous. We've had Chardonnay picked at 22°Brix produce 14% alcohol.

"It is not enough to bring talented viticulturists and winemakers to a place like El Dorado County. Innovative marketing and capital are also going to be needed. The potential, however, is extraordinary."

Bert Urch

Teddie Wolterbeek

YORK MOUNTAIN WINERY

York Mountain Winery is the confluence of two historical currents. Like still waters, the volume of experience the winery represents is not apparent at the surface. The place looks like a small, relatively primitive and thoroughly laid-back, family operation with a penchant for eclectic antiques. This image is not entirely mistaken. It is small, and it's definitely a family operation. Production techniques do favor the traditional and labor-intensive, as opposed to capital-intensive, side of the the spectrum. 75% of their 8,000 cases/year are sold at the winery. This situation engenders an attitude which is more righteously self-sufficient than obsequious or trendy. Vertebrate zoology has never known more accomplished examples of the phrase "laid-back" than Clark Kent and Ratso, two feline stroke addicts who literally hang around the tasting room. They are picked up by hundreds of visitors each week, and immediately adopt limp imitations of a feather boa with its motor idling.

One historical stream involves the property itself. It was established as a winery in 1882 on land originally deeded by President Ulysses S. Grant. The tasting room is an old winery building made of hand-formed bricks, kiln baked on the premises. Two shoulder-high fireplaces lend a cozy ambiance on winter days. The building's timbers were brought by wagon from Cayucos when one of the first piers on the California coast was dismantled. It had been built in the early 1800's by Capt. Jean Cass to service lumber schooners. Until his death in 1941, Ignace Jan Paderewski brought grapes from his nearby ranch to be processed at York Mountain Winery. Paderewski was the foremost pianist of his time. He is equally renowned as a statesman, having served as first premier of the Polish Republic in 1919.

A second legacy involves present winery owner Max Goldman. Max has logged over 50 years in the wine business. He was a founder of the American Society of Enologists, the industry's technical fraternity, and he sits on the Board of Wine Institute, the trade association for California wineries' legal and PR affairs. Trained as a Chemical Engineer, Max made wine for United Vintners and Roma in California and Great Western in New York. He purchased York Mountain in 1970 as a retirement project. His son Steve is the winemaker, and his daughter Suzanne handles sales.

There are 200 acres on the property. The winery sits at 1,500 feet, 7 miles from the ocean. None of the original Zinfandel vineyards have survived. A 5 acre test plot was re-planted in 1971 to approximately equal portions of Pinot Noir, Zinfandel, Chardonnay and Cabernet Sauvignon. Steve feels that Pinot Noir and Chardonnay are the best candidates for expansion. There may have been 80 acres of vines at one time, but Steve thinks 40 acres would be his limit now. Although wines were once purchased for sale in the tasting room, everything except sparkling wines are currently made at York Mountain. They have their own bottling equipment and do case storage on the property.

In 1983, York Mountain was designated by BATF as an official viticultural appellation separate from Paso Robles. U.C. Davis classifies it as a high Region 1. Located on the eastern slope of the Santa Lucia mountains, there is a ridge separating it from the coast. They get some wind, but not enough to damage the vines. Fog is erratic. It shows up maybe 3 days out of 7 at the end of the season. Their warmest days will usually be hot in the morning, then cool off in the afternoon. They only had 6 days above 90°F in all of '86 and '87. When fog comes in during the summer, temperatures can drop to 48°F at night. Soils are shallow and very infertile. They have some "chalk soil," but not as much as places around Adelaida. Still, the high alkalinity can have a corrosive affect and stunt growth. Sometimes an application of kelates is the only answer. Steve Goldman buys the Burgundian argument that limestone soil improves quality because it doesn't retain nutrients or moisture. Vines struggle and produce smaller berries. York Mountain Pinot Noir is always darkly colored and thick bodied with low pH and distinct black cherry aroma. It's won medals 3 straight years at the LA County Fair.

YORK MOUNTAIN

1986

San Luis Obispo County

MERLOT

PRODUCED & BOTTLED BY
YORK MOUNTAIN WINERY • TEMPLETON, CALIFORNIA
ALCOHOL 12½% BY VOLUME, CONTAINS SULFITES

ESTABLISHED 1882

1986 Pinot Noir
450 cases
750 ml

Estate vines are 3 clones of certified stock which have subsequently developed virus; 15-yrs-old, dry-farmed, cane pruned and producing 2.5 t/a on a SE facing slope with sandy clay soil. This wine is 33% Estate, 33% Bien Nacido Vyd and 34% from the old HMR Vyd near Adelaida. Picked early Sept at nearly 24°Brix. 20% whole berries, no stems. Frmtd in open stnls up to 95°F with Montrachet yeast. Punch down 4x/day, M-L finished in spring. Aged in Sirugue and Francois Freres Limousin barrels. Rough filter, then btld Jan '88 at 13.5 alc, .82 acid, 3.35 pH.

1987 Chardonnay
600 cases
750 ml

30% Estate grapes, 70% nearby McBride Vyd. Picked mid Sept at 23°Brix. Overnight skin soak, no SO₂ at crusher. Frmtd in 2 yr old French oak barrels with Prise de Mousse yeast. 65% put through M-L. Sterile filter, then btld Aug '88 at 13.1 alc, .88 acid, 3.3 pH.

1985 Zinfandel
Bailley Vyd
425 cases
750 ml

Grapes from across the street from HMR Vyd near Adelaida on the Westside of Paso Robles. Picked at 24.5°Brix. 7 days on skins. Aged in American oak. Btld Aug '87 at 13.8 alc, .65 acid, 3.42 pH.

1986 Merlot
Far View Vyd
600 cases
750 ml

Vyd on Westside near Templeton. 15-yr-old vines picked at 22.5°Brix, 3.6 pH, .6 acid. Frmtd with Montrachet yeast. On skins 10 days. Aged in 50% American and 50% French barrels for 14 mos.

What are you doing about the high price of barrels?

"I've looked at several options. Used barrels seem the most attractive. Several prestigious wineries sell barrels after 3 years. Barrels which have been used for white wines that did not undergo malo-lactic fermentation are the most expensive at about $75. You can use them for anything. Those which have been used for red wines are half that price because you can only use them for red wines in the future. Red wines will also have extracted more from the wood. We can have these barrels shaved and retoasted for $15. Our total expense is about one-fifth what a new barrel would cost.

"Interestingly, many winemakers think new Limousin oak is too intense for most wines. Limousin's loose-grained wood produces so much flavor so quickly that winemakers say the wine has been 'flashed' in the oak. Most winemakers prefer Limousin barrels when they are 2 and 3 years old. A shaved and retoasted barrel is **not** like a new barrel. It is like a 2 year old barrel with fresh toast.

"Other alternatives include inner staves and fire-coopered American oak barrels. I'm still looking at these options. At this point, however, used barrels are less expensive than either one. Used French barrels have the added benefit of being 8 gallons bigger than American barrels. I'd consider puncheons, but they are impossible for one man to move around."

Steve Goldman

CARNEROS QUALITY ALLIANCE

CQA is not a winery story. That is why we took it out of alphabetic order to conclude the Winery Section with a crescendo. CQA is a marketing idea, and a real good one, but more importantly it is a regional grape growing story. That is what makes it unique and extremely valuable in California.

Over many hundred years of history, European viticultural areas developed concepts similar to CQA. The forces that begat these organizations, however, were often quite different. The rigors of medieval transportation frequently constrained political alliances to units defined by the topography of the land. This same transportation problem, particularly in regions remote from major trade routes or ports, made cooperative sales efforts almost mandatory. Traditional sales channels, and labeling laws, developed in Europe against this backdrop of regional groupings. Commune designations in Burgundy (i.e. Puligny-Montrachet) and quality consorzios in Tuscany (i.e. the Gallo Nero neck labels) are representative of such trends. Grape plantings and winemaking practices were subsequently influenced by the same preconceptions. Regionality is basic to European wine.

The European immigrants who launched

1985

CARNEROS

PINOT NOIR

MADE & BOTTLED BY THE CELLARS OF THE CARNEROS QUALITY ALLIANCE
NAPA, CALIFORNIA. ALCOHOL 12.5% BY VOLUME. CONTAINS SULFITES

California's wine industry would probably have followed these traditional notions, even though the transportation issues no longer applied, were it not for Prohibition. In 1933 the U.S. wine industry began for a second time, with very little connection to its roots. Distribution systems had replaced source of grapes as the most powerful influence permeating the industry. Brand name identity became the key factor in California wine.

CQA is extraordinary because it is the first time in 70 years that California wineries have been able to temporarily submerge their brand name mentality in order to cooperate with growers for promotion of a special regional character in their wine. Industry insiders consider this philosophical giantstep quite astonishing. Nan Campbell, an administrator for CQA, explains the situation succinctly. "Our members don't agree on everything," she says, "but they have carefully identified those things about which they can agree. They work hard to focus activities on these important topics."

The Los Carneros viticultural appellation was established by BATF in September, 1983. It comprises 36,900 acres divided almost equally between Napa and Sonoma Valleys. Less than half the acreage is plantable. There are currently 6,840 acres in vines. Average production is 2.5 tons/acre. The primary influence on Carneros climate is San Pablo Bay to the immediate south which cools the land in summer and warms it in winter. U.C. Davis classifies the area as a Region 1 with 2,100 degree days. Soils are shallow with slow drainage and rich nutrients. 48% of the production in Carneros is Chardonnay and 37% is Pinot Noir. This varietal specialization was originally due to demand by large sparkling wine producers. It is also a fundamental reason CQA has been able to develop into a cohesive organization.

Grape growing in the Carneros area dates back to the 1850's. It is one of the few regions in California which has had a clear and separate, albeit unofficial, identity for decades. In 1985 Francis Mahoney from Carneros Creek, Marcus Moller-Racke from Buena Vista, Mike Richmond from Acacia and vineyardist Angelo Sangiacomo found themselves talking more and more frequently about the uniqueness of their region. They got together to discuss making a movie about the area, and invited some of their neighbors. When a large crowd showed up, they began to realize they were on to something. CQA began by sponsoring research to determine if there was a style of Pinot Noir which distinquished Carneros from other growing regions of California. When results indicated this distinction to be the case, the group decided to promote the region cooperatively through educational programs and a wine blended each vintage to typify the Carneros style. Today there are more than 50 grower members and 12 wineries. Wineries pay $6/ton in dues, while growers pay $4/ton. High assessments like these reflect the strength of the organization.

The study which revealed a particular style of Pinot Noir as indicative of the Carneros region has allowed winemakers with diverse philosophies to share in a very productive activity. Every six weeks they meet to taste each other's wines (blind) and discuss the blend which CQA will use to promote the region. This original research provided a starting point; a set of characteristics which they want to emphasize in the final blend each year. They have all been struck by the sense of teamwork which has developed from these sessions. No single sample is superior in **all** the categories outlined by the research. Therefore, one wine can be praised for its "cherry" nose and another for its body. Everyone contributes. The process of assembling a blend to represent the region both symbolizes the efforts of their organization and provides a practical exercise in how they can work together for their mutual benefit.

Carneros Pinot Noir Research

Dr. Ann Noble, U.C. Davis professor specializing in organoleptic evaluation and author of the Wine Aroma Wheel, was asked by CQA to conduct a scientifically valid experiment to determine whether a recognizable Carneros Pinot Noir style exists.

A tasting was designed to compare Carneros wines with wines from both Napa County (non-Carneros) and Sonoma County (non-Carneros). Wines from both 1981 and 1983 were tasted to minimize differences due to vintage. A panel of 12 trained judges tasted a total of 28 wines (10 Carneros, 9 Napa, 9 Sonoma) two times each in 14 sessions held on different days. All wines were tasted blind, 4 wines per session, and no wine was presented in combination with any other wine more than once. The judges were asked to score each of the attributes chosen to describe Pinot Noir wine (fresh berry, berry jam,

spicy, mint, prune, vegetal, smoke/tar and leather) on a line scale of 1 to 10.

All the judges' results were correlated and subjected to a number of complex statistical analyses. 9 of the 10 Carneros wines were found to be clustered together in one area representing high cherry, fresh berry, spicy and berry jam intensities. The wines from Napa and Sonoma Counties were not clustered with the Carneros wines or with themselves; they were scattered all over the graph.

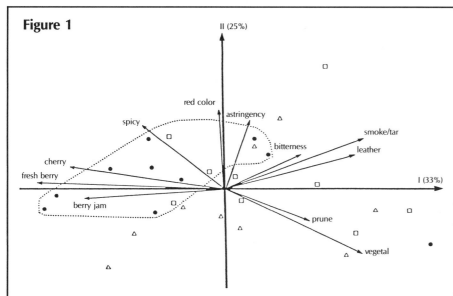

Figure 1. Principal component analysis of the mean ratings of the 28 wines for 11 attributes. The first two principal components are shown. The attribute vectors and the 28 wines with their code Carneros (●), Napa (□), or Sonoma (△), are plotted.

Blending session

EXPLANATION of TERMS

The specifications cited about wines on the winery pages reveal a great deal of diversity in the way micro-vintners make their products. Small wineries often comprise the experimental cutting edge which has made California the most dynamic wine region in the world. These winemakers can take chances with their limited size lots which big, corporate wineries are unwilling to risk. Controversial issues and techniques abound in the wine industry. They lend excitement and drive many a dinner table conversation. The abbreviated explanations in this chapter attempt to add texture and perspective to the choices wineries make, as well as the ones they ignore. These explanations are arranged to approximate the route a wine covers from planting to consumption. The subtitles for each section are gratuitous.

No one suggests that numbers can approximate the smell and taste of a wine. However, a wine's pedigree does have some predictive value. Recognizing vineyards or winemaking techniques which you particularly enjoy may enable you to scoop the marketplace. A wine's "specs" are known long before it is released. It is also much easier to communicate "specs" than it is to provide tasting opportunities when the availability of a wine is severely limited and purchasing decisions must be made quickly.

It is best to use wine "specs" in this book as a reference. When you taste a wine that appeals to you more than others, look up where the grapes came from and how the wine was made. You may discover a pattern to your preferences. You may also find that certain winemakers are tailoring wines just for you.

CLONES: YOU CAN'T TELL THE PINOT NOIR WITHOUT A FINGERPRINT KIT

In vineyards, grapes are usually reproduced by cuttings that are genetically identical to the parent vine. Grapes can also be grown from seeds, via sexual reproduction. Here the offspring inherit genes from both parents and are thus slightly different from either. These slight differences between similar grapes are called "clonal variations." Variation also occurs when cuttings from the same vine are grown in different environments long enough to develop new characteristics.

Differences between clones of the same variety are usually minute, and it takes an expert to distinguish two different clones of, say, Chardonnay. It becomes really complex if one tries to identify clonal differences in the wines, as many variables like soil and climate are hard to isolate and control.

Until recently, the only way for a grower to know what clone of Chardonnay he had in his vineyard was to trace the original cuttings back to the source, a virtually impossible task in most cases. Technology has changed all that. Today, the genetic code of a single vine can be "fingerprinted" and compared to others. We are discovering that there are literally hundreds of clones of each variety planted in California. Some are from a popular or common source (e.g. the Wente clone of Chardonnay) and are therefore widely planted. Others are obscure and scarce. Pinot Noir has shown a striking propensity towards variation. We are just starting to learn the extent of clonal variation and its importance to grape growing and winemaking.

HYBRIDS: MIX AND MATCH

Hybrids are genetic blends, where flowers of one type of grape are pollinated by another and the offspring raised from seed. Each seedling is a clonal variation of its siblings. Researchers raise all the plants and choose those with the qualities they seek. The resulting plant shares characteristics from each parent. Grape geneticists select for particular qualities like special flavors, resistance to disease, high acidity in hot climates, productivity, etc.

Some of the more familiar new grapes in California are products of University research: Ruby Cabernet, a hybrid of Carignane and Cabernet Sauvignon; Carnelian, which blends a Cabernet/Carignane cross with Grenache; and Symphony, a mix of Muscat with Grenache. Researchers at UC Davis develop varieties in experimental vineyards and then propagate them by distributing cuttings to growers and nurseries.

Many Eastern grapes, grown under conditions of frost in winter and extreme humidity in summer, are hybrids of European grapes with disease-resistant American varieties. Most of these French-American hybrids were developed in France during the phylloxera epidemic, and bear names like Seyval, Baco Noir, Marechal Foch, etc.

ROOTSTOCK: THE AMERICAN UNDERGROUND

As a result of a disastrous phylloxera epidemic in the late 19th century, most wine grapes (*Vitus vinifera*) are planted on native American rootstock (*Vitus rupestris, V. riparia*, et al.). Phylloxera is a root louse that virtually destroyed the world's grapevines in the space of a few decades. It originated in the United States and native American vines are, obviously, resistant to it. Budwood from vinifera varieties like Chardonnay and Cabernet Sauvignon is grafted to these native American roots. Thus the top or producing half of the vine is vinifera and the part below ground is an American variety. The grapes produced are true vinifera and not hybrids. T-budding is the technique of converting an established vineyard to a different variety by cutting off the top of each vine's trunk and grafting new budwood into the sides of the cut.

Rootstock does influence growth characteristics of the vine such as drought resistance, proliferation of foliage and volume of grapes produced. The German and French viticultural research facilities, at Geisenheim and Montpellier respectively, are currently taking a leadership role in the hybridization of new rootstock varieties. There is much debate as to whether rootstock has any effect on wine quality and flavor. One claim often heard is that vinifera varieties grown on their own roots produce more distinctly flavored fruit. No one has come up with any convincing evidence, and this assertion, as one would expect, usually comes from growers with ungrafted vines.

VIRUS: LET THE RED LEAF ROLL?

An interesting and far-reaching debate rages in California concerning a systemic virus disease commonly called leaf roll or red leaf virus. All that beautiful red color out there in older California vineyards in the fall is a result of disease. The virus reduces the vines' vigor and holds down production of fruit. It also retards ripening, since the color change begins in the leaves when the grapes reach about 16-19°Brix. Grapes need green leaves with chlorophyll to produce sugar. The virus slows down and eventually stops the ripening process.

Researchers at U.C. Davis set out to eliminate the disease in the early 1960's. Their goal was virus-free vines bearing the maximum tonnage of high-sugar grapes. Davis distributed certified, heat-treated cuttings to nurseries and growers. Today, two-thirds of the state's vineyards are planted to these virus-free vines. Davis spokesmen say these vines give "more production with no loss in quality."

And that's where the argument starts. Some Californian and many European growers feel that two of the most common problems with grapes here are overproduction and high sugar levels. They wonder whether virus infected vines producing fewer, less ripe grapes might not result in higher wine quality. "After all," they maintain, "the aim of grape growing is not healthy vines, but fine wine." U.C. Davis feels that there are better ways to solve the problem than using sick vines. Virus advocates say that certified vines grown on deep, fertile, irrigated soils can't be restrained even by severe pruning or cluster thinning. They call the plants "bull vines" and the grapes "basketball berries." Enemies of the virus respond by asking, "Tuberculosis might make you thin and attractive, but would it be worth it?"

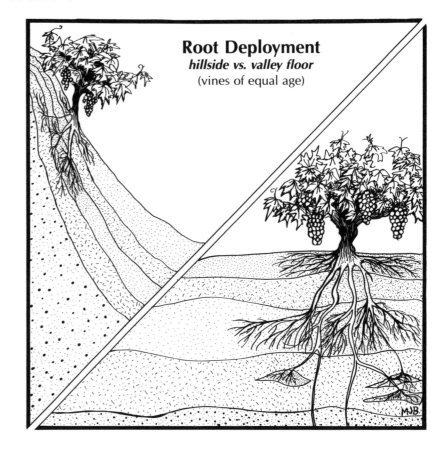

Root Deployment
hillside vs. valley floor
(vines of equal age)

VINE AGE: THE GENERATION GAP

One thing about old vines is that only time produces them. You can't buy them at a nursery. In fact, they have a way of connecting generations. Few individuals ever plant grape vines and then live to see what kind of wine is produced from them after the vines get to be 50 or 60 years old. Making wine from older vines is really an example of harvesting wisdom and labor invested by our forefathers.

California does have some small vineyard plots which are over fifty years old, but there are very few of them. Most early California vineyards have been ripped out, usually to plant other crops as agricultural fortunes changed. In Europe, some vineyards have been in the same place for a thousand years. Of course, these vines have been replanted many times, but Europeans have developed a great sense of value for wines from plots of ground which have been prized throughout history. Europeans also think more highly of wine made from old vines. At several of the top châteaux in Bordeaux, grapes from vines less than 20 years old are used for a second, less expensive label.

Vines start producing grapes after they are 3 or 4 years old. The productivity of the vine increases for the next 5-15 years depending on how much space there is for the roots to occupy. If vines are planted on a steep hillside where erosion has stripped off most of the top soil, they may reach peak productivity at a very low level in just a few years. Conversely on deep, valley floor soils it might take 15 or 20 years for the vines' roots to expand fully and reach the high productivity of which the vine is capable. Productivity will then plateau until the vine is 25-30 years old. After age 30, productivity starts to decline.

European growers are very conscious of limiting productivity in order to improve quality. This standard is even written into the labeling laws of Burgundy. Certainly it is the case that grapes grown in cold climates must limit productivity in order to ripen the grapes fully. Beyond that case, the theory follows that older vines are using a fully expanded root system to supply a constant amount of flavor to a diminishing volume of juice. It is also true that older vines set a larger number of smaller clusters with smaller berries. This fact increases the ratio of skin to juice, which is important because most flavor is produced in a layer right under the skins.

Most California growers consider the economics of the system and replace their vines when they get to be 30-35 years old. These growers are being paid on the volume of the crop, not on the quality of the wine produced. Many small wineries are begun by owners of an old vineyard who can not realize enough income from selling top quality grapes to continue growing them. Vertical integration through direct sale of the wine to consumers is the only way these artistic products can make economic sense.

IRRIGATION: WET VERSUS WILD

California has a very dry climate during the grape growing season. Therefore, irrigation plays an important role in managing productivity of the vines. Liberal application of water throughout the growing season will produce bigger vines with lots of leaves and a much larger crop. Given plenty of sunshine, these vines will produce an acceptable amount of sugar in this large crop. Traditionally, growers have always been paid based on sugar level for grapes they deliver to wineries. In Europe, this system makes sense because sugar is a hard thing to produce in their cold climate. California is another matter.

Extensive irrigation produces large-size berries with diluted juice. If there is enough sunshine, the dilution of sugar in the berries can be overcome. However, acid in each berry is also diluted and big berries do not provide as much skin surface for the volume of juice they produce.

Dry-farmed California vineyards are not universally superior to irrigated ones. Dry-farmed vines can become stressed early in the season and shut down the growth processes of the vine. The second year of drought in 1977 proved this fact by producing not only very small crops, but often very awkward wines. The 1988 vintage may prove a further example. Irrigation is a management tool that conscientious growers can manipulate to produce the best quality possible given differences in the soils and the vagaries of the vintage. It is noteworthy that many growers in the sandy Salinas Valley have learned to eliminate vegetive aroma in their Cabernet Sauvignon grapes by altering irrigation schedules.

CANOPY MANAGEMENT: GOT YA COVERED

Canopy management is a new buzz word in California. French growers have practiced it for decades, but their vines are spaced so closely that foliage must be trimmed to get equipment through the vineyard. More recently, studies at U.C. Davis and in Australia have revealed surprising effects on the composition of grape juice due to quantity of leaves on the vine and the sunlight each receives. Buds hidden away from sunlight on the interior of the vine are not as fruitful as those that receive some indirect sunshine. Leaves buried in the middle of the vine take nutrients which might otherwise benefit the grapes. Finally, dense foliage inhibits air flow through the vine. Air flow can hold down mildew, as well as rot in the grape clusters if the vineyard gets rained on at the end of the growing season.

There are several taste characteristics which winemakers are beginning to think may be effected by canopy management. One is pH. In areas where pH rises rapidly before the grapes are ripe, removing unproductive leaves can help. A specific smell, which is variously described as "grassy," "herbaceous" or "vegetal," also seems to be tractable through canopy manipulation. It is particularly apparent in Sauvignon Blanc and Merlot, but also to some degree in Chardonnay. Proponents of canopy management argue that the existence, or concentration, of that smell is unrelated to volume of grapes produced per acre, but is dependent instead on the amount of foliage produced by the vines.

Canopy management is accomplished in four stages: trellising; winter pruning; suckering; and hedging.

Many traditional older vineyards were head pruned fairly low to the ground. New growth each year came from a crown to form an umbrella shape. Today most vineyards are trained along trellis wires to form cordons, or arms, which create vine rows. The number, height and spacing of parallel cordons can be varied to open the vines up for more or less light as well as encouraging or discouraging vigorous vine growth.

Pruning is done while the vine is dormant each winter. Various techniques are used. They are all intended to reduce the number of buds which will produce new growth the following summer. Choosing the number and the location of buds which remain on each vine allows the pruner to shape the vine and control the crop size.

Removing entire canes which were not planned for during the pruning procedure is called suckering. Generally these canes are not very fruitful anyway. Removing them reduces the following year's pruning costs as well as opening the vine up so sunlight can penetrate to the grapes and next year's buds. Having fewer leaves slows the ripening process. The result is higher acid, lower pH and a longer hang time to achieve a particular sugar level.

Cutting back growing tips on canes is called hedging. It is done toward the end of the season to improve air circulation in case of rain. It also makes picking easier. Unlike pruning and suckering, hedging can be done quickly with mechanical shears — just like giving the vine rows a military haircut. Most grape clusters form at the first or second nodes as the cane grows out of a bud near the trunk or cordon. Therefore, the grapes are in the center of the vine and can be left undisturbed by mechanical hedging.

pH: THE ACID TEST

Total Acid measures approximately how many molecules of acid there are in a given wine. It is usually expressed in grams per liter or, as here, in percent by volume. The optimum range for most varieties is between 0.6% and 0.9%; 0.5% would certainly be considered low with 1.0% on the high side for a finished California wine.

pH measures the concentration of hydrogen ions and their reactive potential, i.e. how much the acid molecules have split (or dissociated) into their positive/negative ions. pH is expressed on a 0 to 14 scale: 7 represents a neutral solution like water. Movement up from 7 toward 14 records increasing alkalinity. Thus Maalox might read 10.50 with Drano or lye probably about 12.50 pH. Increasing acidity is read downward from 7 toward 0. Thus lemon juice might read 3.00 while battery acid would register a more extreme 1.50 pH. Wine usually has a pH between 3.20 and 3.80. A 2.95 pH would be very acidic for California wine. A 4.05 pH would be disturbingly weak.

Winemakers generally consider pH to be a more important number than Total Acid. pH has a more direct effect on taste, color, microbiological activity and longevity of a wine. Unfortunately, pH is considered an extremely difficult concept to explain to consumers. Many people become confused by the fact that high acid means low pH. Measurement of pH also requires more sophisticated equipment than measurement of Total Acid. The result is that most winemakers talk about pH among themselves, and talk about Total Acid when "pressing the flesh" in the marketplace.

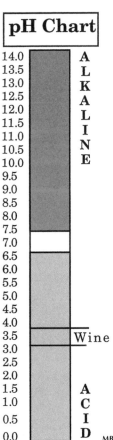

pH Chart

14.0	A
13.5	L
13.0	K
12.5	A
12.0	L
11.5	I
11.0	N
10.5	E
10.0	
9.5	
9.0	
8.5	
8.0	
7.5	
7.0	
6.5	
6.0	
5.5	
5.0	
4.5	
4.0	
3.5	Wine
3.0	
2.5	
2.0	
1.5	A
1.0	C
0.5	I
0.0	D

MB

Acid In Europe And California: Two Sides Of The Golden Mean

When grapes ripen, sugar is manufactured in the leaves and stored in the berries as they grow toward maturity. Acid in the berries is diluted by water drawn up from the roots. It is also disguised by the developing sugar. The taste of the grape gradually changes from "green and sour" to "sweet" as the percentage of acid drops, the pH gets higher and the percentage of sugar increases.

In Europe, particularly northern France and Germany, cold climate makes it difficult to ripen grapes completely. Poor quality is usually demonstrated by extreme levels of acid and little aroma in the grapes. These wines typically have thin body because insufficient grape sugar produces a low alcohol level, which in turn fails to extract enough solids into the wine.

In California the opposite situation pertains. There is more than enough sunshine to ripen grapes throughout the inland valleys, where vines have been planted most frequently over the years. California's problem is usually over-ripeness. Poor quality wine in California tends to be hot with alcohol, flabby with low acidity and beset with raisin-like smells.

Winemaking practices in Northern Europe and California parallel each region's climatic conditions. The styles of wines that result are usually endorsed by the palates and attitudes of local wine tasters and the public relations campaigns of the wineries. In France and Germany it's often advisable to add sugar to grapes that don't ripen fully. In California that practice is unnecessary and illegal. In France, growers are not allowed to irrigate during the summer, a viticultural technique widespread in California. Of course, it rains with predictable and often vexing regularity in France more summers than not.

Acid adjustment in winemaking falls squarely into this spectrum of debate. California winemakers often add tartaric acid to low acid musts to ensure a quick, clean fermentation, and to achieve balance in the resulting wine. They reason, logically, that any excess acid can be removed by chilling the finished wine so that superfluous tartaric acid precipitates out as cream of tartar (cold stabilization). It is generally thought that the best vintages in California are the ones requiring the least acid adjustment. Just as the best vintages in France are thought to be the ones requiring the least chaptalization (sugar addition).

It's A Balancing Act

It is impossible to state an ideal acid or pH level for wine. Each wine is an individual entity with its own structure. Residual sugar, tannin, flavor intensity, alcohol level and bouquet development will all influence how much acid may be desirable to maintain balance. Individual preferences will differ, but the goal is to present a harmonious profile without single components obtruding. Sugar masks acid, and sweet wines generally need high acid levels to be in balance. Conversely, acid and tannin seem to accentuate each other. That is why the balance between them has so much to do with how long a red wine should age in the bottle for maximum sensory enjoyment.

This question of longevity is under debate in California. It was once thought that heavy body and lots of tannin automatically meant long-lived wines. Such a model is probably accurate for European wines where high acid is the norm, with alcohol and tannin much less common. High levels of tannin and alcohol in California, however, usually indicate overripe, low-acid grapes. Current thinking is that high-acid wines may seem less pleasant when young, but are more likely to develop well with age. Only time will tell. The overall trend in California is definitely away from inky, tannic monsters, and toward wines with higher acidity and lower alcohol.

It should be emphasized that 'balanced' does not have to mean bland. It is more impressive to see a tree teetering on a rock than to see a yardstick performing the same feat. That scene is more impressive still, and more stable, when pickup trucks are parked on top of both ends of the tree. Great wines require both character **and** balance.

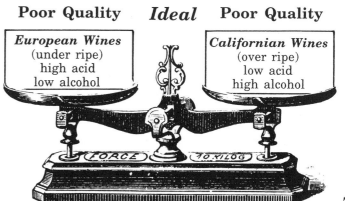

Poor Quality   *Ideal*   **Poor Quality**

European Wines (under ripe) high acid low alcohol

Californian Wines (over ripe) low acid high alcohol

HANG TIME AND RIPENESS

In northern Europe, vines bud later than in California because of the cold climate. They would also ripen more slowly were it not for the longer daylight hours from May through July in northern latitudes. Still, it is rare for grapes in Burgundy, Bordeaux or Germany to develop more than 23% sugar before the rains and cold weather of fall threaten the harvest. In these historic wine regions, the phrase "too ripe" is analogous to phrases like "too rich" or "too well built" in California. If nothing ever reached this imaginary point, you didn't need language to describe passing it. Grape sugar became a traditional standard for evaluating ripeness.

The amount of sugar in grape juice is usually determined by floating a hydrometer in it to measure specific gravity. Scales calibrated in various ways at different temperatures are used to report this amount. Germans use the Grad Oechslé. Australians prefer the Baumé scale. Americans like the charmingly named Balling scale. °Brix is widely understood to indicate percent sucrose by weight. These days, sugar measurements are taken easily in the vineyard with a device called a refractometer. A drop of juice on the lens bends light such that a Brix scale can be read through the eyepiece. The most difficult part of the operation is selecting a sample of berries which accurately represent the crop to be harvested. Individual berries may differ depending on where in the cluster, vine or field they've been growing.

California confounds the traditional ripeness standard though. Sugar is easy to produce in California grapes. Moreover, growers in California rarely have imminent rainstorms to dictate the beginning of harvest. The decision of when to pick in California isn't any more important than it is in Europe, but it involves more variables. California growers talk about "optimum ripeness" as the middle of a gradient, not one of its endpoints.

When vineyards began being planted in cool areas along the California coast, growers discovered sugar standards for ripeness in Napa Valley didn't necessarily apply to these new areas. Napa growers thought 23.5°Brix was a minimum for making top Cabernet Sauvignon. In the Salinas Valley Cabernet had to stay on the vine until December to achieve that sugar level. More importantly, when it got there its acids were down around its knees, and the flavors brought cheap Port to mind.

Phrases like "physiological ripeness" sprang up to describe empirical changes the berries went through involving smell, feel and color. Growers charted the sugar, acid and pH of their grapes during the last month of the season. They found none of these measures progressed in a straight line. Heat affected sugar, but so did access to water. Sometimes the sugar would plateau for a week, then acid would drop precipitously. Are the grapes ripe at the beginning of the week when the sugar stops climbing, or at the end of the week when the acid starts dropping? The jury is still out, but apparently "hang time" plays a role in maturity. In cool climates, grapes may develop all the smell and flavor components of ripeness at lower sugar levels than they do in hot climates. Perhaps maturity is a function of time on the vine, while sugar is a function of sunlight.

BOTRYTIS: THERE'S A FUNGUS AMONG US

Botrytis cinerea is actually a very common fungus. One often sees it in a box of strawberries left too long on the counter. Under most conditions it weakens the skin of grapes and allows various molds and bacteria to destroy the fruit. In those circumstances it is called gray rot, a type of spoilage. There are, however, certain conditions that turn Botrytis into a beneficial parasite known around the world as "noble rot." "Pourriture noble" in France produces the luscious wines of Sauternes from Sémillon and Sauvignon Blanc grapes, as well as the Coteaux du Layon wines from Chenin Blanc. In Germany, "edelfäule" is responsible for Auslesen, Beerenauslesen and Trockenbeerenauslesen from White Riesling and occasionally Gewürztraminer. It also produces the Tokay Aszu of Hungary.

The fungus needs moisture, moderate temperatures and still air for its spores to germinate. Its thread-like mycelium penetrates the skin of the grapes. Then, if conditions change to dry, moving air without too much heat, water will evaporate from the perforated berries. Sugar, acid and flavor are concentrated in these dessicated grapes. Volume is tremendously reduced though. An entire vine may produce only one bottle of wine. The risk of spoilage, the sharply reduced quantity and technical vinification difficulties explain why botrytized wines are so expensive.

A distinction should be drawn between botrytis-infected grapes and those which are merely over-ripe. Grapes left too long on the vine will turn to raisins. Wines made from grapes like that will be low in acid, high in alcohol and smell of carmelized sugar. Wines made from truly botrytized grapes will have plenty of acid to balance their high sugar content. In many cases, botrytized wines end up with low alcohol because every 4% of the sugar acts like 1% of alcohol to inhibit the fermentation ability of the yeast. In California botrytized grapes have been harvested with sugar as high as 48%. Such a wine would end up with 30% residual sugar and 9% alcohol. It would also be extremely hard on filters. One winemaker described the experience of cleaning up one of these wines as "trying to pump Karo syrup through a brick wall."

PICKING AND TRANSPORT: ROUND 'EM UP AND MOVE 'EM OUT

RG

Picking grapes is tremendously hard work. It is only marginally easier to supervise the harvest. Recognizing the precise moment of optimum ripeness is one thing. Removing tons of grapes from vines to the crusher is quite another. The logistics of hiring 10-40 people make it difficult to reschedule a picking date if overcast skies slow the ripening process down by a week. Hot weather is worse. Everybody's grapes ripen at once causing an inadaquate supply of pickers to leave scheduled jobs as demand drives wages up elsewhere. Finding a picking crew is never simple anyway. The folks willing and capable of doing the job usually speak Spanish exclusively, live without telephone service and avoid contact with strangers. You don't make an appointment for a crew with your local employment office, nor do you find one in the Yellow Pages.

It is often important to harvest the crop quickly, and experienced pickers make a big difference. For perspective, I am highly motivated on those infrequent occasions that I pick grapes for myself. I have no physical disadvantages and pride myself on a background that included healthy doses of manual labor. In my robust youth, half a ton a day was the best I could do. Good pickers in California routinely do three times that amount and earn $100-150 a day.

Head pruned vines and/or steep vineyards **must** be picked by hand. In addition to the labor of searching through vines for the clusters, there is the business of carrying 40-pound buckets or lug boxes to the end of the row where they can be loaded on mechanized vehicles. Bees, intoxicated by sugar from ruptured berries, mob the scene, but never sting anyone. The advantage of picking by hand is an ability to choose what goes into the wine. Of course, lack of rapport with the crew can diminish this advantage. Unripe second crop and bunches infested with mold, raisins or "water berries" are undesirable. Leaves, rocks and beer bottles are common enough to have their own name, MOG (matter other than grape).

Mechanical harvesters have some financial advantages, but those are not significant for small growers. The machines do require vines to be trained onto trellis wires. The big advantage of mechanical harvesters is the speed with which they accomplish the task, and the way they can work with headlights in cool nighttime temperatures. The first mechanical harvesters in the late '60s were clumsy machines which beat vines up pretty badly. They straddled a vine row and struck the trellis wires to knock clusters onto a conveyor belt. Juicing of the berries and the tremendous amount of leaves collected were problems. Today's machines vibrate against the vine itself while blowers remove leaves from the harvested grapes.

The phrase "Estate Bottled" has a valuable connotation. Unfortunately, its legal meaning is so nebulous as to render it a refuge for scoundrals. Caveat emptor. The connotation is that the grapes are grown in the same location as the wine is made and bottled. That is always an advantage. Transporting grapes runs the danger of crushing berries at the bottom of the container, thus promoting oxidation. Using SO_2 as an anti-oxidant is a compromise solution favored by large wineries. When you see 2-ton gondolas lined up for hours in the sun waiting to be checked into the crusher at a factory winery, you can easily imagine the degradation of the resulting wine.

The best protection is to transport in small containers at cool temperatures. Many micro-vintners go so far as to transport their grapes in 40-pound lug boxes. They try to pick at dawn, and they can usually get their small sized loads on the road by mid-morning. Other wineries use covered half-ton bins sparged with inert gas. An uncommon, but valuable piece of equipment, is a field crusher with a stainless steel tank. Grapes can thus be crushed within a few minutes of picking and put into an anaerobic environment to maintain aromatic constituents intact.

RG

SO₂: Label Those Preservatives

Sulphur dioxide inhibits the growth of micro-organisms. As such it is a common preservative in many bottled products that contain sugar, like lemon juice and soft drinks. It also acts as a powerful anti-oxidation agent. In that capacity it is extensively used on restaurant salad bars to keep lettuce from turning brown. Winemakers have used it for centuries by burning sulphur wicks in empty barrels to keep spoilage bacteria from infecting the wood. It is common for high-tech winemakers to point out that "grape juice doesn't want to become great wine, it really wants to become vinegar." SO_2 is one of the tools that most winemakers consider essential in preventing this tendency.

Wineries add SO_2 to grapes during transportation from the vineyard to reduce oxidation and the browning it causes. They also add SO_2 to the crushed grapes before fermentation to inhibit the wild yeast. In the barrel, SO_2 is used to stop the growth of surface yeasts and/or inhibit an unwanted malo-lactic fermentation. In the bottle, SO_2 helps stop oxidation which might result from poor storage conditions in less-than-sophisticated retail stores.

Free SO_2 effects human senses more as a feel than as a smell. It irritates the mucus membranes and gives a jolt that most people would recognize from a just-struck match. Sensitivities to SO_2 vary greatly. Some people will begin to weep in the presence of a wine with 50 ppm while others will be completely oblivious to 150 ppm. It is a mistake to confuse sulphur dioxide with hydrogen sulphide (H_2S, which emits a rotten egg smell) by merely refering to "too much sulphur" in a wine.

When SO_2 is added to wine just before bottling, the winemaker has to guess how long it will be before the bottle is opened. Over time the free SO_2 will become "bound" into the wine while performing its prescribed duty. If the winemaker adds 80 ppm "free" thinking that the bottle won't be opened for several years, sensitive individuals who open the bottle in six months are going to get a headache. Should you encounter this situation, merely swirl the wine for a few minutes and the free SO_2 will blow off.

A few small winemakers do not use SO_2. They reason that today's technology allows them to protect the wine from oxidation with other means. Most winemakers would give them an argument. Other winemakers feel that SO_2 used at the crusher binds up aromatic constituents which are desirable in wines like Riesling. In Chardonnay, too much SO_2 can dull the appearance. It is becoming more popular to limit SO_2 early in the winemaking process. In any case, the government required sulphites to be mentioned on labels of any wine with more than 10 ppm beginning in 1987. Unfortunately, these regulations do not make any distinction between sulphites created naturally by the yeast fermentation and those that are added. Nor is there any indication on labels of the amount added and when the addition occurred.

Back label from Au Bon Climat's $20 Pinot Noir

SKIN CONTACT: IF I SAID YOU HAD NICE BODY, WOULD YOU HOLD IT AGAINST ME?

White wines are fermented grape juice. Red wines are fermented grape juice **and** skins. Red wines are generally more complex than white wines because the grape skins contain hundreds of components in addition to coloring pigments. The amount of time that any wine stays in contact with the skins is an important determinant of style.

Some wineries will leave the skins of white grapes in the juice for a period ranging from a few hours to a day and a half. This technique may be simply "settling" of the juice, which allows pulp to drop to the bottom of the container. An alternative is to macerate the skins in the juice. Since the mucilaginous layer between the skin and the pulp contains most of the aromatic constituents, maceration intensifies the smell of those wines. It also adds body as solids are extracted from the skins. However, there can be a downside. Sometimes bitter tannins will also be extracted and occasionally off-smells will develop during fermentation. The opposite of "skin soak" would be the more common technique of spinning white juice at high speed in a centrifuge prior to fermentation. This procedure removes suspended solids and thus guards against visually unattractive protein hazes which might develop. Centrifuges are expensive pieces of equipment, unlikely to be found at small wineries. They also heat up the juice.

Red wines offer the winemaker several options in terms of time on the skins. Common practice is to press the wine off the skins at the completion of fermentation. This idea is prudent because the cap of grape skins that rises to the top of a fermentation vessel provides a hospitable medium for the growth of spoilage bacteria once CO_2 stops coming out of the wine. An interesting alternative has been practiced for a long time in Europe and is starting to see more practitioners in California. It is called "submerged" or "sinking" cap. In this technique the skins are held under the top of the wine, and the vessel is closed. The newly created alcohol in the wine acts as a solvent to extract more materials from the skins, increasing body and flavor. Proponents of this technique claim that harsh, bitter tannins are "reabsorbed" from the wine, making it drinkable earlier. The mechanism whereby this may occur is not clearly documented. Another explanation may be that the pH of the wine rises rapidly while the skins are soaking, thus making the tannin less detectable.

During red wine fermentations it is always necessary to keep the skins immersed in the must as completely as possible. Pumping juice from the bottom of the tank over the top of the skins is the method employed by all large wineries. Some micro-vintners choose to punch the cap down into the fermenting must instead. It's physical work. At the start of fermentation the cap is fairly loose. As fermentation progresses, heat and CO_2 build up and any pulp in the skins disintegrates. Thus the cap becomes drier and more compact. If the fermentation tank is tall and skinny, the cap may be 4' thick. Bill Frick weighs 220 pounds, but says he can stand on his 10" diameter punch plate without breaking through if the skin to juice ratio of the grapes is high. "First I try jumping up and down," he says. "Then I find a smaller punch plate to get me started." The idea is to force all the skins to the bottom of the tank, then twist the puncher to break the cap apart. It takes about 15 minutes to finish a 750-gallon fermenter. Heat and CO_2 rush up as the first punch is made, but CO_2 is heavier than air so the person doing the punching is not in much danger on top of the tank. S/he can get a surprise while climbing down and trying to walk out of the winery though.

The thoroughness of the punching job is a personal contribution micro-vintners make to their wine. It should be done at regular intervals. That means sleeping in the winery and getting up several times each night to perform this strenuous exercise.

RB

161

FERMENTATION TEMPERATURE: LIGHT IT UP

It is customary to summarize fermentation with the simplified Gay-Lussac equation which shows a molecule of sucrose being broken into two molecules of ethyl alcohol (C_2H_5OH) and two molecules of carbon dioxide (CO_2). The percent alcohol in the finished wine will be slightly more than half the percent sugar in the grapes. This conversion rate can apparently be altered by the yeast, the temperature and the fermentation vessel, among other things. Some California wineries experienced strangely elevated conversion rates on Chardonnay during the early '80s, for instance. Nevertheless, Gay-Lussac doesn't begin to do fermentation justice. The reaction actually involves a great many intermediate steps. Many of these are enzymatic reactions and reversible equations which can be driven one direction or the other by conditions like temperature, available oxygen, presence of SO_2, etc. The trace amounts of by-products formed in this manner are extremely important to the eventual smell of the wine. They are the magic of

CL

fermentation. It is such a complex reaction, with so many variables, that science is unlikely to ever control it completely. That is why winemaking is an art.

Eduard Buchner got the Nobel Prize in 1907 for showing that sugar molecules pass through the cell walls of yeast to be broken down by enzymes inside. The majority of yeast strains work most vigorously at 75°F. They die above 115°F and become dormant below 45°F. In between these two extremes, the speed of the fermentation will be governed by the temperature. When sugar molecules are broken down, they release energy and generate heat. In very large containers this heat can rise to the point that it kills the yeast before all the sugar is consumed. That problem is called a stuck fermentation, and it requires a great deal of expertise to get going again. On the other hand, a winemaker may want to halt a fermentation in order to retain some residual sugar in the wine. That can be accomplished by chilling the wine below 45°F and filtering out the yeast.

Fruity aroma can be volatilized at higher temperatures and lost. Therefore, wines which emphasize the delicate scent of the grapes are best when fermented at cold temperatures. Removing the natural heat generated by the fermentation requires a cooling system. Most California wineries use stainless steel tanks with jackets through which a coolant can be passed. Jacketed tanks can control the temperature of the fermentation to within 0.5°F. This technology has improved white wines significantly, but the tanks are expensive. They have only become common in the last 20 years. White Riesling fermented at 52°F may take several months to finish, which means its tank won't be available to ferment any other wines. Another method of cooling fermentations is to insert stainless steel coils into the must (fermenting wine) itself. This technique was first introduced to California by Robert Mondavi at his family's Charles Krug winery in the 1950s. Chardonnay fermented below 55°F in stainless steel will retain a fresh, fruity aroma. Fermenting Chardonnay in a barrel makes temperature control below 65°F very difficult, although there will be certain flavor characteristics gained in the process. Hence, barrel fermenting Chardonnays is a stylistic question.

Red wines are usually fermented at warm temperatures to help extract pigments from the grape skins. A typical red wine fermentation will run between 75°F and 90°F. At these temperatures, all the sugar will be consumed, and the wine will "go dry," in 5-7 days. Red wines are often fermented in open-topped, wooden containers since cooling is generally not required, and the grape skins need to be "punched down" into the liquid several times a day. Small quantities are less likely than big ones to generate enough heat to result in a stuck fermentation.

YEAST: THE MICRO-BIOLOGICAL PALETTE

Yeasts are a large class of micro-organisms, and there are considerable variations among those that cause alcoholic fermentation. Terry Leighton, a micro-vintner and microbiology professor at U.C. Berkeley, says, "We're 50 years behind the dairy industry in exploiting micro-organisms. There, they take essentially the same raw material (milk) and produce hundreds of different cheeses. We have so many different grapes, but only use a couple of the microbiological agents available to us."

California winemakers can choose different strains of yeast, seeking tolerance to low pH, high sugar, cold temperature or a host of other conditions. Virtually every strain selected will be some variety of the genus Saccharomyces (either *S. cerevisia* or *S. bayanus*), since these ellipsoidal yeast cells are easily recognized under a microscope and show a healthy tolerance for alcohol. Several of the small wineries in this book use multiple yeast strains for added complexity. A further refinement is to introduce them at different times. For instance, a cold tolerant yeast may be used to start the fermentation. That will be followed by a very aromatic one. At the end a vigorous fermenter will be introduced to make sure the wine goes completely dry.

Many wild yeast varieties found on grapes will only ferment to between 4 and 7% alcohol. These wild yeasts are more likely to produce trace amounts of higher (more than two carbon) alcohols, and esters with pronounced odors. If these odors are pleasant, the wine is enhanced. If they are disagreeable, as can often happen, the wine suffers. Predicting the outcome of a wild yeast fermentation is very difficult unless one has extensive experience with the vineyard involved.

Grapes have a waxy "bloom" on their skins to which wild yeasts adhere. In older European vineyards this "wild" microflora has become stable from berries falling to the ground each winter and from the practice of plowing pomace (used grape skins) into the vineyard as fertilizer. The resident yeast population is static, since the percentage of new yeast which arrives on the wind each year is barely significant. Thus French and other European vineyardists have been able to let the "natural" yeast ferment their grapes, and expect to get much the same results year after year. Often their wines have benefited from complex aromas generated by yeasts which evolved over hundreds of years in the special conditions of their vineyards.

California vineyards are generally not old enough to have developed static yeast populations. A large percentage of the yeast on the grapes arrives each year as new, wind blown strains. Most California winemakers introduce a vigorous inoculum of commercial wine yeast which has been isolated from one of the famous growing areas of the world like Champagne or Montrachet. The performance of these selected yeast cultures can usually be predicted with an acceptable degree of confidence. Some California laboratories are producing commercial yeast strains from noteworthy California vineyards as well.

It should be reported that European winemakers and grape growers are discovering the two-edged nature of technology, just like their counterparts in California. Contemporary anti-rot fungicides allow Europeans to harvest many vintages which would have been total losses twenty years ago. Unfortunately these fungicides also wipe out the indigenous yeast populations. European winemakers today find it much harder to achieve spontaneous fermentations. They are beginning to employ commercial yeast cultures, in many cases buying them from US laboratories.

The effect of differing yeast strains on wine aromas and flavors can be quite significant. Moreover, yeast experiments yield quick results compared to lengthy vine-growing trials. The technology of yeast research and production has leap-frogged ahead in the last few decades. Dr. Leighton, however, says that recombinant DNA is not an essential part of such programs. "The important characteristics are controlled by several genes at once, so classical genetic techniques (breeding) work better than really high-tech stuff at this point," he reports. It will be interesting to see the results of such experiments applied to fine wines.

LEES: GET DOWN AND GET DIRTY

Yeast cells die after reproducing a certain number of times, or when they can't tolerate adverse conditions like extreme temperature or high alcohol content. Along with tiny pieces of grape pulp, these dead yeast cells fall to the bottom of the vat or barrel. This occurs when the alcoholic fermentation finishes and the yeast is no longer buoyed up by carbon dioxide. The sediment is called "lees."

The yeast cells gradually split open, a process called "autolysis." Flavors and odors are released into the wine. Some winemakers rack wines off the lees immediately to avoid these flavors. Others recognize the complexity of wines like Champagne aged on the spent yeast, and seek similar flavors, body and bouquet. Leaving a wine on the lees, however, carries the risk of off-odors such as H_2S and mercaptans. These problems are most likely when a thick deposit of lees builds up in one place, trapping some of the autolyzing cells in a covered layer. Rolling barrels to spread the lees evenly over a larger area can help reduce the risk.

There is also a difference between the large volume of dead yeast cells and pulp which falls out of a wine quickly, and the small volume of later generation yeast cells which precipitate gradually over three weeks following fermentation. The first bunch is graphically termed "gross lees," while the remainder is called "fine lees." Few winemakers fear a couple of months on the fine lees. Putting one's wine into barrels "dirty" (i.e. on the gross lees), and stirring them up regularly, is considerably closer to the edge of prudence. Winemakers who practice this technique must monitor their barrels very carefully, which effectively limits the option to producers of tiny volumes.

MALO-LACTIC FERMENTATION: DROPPING ACID

There are other micro-biological processes occurring in wine besides the alcoholic fermentation. One of the most important, especially for red wines, is malo-lactic fermentation. This is caused by bacteria (*Leuconostoc*) that metabolize the natural malic acid in the grape to yield lactic acid and carbon dioxide. There are also trace amounts of by-products generated along the way, most notably diacetyl and ethyl lactate. Opinions vary about these distinctive compounds: if you like the smell, you call the wine buttery; if you don't, you say it smells like margarine or rancid butter.

Perhaps the most important change in a wine brought about by malo-

lactic fermentation is a dramatic pH increase. When a carboxyl group is removed from the malic acid molecule, the resulting lactic acid molecules are not as reactive. This significantly softens the wine's perceived acidity. There is also a subtle change from fresh, fruity flavors to a more vinous, complex character in the wine. Grapes grown in certain locations seem to have more malic acid (relative to the tartaric acid which is usually predominant) than grapes grown in other spots. The greater the proportion of malic acid, the greater the effect of M-L will be.

Almost all California red wines go through malo-lactic. Very few aromatic whites like Gewürztraminer or Riesling do. In dry whites like Chardonnay, the secondary fermentation is an important determinant of style. Bacteria are less able to function in low pH, high acid wines. Thus, wines that would most profit from the process are least likely to go through it naturally. In a similarly perverse way, high pH wines which might not have enough acidity are the ones most likely to undergo spontaneous malo-lactic fermentation.

Winemakers can manipulate conditions to favor or inhibit M-L. Generally the bacteria favor warmer temperatures (70-75°F) and are fed by nutrients from autolyzed or decaying yeast. Thus, wine is more likely to start (or complete) M-L if it is left on the lees longer and has warmth supplied by spring weather or artificial heating like an electric blanket placed over the barrel. Most California winemakers who want M-L, innoculate the wine with an appropriate culture like M-L 34 from U.C. Davis or PSU-l from Pennsylvania State University. To inhibit M-L, winemakers use SO_2, cold temperature, early racking off lees and sterile filtration to remove bacteria. They also try to keep non-M-L wines away from barrels which have contained active M-L wines, as the pores of the wood harbor the bacteria. Once a dry wine has gone through M-L, it is biologically stable and does not require sterile filtration before bottling. Most non-M-L wines are sterile filtered to prevent re-fermentation in the bottle, with resulting off-odors and CO_2 bubbles.

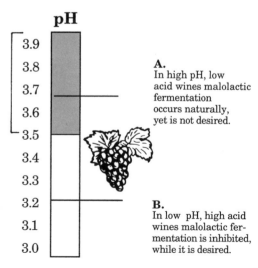

pH

3.9
3.8
3.7
3.6
3.5
3.4
3.3
3.2
3.1
3.0

A.
In high pH, low acid wines malolactic fermentation occurs naturally, yet is not desired.

B.
In low pH, high acid wines malolactic fermentation is inhibited, while it is desired.

MB

One strain of M-L bacteria is unusually tolerant of low pH conditions. It has become a valuable tool for winemakers who wish to pick Chardonnay early, and then "work it up" in the winery through barrel fermentation and forced M-L. Such wines have extremely long aging potential. This strain is called MCW (Matanzas Creek Winery) because it was discovered there by Merry Edwards. The original winery building on the property had previously been a dairy shed. Merry noted that occasional batches of low pH Chardonnay began malo-lactic fermentation whether she wanted them to or not. When it was decided to sterilize the building and paint it, she took a piece of the floor to a lab in Santa Rosa where they isolated this unique strain of M-L bacteria.

BRETTANOMYCES: REMINDS ME OF A DAY AT THE TRACK

Another microbiological agent found in some wines is the surface yeast Brettanomyces. Its name is a Latin tribute to its isolation from English beer in 1904. It is occasionally called "Deckera," but that may be a mistaken reference to a separate genus, Kloeckera. Like so many other micro-biological smells, Brettanomyces can contribute positively to bouquet in sub-threshold amounts. When it dominates the nose, it is usually described as "barnyard" or "horse stable" . . .and we're not talking about the farmer's aftershave here. Peter Franus, winemaker at Mt. Veeder, says it reminds him of shoe polish. "Some wines with absolutely stupendous reviews from the critical press are loaded with it," he explains. "People respond as if it were a European regional characteristic because it is so recognizable and so common."

Wineries can check their wines for "Bret" by having cultures grown on Petri dishes in a laboratory, but they have to specifically request this analysis. Because it is a large yeast cell which can be filtered out of wine, it is much more likely to show up in reds than in whites. Franus also says there is some evidence Bret can be present in wine, but not produce off-odors under certain conditions. A wine with 0.2% residual sugar might show the smells, while a bone dry wine would not. It seems to thrive on aeration and hate SO_2. Since barrels can harbor Bret, it is always a good idea to top older barrels up with wine from new barrels instead of the other way around.

BARRELS: WOOD YOU BE MINE

Barrels, along with glasses, bottles and grape clusters, symbolize the whole wine experience. Cooperage, the art of making barrels, is a highly refined woodworking skill passed on through a system of apprentices and only mastered in a few specialized places. For comparison, consider that one of the French coopers working in Napa Valley might be able to turn out 10-12 handcrafted barrels per day. A whiskey barrel factory in Kentucky might turn out 3,000 barrels in the same time. The French cooper bends staves over a small fire made of shavings. The process is gradual and it lets the cooper control the amount of "toast" as the inside surface heats up, carmelizing the carbohydrates in the wood much like one would gently toast a marshmallow. At the whiskey barrel factory a machine on the assembly line would put the barrel over a gas jet where the inside will be charred in a matter of seconds with one giant swoosh of flame.

There are many variables when discussing cooperage and it is easy to get into an argument about which one has the most effect on wine. Most American oak is *Quercus alba* which has a strong lactone smell. European oak is principally *Quercus robur* and *Quercus sessilis,* which have more extractable solids and more phenolics. The way barrels are made is another factor. So is how the wood has been treated. Some wood is air dried for years before being split into staves. That technique is con-siderably more trouble than kiln drying the wood and then sawing it.

Three major names for barrel oak are (rather generically) American, Nevers and Limousin. It would be more accurate to refer to Nevers as "tight-pored from the center of France" since there is practically no forest at Nevers left. Limousin is the loosest-pored, or most permeable to the wine, of the three. It is often used for Pinot Noir and Chardonnay because it has a soft, vanilla smell. Nevers has tighter pores and tends to give up flavor more slowly because the wine can not penetrate as far into the wood. Its cedar-like nose goes well with the Bordeaux grape varieties. American oak is the tightest, most dense, of the three woods. It is primarily grown in Missouri and Kentucky. It has a coconut-like nose. Experiments seem to indicate that one can tell the difference between the same wine aged in different barrels when the wine is young. As the wine develops bouquet in the bottle, these differences become less distinct. After 5 or 6 years of bottle age, it is very difficult to tell them apart.

The size and age of the barrel, however, are important considerations. Barrels do two things. They confer flavor as the wine extracts tannins from the inside surface of the wood. They also allow a gradual interaction with oxygen which softens the wine and develops bouquet. Both of these activities proceed as functions of the surface area related to the volume of the wine in the barrel. As barrels get bigger, the volume increases as a three dimensional figure while the surface increases as a two dimensional figure. A 52-gallon barrel will age wine several times faster than a 130-gallon puncheon. This size factor always stays the same on the issue of oxygen interaction and subsequent softening of the wine no matter how old the barrel becomes. However, the wood extracts which flavor the wine are gradually used up as the alcohol leaches them out of the oak. Therefore, wine needs to stay in a used barrel much longer than in a new one to get the same amount of flavoring. After 4 or 5 years, barrels become effectively neutral on the wood extracts issue. At that point they can be shaved to expose new wood, but that technique weakens barrels structurally. Another idea being tried at some wineries is called "inner staves." It involves putting pieces of new wood inside used barrels.

Another controversy is called the "turned bung" theory. The traditional idea has always been that the barrels "breathe" through the wood to give wine this limited, gradual interchange with oxygen which causes changes we call "maturation." Most wineries spend a lot of effort going around monthly to "top up" their barrels so that the air space that forms will not provide an unlimited source of oxygen which would turn the wine to vinegar. When Dr. Richard Petersen was at Monterey Vineyards, he did some interesting experiments with pressure gauges attached to the ends of barrels. He determined that barrels pull an increasingly large internal vacuum as small molecules of water and alcohol evaporate through the wood. This evaporation amounts to approximately 5% of the wines' volume each year. Larger air molecules have trouble penetrating the oak, so a vacuum builds up. Dr. Petersen found this vacuum suddenly disappeared periodically. He reasoned that it built up to a point that one of the barrel staves flexed allowing a jolt of air to enter. Petersen concluded that more air gets into barrels from topping up than from the vacuum space that forms. If the bung of the barrel is pounded in securely and the barrel then rolled partly over to keep the bung moist, the barrels could be left alone throughout the aging period. There is some historical precedent for this technique. It is practiced in both Bordeaux and Portugal. Dr. Petersen says it results in wines that receive less oxygen, and that these wines are different. He does not say that these wines are necessarily superior.

RG
Shaving

RG
Toasting

ASSEMBLAGE: A LITTLE OF THIS, A LOT OF THAT

There were more grapes planted in California in 1926, during the middle of Prohibition, than at any other time in the state's history until recently. Most of those grapes were not top varieties. They were meant for legal home winemakers. No one stood to profit from better quality wine. Following Repeal, an effort was made to promote varietal labeling in order to create demand for better quality fruit. This initiative was, at that time, unique in the world of wine. Maynard Amerine gets most of the credit for it. Over the next 50 years, varietal labels implied that blending would cheapen the product. That notion is, of course, correct in some instances. It all depends on who is doing the blending (or assembly) of the wine and what their motives might be.

If their intention is merely to stretch valuable wine, then U.S. label regulations can be accused of complicity in a fraud. Until 1983, it was legal to call wine Chardonnay which only contained 51% of that grape. In 1960 some 70% of the white grapes made into wine in California were Thompson Seedless. Skeptics can be forgiven for assuming this fact reveals the identity of a 49% component in many Chardonnays of that era. Vindication for the labeling law lies in realizing how quickly noble wine varieties have replaced lesser quality grapes throughout California.

In 1982 the Bureau of Alcohol, Tobacco and Firearms, which governs U.S. wine labels, held hearings on new regulations which proposed raising the varietal standard to 75% of the grape named on the label. Many consumer witnesses testified that something called Chardonnay damn well ought to be 100% Chardonnay. These advocates demonstrated how completely varietal labeling had captured Americans' concept of wine quality. They also showed a rather cavalier disregard for the marketplace's ability to decide questions of price and quality. Perhaps they were reflecting a distrust of big business and big government nurtured during the '60s.

A few witnesses chose another tack. They pointed out that many of the world's greatest wines are blends of several grapes. They opined the time had come for a new labeling initiative that would encourage a search for America's best blends. Deregulation if you will. They advised letting wines sell on the integrity of the winemaker. Let the marketplace arbitrate what constitutes good quality. Their point was not taken. But since then, more and more wineries have moved in that direction, particularly involving Cabernet Sauvignon which can be overpowering in its naked splendor.

These wineries all face the marketing challenges inherent in explaining a wine with a proprietary name, but some (like Phelps' Insignia and the Mondavi/Rothschild Opus I) have had great success. The theory is sound. Grape varieties react differently to the changing conditions of each vintage. Some years a wine with more than 75% Cabernet Sauvignon will be magnificent. Other years Cabernet Sauvignon will be improved by adding more than 25% Merlot, Cabernet Franc, etc. By letting an expert make this decision, the best wine possible can be constructed in any vintage.

The same idea holds true for vineyards as it does for grape varieties. If you own a vineyard or have a long-term contract, you just about have to use those grapes no matter what condition they're harvested in. Winemakers who shop around at least have a chance to buy grapes which have done particularly well in a specific vintage. If they are talented, and extremely conscientious about assembling a blend, they can usually make fine wine **every** year. As a consumer, putting your faith in a winemaker of this type is a viable alternative to putting your faith in the pedigree of a vineyard. Either idea is superior to putting your faith in a brand name, which may only be linked to a person or a vineyard temporarily.

Assembling a blend is truly creative art. Like colors, some wines will enhance each other while others cancel each other out. The chemistries of each wine may hold surprises when they are combined. Additions as small as a few percent of a particular wine can dramatically change the character of the final result.

Eventually economics must be factored in as well. Let's say you have three wines available for the blend. X, Y and Z can represent the volume of each wine you have. If you decide aesthetically that the best possible blend uses X+.60Y+.78Z, you can't go home yet. You still need to figure out what to do with .40Y and .22Z. It is very hard to be an artist and a businessman at the same time. Wineries that wax eloquent about the brilliance of their top of the line blend are more credible if they also sell some cheap generic.

If X, Y and Z are also different grape varieties and you can't make yourself accept one as 75% of your masterpiece, you have a further problem. What're ya goin' ta call this sucker?

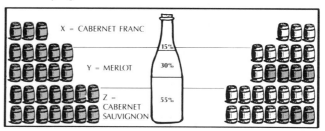

Corks: Put One In Your Ear And Tell The Waiter "Sounds Fine. Serve It."

Dom Pérignon is credited with the discovery of sparkling wine. He didn't do that. Dom Pérignon **should** be venerated for launching cork as a bottle closure.

Wine corks do a difficult job. They compress to enter the neck of a bottle, but remain resilient enough to maintain a tight seal on an uneven surface over decades. They perform this task at various temperatures and moisture contents. They are almost impermeable to wine, air and micro-organisms. They do not impart smells or flavors even in direct contact with an alcoholic and acidic solvent. Modern plastics technology has not produced a better answer.

Corks can lose some of their resiliency if allowed to dry out. Lay bottles for long-term storage on their sides to keep corks moist. Corks are not absolutely impermeable. Cheer up a bottle which appears to be weeping by drinking it. Seepage through the cork is not prima facie evidence of spoilage. True, it does provide a potential pathway for air and bacteria to enter the bottle, but these processes take time to work. Consume wines, whose corks have begun to leak, within a couple of months and they will likely be fine.

When a bottle of wine is heated, gases in the ullage space expand 30 times more than the wine and 180 times more than the glass. Wine may be pushed through the cork, or the cork may be pushed out slightly. Greater than the danger of oxidation is the risk that the wine itself may take on "cooked" smells from prolonged exposure to temperatures over 100°F. When a bottle cools, pressure is exerted the other way. Small amounts of oxygen which enter the bottle in this fashion can be incorporated into the gradual aging of the wine. Ullage of an inch or so is common in 20-year-old bottles which still contain magnificent wine. As long as the cork has not become loose enough from expansion and contraction to allow unlimited access to oxygen, there will not be a problem.

Most wine corks come from Portugal. The cork oak, *Quercus suber,* must be 40 years old before the initial harvest can be made. Growers must wait 10 years between harvests from an individual tree. Obviously supplies can not be dramatically increased overnight. When Gallo began using corks in the early '80s, prices nearly doubled.

To make corks, bark is stripped from trees in large sheets during the summer. These sheets are soaked in very hot water, then air dried for months. The bark has xylem and phloem running up and down the tree to transport elaborated sap between roots and leaves. These pores become partially plugged by tyloses as each layer matures, but they represent potential passageways through a wine cork. Lenticels also penetrate the bark of a cork tree from the outside to the heartwood. Top quality wine corks should be punched out of the bark perpendicular to the directions of these potential flaws.

The quality of cork is determined by how dense it is. The best corks come from the slowest growing trees. Imperfections sliced out of the ends of wine corks leave little grooves. Fewer grooves mean better corks. Brown barky areas, or oxalic acid used to bleach them, indicate low quality. The length of a cork is a price consideration. Wines meant to be bottle aged for a long time should have long corks; 2.25" is a long cork, 1.5" is a short one. Parafin coating and "chamfered" (beveled) ends are merely ways to ease insertion and extraction of corks from wine bottles. Winery logos printed on the side of corks have long made them seals of authenticity.

As sheets of cork bark are drying, they may be infested with a fungus which renders them useful only for shoes and bulletin boards. Experts cull this tainted cork by smelling the sheets. Sometimes they have on off day. "Corkiness" in wine seems to be quite random. Encountering it in one bottle rarely means that other bottles from the same case will be affected. This "dank, musty, moldy" smell is caused by 2,4,6-trichloroanisole, commonly called tyrene. Some people are much more sensitive than others to tyrene.

GRAPE VARIETY & WINEMAKING STYLE

INTRODUCTION

Wheat, oil, detergent and vodka are examples of fairly standardized commodities. Wine is at the opposite extreme. There are tens of thousands of very different wines produced every year. Digesting this massive amount of information is a constant struggle for most consumers and a perverse source of delight for a few others. Dividing the field into general cubbyholes is the only hope for most of us. Grape varieties are a real good way to start separating the field because that is how most American wines are labeled. There are only 20-25 categories based on grape varieties which also correspond to major sets of winemaking techniques and taste/smell characteristics. Let's call these "styles." Once you come to recognize these broad varietal/enological styles, it will be easy for you to serve wines appropriately.

The conditions in which grapes are grown vary widely due to regional features like elevation, and vintage factors like weather. Some grape varieties are simply better suited for particular conditions than others. Throughout history, this process of matching grape varieties to expected growing conditions was the most important element in quality and style. Since the middle of the twentieth century, however, the role of the winemaker has become increasingly pivotal. Technical advances in equipment and analysis have turned winemaking into a dynamic blend of science and art. Today winemakers can choose among many alternatives in the way they handle the grapes, the temperatures at which they ferment them and even the microbiological players in the process.

Few wineries work to a recipe. Almost any winemaker will say, "I determine what the grapes can give me, then try to stay out of their way." It sounds like babysitting. Actually it is more like sculpture. You start with a block of marble and gradually take away everything that isn't part of the finished piece. It is hard to add much, and virtually impossible to replace something removed by mistake. Conventional standards do outline gross features which are generally expected in wines made from major grape varieties. Most winemakers try to influence nuances of smell and flavor within these bounds. Still, the options available to winemakers are so numerous the task will always remain more of an art than a science.

Worldwide, hundreds of grape varieties are made into wine. Most differentiate themselves in the vineyard or the winery, if not in the glass. Some are vigorous producers. Some are resistant to particular pests or mildews. Others compensate for mediocre growing conditions by budding late, or ripening early, or drying off easily after a rain, etc. Alicante Bouschet is one of the few wine grapes with a red pulp. Thirty years ago it was widely used to add color. Grenache is a fragrant wine grape which retains good acid even in hot climates. Grenache is frequently used in blended wines from California's Central Valley, as well as several from southern France (Châteauneuf du Pape). Table grapes are chosen to have large, pulpy berries with thin skins, high sugar and low acid. These characteristics make them enjoyable to eat. They don't, however, make very good wine. Thompson Seedless was once known colloquially as the Fresno Chardonnay because its neutral flavor and high yield made it a good extender for more expensive varieties in wine.

Some excellent wine grapes are not extensively grown yet in California. These include Nebbiolo and Sangiovese from Italy as well as Viognier and Syrah from France's Rhone Valley. All four are receiving more attention in California each year.

Of the wine grapes which are commonly grown in California, six groups clearly stand out from the crowd. Gewürztraminer, White Riesling and the Muscats comprise the white group best known for dominating, fruity aroma and soft (read semi-sweet) structure in the mouth. Sauvignon Blanc is probably the most distinctively flavored, and most searingly acidic (interpreted as "dry" by most people), white. Chardonnay is the most complex white by virtue of the way it is aged in barrels and its ability to develop bouquet in the bottle. Pinot Noir is the most accessible red; famous worldwide for its sensuous structure and berry-like aroma. Zinfandel is the most unique red (virtually a California exclusive) and economical besides. Cabernet Sauvignon leads the red group (including also Merlot and Cabernet Franc) most renowned for aging ability and dominating bouquet.

The purpose of this chapter is to detail the growing, winemaking and serving options available within each of these six major varietal categories.

CHARDONNAY

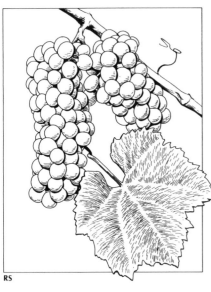

RS

Wine professionals use a linquistic convention which pointedly illustrates the unique features of Chardonnay wine. The word "aroma" is used for the fruity or floral smells derived from freshly crushed grapes. The word "bouquet" is used for smells which derive from the winemaking and aging processes. Thus, woodiness and yeastiness are examples of bouquet. So is the smell that develops from the gradual, continuous oxidation of the wine's components as they age in the bottle. (Rapid, unlimited oxidation causes spoilage, i.e. volatile acidity; which is only considered a component of bouquet up to the point that you recognize its identity.) The delight of most white wines is their fresh, fruity aroma. As such, those wines are degraded when the aroma begins to fade over time. Chardonnay draws its superb reputation from the fact that it is often made, and ages, more like a red wine than a white. Chardonnay develops additional bouquet in the bottle which first complements, then replaces, the aroma of the young wine.

The great white Burgundies of the Côte d'Or and Chablis are all made from Chardonnay. It is a component in the best Champagnes. It produces excellent wine in Australia as well as in France and California.

◆ VITICULTURE

Chardonnay is not a member of the Pinot family. Pinot Blanc is the white version of Pinot Noir found interplanted among Chardonnay vines in some of the best Burgundian vineyards. But Pinot Blanc is rarely found in California. Most of the grapes called Pinot Blanc in California are actually the Melon, which is currently best known for making France's Muscadet wines. Confused? Just imagine a California viticulturalist visiting northern Burgundy in the late 1880's and asking a French grower for cuttings of his best Pinot Blanc. "Mais oui, (Yankee running dog) take these."

True Pinot Blanc has higher total acidity than Chardonnay, lots of tannin in the skins and a propensity to darken quickly. Melon has low total acidity, even when grown in very cold climates.

Chardonnay grows vigorously, but will only bear a large crop in deep, fertile soils. Large production severely compromises wine quality. Clusters are small, compact, cylindrical and winged (having one separate, smaller section attached to the main stem at the top). Berries are small, round and thin-skinned. Chardonnay buds early in the season which makes it quite vulnerable to spring frost. It is sensitive to powdery mildew and botrytis which leads many growers to spray it with sulphur if moisture threatens the harvest. Sulphur on the grapes can result in wines with an H_2S problem. However, Chardonnay also ripens early which allows harvest before the onset of rain in most California vintages. Compact clusters and thin-skinned berries mean that Chardonnay is likely to suffer extensive bunch rot if caught by an early rain.

The color and turgidity of Chardonnay berries change noticeably as ripeness approaches. Prior to ripeness the grapes are green, hard and opaque. After ripening they become much more pliant to the touch and turn an amber yellow color with translucent skins. The point along this gradient at which they are harvested will have a lot to do with the style of wine which is made. As the skins become translucent, clusters exposed to direct sunlight are in danger of sunburn. Early maturity and soft-pulped berries make Chardonnay a likely candidate for bird damage. This litany of potential problems may begin to explain the high price of Chardonnay wine. Cool climate regions are strongly indicated.

Although different clonal selections have been identified, there is very little agreement on names to apply to them or characteristics which may be available. Some winemakers claim to notice differences in aroma. Differences in berry size and tonnage per acre are easier to document. Prior to Dr. Olmo's work at U.C. Davis in the '60s, Chardonnay rarely produced more than 2 tons per acre in California. Clonal selection has now raised the state average to 4 or 5 tons per acre. The phrase "small-berried old clone" is more of a backlash to this transition than it is a reference to any specific clonal selection.

In 1960 there were only a few hundred acres of Chardonnay in California. Chalone, Hanzell and Stony Hill pioneered the grape variety here, as well as the artisan-sized winery concept. By 1990 California may have more acres of Chardonnay planted than France does.

◆ ENOLOGY

Few wines reveal the manipulations of the winemaker more clearly than Chardonnay.

Leaving the juice on the skins for 6-36 hours after crushing will add viscosity in the mouth and complexity in the nose. Alternatively, centrifuging the juice will ensure a clean fermentation and lighter, less controversial wine. SO_2 additions will minimize competitive microbiological activity and stop oxidation of phenolic compounds which may have been extracted from the skins and pulp. However, SO_2 will also bind up aromatic constituents and dull the wine's color. The temperature of the grapes at harvest, and the time they spend moving between the vine and the winery, will dictate many of the decisions about skin soak and use of SO_2.

Fermentation in small barrels will add a toasty quality to the wine, but lack of temperature control may diminish aroma. Leaving the wine on the lees in the barrel for 1-9 months will obviously increase rich, yeasty smells, but runs the risk of developing off-odors. Fermenting in stainless steel tanks is less work, but the tanks are expensive. Several pure strain yeast cultures are popular for Chardonnay fermentations: Prise de Mousse is a newer candidate offering control of foaming during the tumultuous (read messy) phase of barrel fermentation; Epernay 2 is a safe standard which will not interfere with the wine's aroma; Montrachet is a traditional culture offering complexity with a slight risk of H_2S development under certain conditions.

Whether or not a Chardonnay goes through malo-lactic fermentation will have a significant effect on smell and taste character. For hundreds of years this factor was governed by the ripeness of the grapes and the incidence of malo-lactic bacteria in the barrels. It was neither controlled nor well understood by the winemaker. It was a happy accident which certainly helped those cold climate Burgundian wines lucky enough to undergo it. Today, knowledgeable winemakers can choose to induce, or inhibit, malo-lactic fermentation in all, or specific portions, of the Chardonnay they make.

Most Chardonnay is aged in small oak barrels. The choice of wood, the age of the barrel, the amount of time the wine stays in the barrel and the method used to cooper the barrel will all contribute to the flavor and bouquet of the wine.

◆ STYLES

It is possible to separate most Chardonnays into three stylistic groups. Cross-overs do occur, of course, but many winemakers are inclined to aim in one of these directions:

◇ **SOFT FRUIT, DRINK AGE 1 TO 3.** The aroma of Chardonnay grapes can range from "peach" to "grapefruit" with "Pippin apple" generally considered a fair midpoint description. "Peach" represents the warmer, riper end of the spectrum. The citrus notes (alluded to by "grapefruit") seem to come from cooler climates and low pH wines. These smells may be favored by a greater proportion of citric acid, just as apple smells may be favored by a larger proportion of malic acid. Exotic aromas (often called "pineapple") seem to result from ripe, high pH grapes grown in cool climates, i.e. Monterey. A little bit of botrytis in Chardonnay can add smells ranging from "winter squash" to "pumpkin."

Winemakers who wish to emphasize aroma in Chardonnay will usually ferment in stainless steel tanks at temperatures under 55°F. They will harvest the grapes at least as ripe as 23°Brix. They will minimize competing smells from malo-lactic fermentation or yeast autolysis. They will age in older oak barrels for a shorter length of time.

This style of wine is easier to produce in California than it would be in colder climates. It is particularly advantageous financially because the wines are ready to drink within one year. These wines have broad appeal for the mass market as they require little experience to appreciate. Since 1985 the practice of leaving half a percent of residual sugar in Chardonnays of this style has become quite common. This small amount of sugar is not immediately identifiable to the average consumer. It softens one's perception of the individual elements in the wine similar to the way bottle maturation would. It improves mouth feel. Unfortunately, Chardonnays with half a percent of residual sugar do not age very well. They take on "poached pear" or "apricot" notes and begin to taste "flabby" after their third birthday.

Distinct aroma is the primary pleasure of this "drink early" category. It is likely to come from riper, lower acid grapes. But strong aroma does not necessarily imply premature senility. Good acid and low pH are indicators of longevity, and they can occur along with intense aroma. Conversely, some Chardonnays are made from young, overcropped vineyards. Such wines rarely have much aroma, and they never develop worth a damn.

◇ **TOASTY, DRINK AGE 2 TO 5.** The initial bouquet of Chardonnay comes largely from yeast, wood, and malo-lactic bacteria. These smells can be differentiated, though they do tend to similarity. Malo-lactic fermentation is the source of the smell many people describe as "buttery." It will be most noticeable in higher pH wines made from riper grapes. Extreme, overdone examples will reek of "butterscotch." A lighter smell, reminiscent of baking bread, comes from the yeast. It will be present in most barrel fermented Chardonnays and strongest in wines left on the lees for extended periods of time. Barrels will contribute smells ranging from "vanilla" to "coconut" depending on the source of the oak. When barrels are made by traditional coopers, carbohydrates on the inside surface of the wood are carmelized to varying degrees as the staves are bent over a small fire. Heavily "toasted," new barrels can make Chardonnay smell like roasted sesame oil if the wine is left in them too long. All these examples of initial bouquet can be smelled more easily in wine served at room temperature than in wine served from an ice bucket. Likewise, they often show up more clearly in the finish, or aftertaste, than they do in the nose.

This style of Chardonnay is more expensive to produce than the first one because it requires the winemaker to do much more work. The effects are intensified by higher pH and higher alcohol levels. It is easier to accomplish this with grapes from warmer regions. It is a very easy style to recognize. Simply look at the color. These wines will be darker and more yellow than the others. You can recognize fellow aficionados from across the room. It tends to be a controversial style though, because the strong flavors dominate subtly seasoned food. I accept that point. I also know that food is just about as likely to be subtle as New Yorkers are likely to be well dressed intellectuals and Southern Californians are likely to be airheads with stunning bodies. It happens, but it's hardly automatic.

Toasty Chardonnays often seem awkward when they're first released at age one. Smells appear as separate entities. So do taste sensations. These wines need a year or two in the bottle to harmonize. As the smells and flavors marry, the wines become rich and beguiling. Per usual, restraint is a virtue. This style is particularly enjoyable when served chilled because the buttery sensation explodes on the palate and lingers for a long time. Occasional examples of this style will age well, but most get pretty tired after their fifth birthday. When these wines go over the hill, instead of getting weak, they start to seem oxidized.

◇ **WORKED UP, DRINK AGE 3 TO 8.** A third style is important. It requires participation by the consumer. That sort of interaction always improves one's sense of appreciation. This style is difficult to find. It relies heavily on the development of bouquet over several years in the bottle.

The grapes are picked early or grown in very cool climates. Hence, the wine is extremely acidic and lacks expansive aroma early in its life. Much of the wine's initial flavor comes from skin contact, extended time on the lees and new wood. These wines must be induced to go through malo-lactic fermentation, but it requires a particularly vigorous inoculum because their naturally low pH inhibits the bacteria. A marvel of these wines is the way fruit aroma grows gradually to fill in the skeleton of acid and tightly restrained winemaking bouquet. Imagine a tall, gawky, painfully thin teen-age girl compared to her friend the shorter, voluptuous, highly coordinated cheerleader. Now imagine both of them at age 40.

These Worked Up style of wines are increasingly rare because of three factors: (1) the success, and predatory nature, of discount stores in America has rendered almost extinct the merchant capable of giving consumers knowledgeable advice on cellaring wines; (2) price point competition in retail stores has driven top wineries to sell most of their wine to restaurants, where the cost of space is too dear to cellar wines at all; (3) interest rates and highly leveraged ownership have taken many of the inventory decisions at wineries or middlemen distributors and placed them on a banker's desk. The result is a predisposition toward wines which will reach their maximum potential quickly.

It is a shame. The style of Chardonnay we ignore in such an environment is a unique experience. At age six it starts to take on the most extraordinary bottle bouquet. It becomes softer, yet more insistent. It expands without losing its focus. There is symmetry to the flavor profile. The nose is almost human. It always reminds me of mousing in front of a fireplace, i.e. part physical, part timeless and part naughty. You can't buy this experience. It is an event produced by your wine cellar; an added value — an investment of time instead of money. As Marilyn Otteman says about her Estate Chardonnay, "She stands back and waits for maturity on your part."

SAUVIGNON BLANC

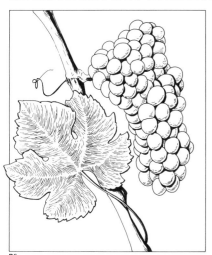

RS

Fumé Blanc and Sauvignon Blanc are the same thing. Legend has it that Robert Mondavi realized nobody was ordering Sauvignon Blanc in restaurants. He guessed Americans were afraid their tongues would cramp if they tried to pronounce the "gn" sound. (It's easy. Say "SOW vin yown.") Mondavi borrowed the phrase "Fumé," which the French town of Pouilly attaches to its name when distinguishing wines made of Sauvignon grapes from those made of Chasselas. Everybody loved saying "Fumé," and the wine started to move like herring at a sea lion bachelor party. Moreover, Sauvignon Blanc often does produce a "smokey" flavored wine.

Sauvignon Blanc from Sancerre, Pouilly's neighbor in the Loire Valley, was Marie Antoinette's favorite wine. Blended with Sémillon, Sauvignon Blanc also makes white wine from the aptly named Graves district in Bordeaux. When infected by the botrytis fungus, that same blend of grapes make Sauternes, the world's longest lived sweet white wine. Chile's best white is Sauvignon Blanc produced near Santiago.

Clusters of Sauvignon Blanc are small, conical and well-filled (not as tight as "compact"). Berries are medium-sized, oval and covered with a heavy waxy coating (called bloom) which makes them look somewhat smokey. The skin of the berry is of medium thickness, and the pulp is resilient, which allows the grape to resist botrytis. Sémillon, being larger, softer and thin-skinned, is a more accomodating host for that fungus. Sauvignon Blanc is pale green when ripe; Sémillon is rich yellow with a pinkish tint. Sauvignon Blanc ripens early in the season; Sémillon in the middle. Sauvignon Blanc is particularly subject to coulure, a condition where some portion of berries fail to form because of adverse conditions during flowering.

Sauvignon Blanc and Sémillon both grow with great vigor. They can produce 6-9 tons per acre in heavy clay soils. With more limited production, Sémillon will yield a soft, fig-like aroma. Sauvignon Blanc is the one receiving most of the viticultural attention however. It shares, with Cabernet Sauvignon and Bell peppers, a very distinct aromatic constituent called 2-methoxy-3-isobutylpyrazine. When under-ripe, i.e. in cold climates or when overcropped, this smell can be quite strong. You would probably call it "herbaceous" if you liked it. Otherwise you might say unkind things like "vegetal" or "canned asparagus." As the grapes get riper, this smell diminishes — first becoming "grassy," then "flinty," then "earthy" or "smokey." When very ripe, Sauvignon Blanc can take on a "spicey" or "melon" quality. Removing leaves in mid-season to allow more sunlight to penetrate the vine's canopy seems to be one way of reducing "grassy" character in Sauvignon Blanc.

◆ VITICULTURE

Sauvignon Blanc is an important varietal for California because examples from warm inland valleys have been winning worldwide competitions since the late 1800's. Sauvignon Blanc's naturally high acid and "green olive, herbaceous" aroma are attractively modulated by the increased ripeness that can be achieved in warmer climates.

Jean Wente (*The Book of California Wine*, U.C. Press 1984) unequivocally traces the origin of Sauvignon Blanc and Sémillon vines in California to cuttings brought by Charles Wetmore in 1878 from Ch.d'Yquem. Descendents of those vines, planted in Livermore Valley's El Mocho Vineyard, were distributed throughout California, and one of them became U.C. Davis's heat-treated clone No. 1 of Sauvignon Blanc.

◆ ENOLOGY

The climate and conditions in which Sauvignon Blanc grapes grow are much more important to the smell and taste of the wine than winemaker manipulations are. Sauvignon Blanc is a relatively simple wine to make. For that reason, it is a pretty reliable purchase if one doesn't know much about the wineries or brand names available.

Mechanical harvesting doesn't seem to degrade Sauvignon Blanc the way it can the more delicate varieties. However, it is an advantage to employ some technique to cull moldy bunches in case of rain during harvest. Chardonnay is hurt more by rain because every bunch is likely to be affected to some degree, but Chardonnay also ripens earlier. Sauvignon Blanc has a greater chance of being caught by rain, but it can be separated into clean versus questionable bunches if a winery is small enough to expend the time and effort.

Most Sauvignon Blanc is fermented in stainless steel tanks. Temperature control is not crucial because the characteristic "herbaceous" smell will not be significantly effected by the difference between fermenting at 50°F or at 65°F. Choice of yeast will contribute flavor notes, but they'll be subtle. Most winemakers inhibit malo-lactic fermentation, and the wine is rarely left on the lees.

At top quality wineries, some Sauvignon Blanc is barrel fermented. The usual technique is to let the tumultuous first phase of the fermentation subside in stainless steel tanks before putting the must into barrels at about 10°Brix. When barrel-fermented Sauvignon Blancs are released, they seem to have a mint overtone, but it fades after about six months. These higher priced wines are also likely to spend 3-6 months in small oak cooperage.

The most common manipulation practiced on Sauvignon Blanc is an adjustment of total acid and pH. In hot years, tartaric acid is usually added to lower pH. In some wines, pH moves in direct proportion to the amount of acid added. In other wines, huge amounts of acid addition are necessary before the pH begins to budge. Some Sauvignons throw protein sediments, or begin to take on slightly reddish color tinges if the pH ends up in a certain range. That is the reason big wineries usually heat stabilize Sauvignon Blancs by warming, and then filtering, them before bottling. There are no ideal numbers for acid and pH. Both have to be balanced with the flavor intensity and body of the wine. Lately, the alternative of leaving a few tenths of a percent residual sugar has also been tried.

Experience with a particular vineyard is the most valuable asset any winemaker producing Sauvignon Blanc can have. The wine's flavor profile is largely determined in the vineyard. Nuances of bouquet can add the complexity that makes a good wine into a great one, but they must be tailored to that particular wine's flavor profile. Acid, pH and alcohol (read body) can be balanced in the winery. It's always preferable though, to manage these characteristics in the vineyard and only fine tune them in the winery.

◆ STYLES

The distinctive flavor of Sauvignon Blanc is both an asset and a liability. It is easily recognizeable. People tend to have strong opinions about it. Like Polar bears, Sauvignon Blanc is ideally suited for certain situations and horribly inappropriate for others. Don't serve it at Thanksgiving if your mother-in-law only agrees to a glass of wine once a year to show you what a good sport she can be. Sauvignon Blanc can be produced for half the cost of Chardonnay. You must decide for yourself whether that improves, or besmirches, its image. At one end of the scale Sauvignon Blanc is the backbone of several excellent wines sold in large containers. From Mondavi's Bob White to Christian Brothers' Napa Fumé to Gallo, the wine is honest and cheap and widely available. Rumor has it that Mondavi crushes 15% of the Sauvignon Blanc grown in California. These are significantly better wines than you can get for a comparable price anywhere else in the world. It may not be art, but if we could build cars, TVs and stereos this well, America would not be a debtor nation.

At the other end of the scale, Sauvignon Blanc occasionally achieves brilliance. It catches your attention with the bold stroke, the massive element, the obvious difference. Then, it juxtaposes fine detail against this powerful first impression. Superb Sauvignon Blanc leaves you with a sense of unnatural restraint; Mike Tyson in lace underwear.

◇ **SHARP GREEN STYLE.** These Sauvignon Blancs will generally be the most acidic of white wines. As such, they are the perfect foil for strong flavored, oily fleshed seafood like salmon and oysters. Examples usually come from cool climates which, in California, means coastal vineyards. They present the "grassier" or "flintier" side of the varietal spectrum. These wines will quickly become the favorites of any militant vegetarians you know. They have enough acid to stand up to salad dressing, and they add whole new dimensions to sauteed zuchini or goat cheese. Anything herbed with cilantro, dill, basil or marjoram will be a marvelous match. Serve these wines cold so the "herbaceous" scent comes out slowly. Take two Rolaids prophylactically before bed.

◇ **SOFT EARTHY STYLE.** Techniques for muting the Bell pepper varietal character in Sauvignon Blanc include blending with Sémillon, harvesting riper low-tonnage grapes and introducing a lot of wood. Flavor descriptors range from "mushroom" to "melon." This style is heavier bodied than the one above. It matches up best with grilled fish, cheese sauces and bean or potato casseroles. Serve these wines just below room temperature. Try aging a few examples for 5 years to see if they gain complexity.

AROMATIC WHITES

J. RIESLING

RS

Several grapes produce distinctive scents as they ripen on the vine. The ability to preserve this fresh fruity smell over a period of years is one reason wine was considered magical throughout recorded history. Gewürztraminer, White Riesling and Muscat demonstrate this aromatic property clearly. All three share a common olfactory compound, a terpene named linalool. It is also found in melons and roses. Muscat has so much linalool scent that 10% Muscat added to an otherwise nondescript wine will create a passably counterfeit Riesling. There are different Muscat varieties, and each one makes up with intensity of aroma what it lacks in complexity of flavor. Many people find Muscat wines "grapey" instead of "vinous." It is an easy wine to like and often inexpensive. Spumantes from Asti in Northern Italy are widely known examples. More highly regarded are liqueured Muscats from Australia and fortified Setúbals from Portugal.

Gewürztraminer and White Riesling are probably native to foothills surrounding the Alps. The extraordinary cuisine of Alsace has surely developed with them in mind. Gewürztraminer is the easiest of the aromatic wines to identify, although few Americans will risk trying to pronounce it in public. (Just say "guh VERTS trah mean her"). Its scent is usually called "floral," as opposed to "fruity."

Using "Johannisberg" instead of "White" as a proper noun to qualify the greatest of several varieties called Riesling commemorates an area along Germany's Rhine River which made the grape famous. Legend has it that Charlemagne noticed a hill on the north side of the river where snow first melted in the spring. He decreed a vineyard should be planted there. Benedictine monks dedicated their monastery on that hill to John the Baptist at the end of the eleventh century.

◆ VITICULTURE

Gewürztraminer is a particularly pungent strain of the vine family called Traminer. "Gewürz" is German for "spicey." This selected clone is a shy bearing variety of early budbreak which ripens early in the season. Clusters are small, conical and compact. Berries are small, oval and pink colored with thick skins. Harvest timing is extremely important because the distinctive aroma develops rapidly. It will dissipate in a matter of days if temperatures are too hot. Cool climates produce the best wines. Botrytis occurs, but only irregularly. The berry's thick skin and early harvest date mitigate against noble rot. Tight little clusters and small berries, however, are easily destroyed by molds and ignoble rot if heavy rain should occur prior to the harvest.

White Riesling is a less delicate vine than Gewürztraminer. It grows with moderate vigor and will bear 6 tons per acre when encouraged to do so. Better wine is made though, from vines that struggle for survival. Along Germany's Mosel River that distinction is quite clear. The river runs north. Whenever it encounters extremely hard slate soils, it bends either to the west or the east. The deep, fast moving side of the river cuts steep, south facing precipaces north of the river. The slow moving, shallow eddies on the south side of the river create gradual slopes of deep residual soils. White Riesling grows in both places. It produces half as much crop on the steep, infertile rock north of the river. These wines, however, are vastly superior to those produced in the more hospitable soils on the south side of the river.

Clusters of White Riesling are small, winged and very compact. The berries are small, round, greenish-yellow and soft when ripe. It is easy to recognize White Riesling because the tender, but reasonably thick, skin is speckled with tiny cork-like openings called lenticels. This grape variety is a mid-season ripener. It produces its most aromatic results in cool climates, but it needs more sun than Gewürztraminer or Pinot Noir.

White Riesling is subject to a vast array of molds and fungi, including botrytis. California's arid climate helps retard the most malevolent ones. If two days of warm, wet weather (a tropical storm in September) is followed by a cool, dry breeze from the north, botrytis can form without interference from competitors. In less than two weeks the berries turn fuzzy purple-brown and shrivel. Acid, sugar and flavor are concentrated to as much as double their normal levels. The history of botrytized White Riesling in California only dates from 1973. Nevertheless, by 1978 California wineries had already produced wines surpassing the maximum sugar level ever reached in 200 years of German Trockenbeerenauslesen.

◆ ENOLOGY

Selective harvest of botrytized berries is labor intensive. Trained pickers go through the vineyard many times. Increased risk to the grapes from inclement weather, and the steepness of the vineyards, make German examples of this wine phenomenon much more expensive than their California counterparts. A large volume of these wines could be made in California if a market existed to buy them. The winemaking process, however, demands considerable expertise. Less than a dozen California vintners have experience with the specialized physical handling botrytized grapes require.

An important step in making aromatic white wine is to maintain grapes in pristine condition enroute to the winery. Picking at cool temperatures in the morning is desirable. So is picking into small containers so the weight of the grapes won't begin squashing fruit prematurely. Wineries located in close proximity to the vineyard have an added advantage. Historically SO_2 has kept grapes and juice from oxidizing between vine and crusher. However, many small wineries believe that SO_2 also binds up aromatic constituents molecularly. It has recently become popular to eschew SO_2 in favor of quick, cool, gentler handling of the grapes.

Aromatic compounds in all grapes collect in a mucilaginous layer between the skin and pulp. The scent of a wine can be greatly enhanced by a period of skin soak prior to fermentation. This technique is a delicate balance, especially with Gewürztraminer. If juice is left with these thick, reddish colored skins too long, it will become tinted and bitter. The contribution of skins to a wine's smell is amply demonstrated in Setúbal near Lisbon. Muscat is made and aged like Port there. Just before bottling, older barrel-aged wine is allowed to macerate with fresh skins from the new vintage. The results are spectacular.

Cold fermentations in jacketed stainless steel tanks have revolutionized aromatic white wines from California. This technology was pioneered in Germany. The equipment is expensive. California has been able to adopt these techniques more rapidly than many wine growing areas because of the large amounts of capital which have flowed into California's wine industry since 1970. Special strains of yeast, which ferment well at low temperature and favor production of fruity esters, have gone hand-in-hand with equipment for temperature control. Steinberger is the name of a current yeast favorite, and Wadenswill appears to be gaining adherents. Temperature controlled fermentations can be halted to leave residual sugar and keep alcohol levels low in delicately styled wines.

A second revolution has occurred in techniques which allow residual sugar to remain in bottled wine. Twenty years ago, the most common way to keep sweet wines from refermenting in the bottle was to add sorbate. You would recognize sorbate as a "bubblegum" smell. The only alternatives were to get the alcohol high enough to inhibit yeast activity, or to pasteurize the wine by heating it. Today, most aromatic whites are "sterile filtered," by passing them through a membrane with pores tight enough to remove all yeast cells. Winemakers may now choose to halt the fermentation with residual sugar left in the wine, or to employ the maté (sweet reserve) system. In the latter case a portion of unfermented juice is added back after the main portion has fermented all the way to dryness.

◆ STYLES

Residual sugar indicates the primary difference among aromatic white wine styles. Climate indicates a secondary point. Cold regions produce delicately scented wines; warmer regions give more luscious, intense examples. This is the same difference between Mosel wines (extremely cold) and Rheingau wines (merely cool) in Germany.

◇ **DRY.** This style has always been the forte of Germany and Alsace. Gewürztraminer is particularly attractive when made well in a dry style. Its flavor is much "spicier" than its nose, which would be better described as "perfumed." It also has a long, lingering finish. It matches up to a wide range of food with lightly barbequed curried chicken and any oriental pork dish being special treats. These wines are usually fine through about three years following the vintage.

◇ **MELLOW.** Most of California's aromatic whites have about 1.5% residual sugar. These are very pleasant wines for guzzling with bland cheese and volleyball on a summer's afternoon. Ladies of breeding may wish to sip them with fruit salads. Look for refreshing acidity and distinct aroma. Serve chilled to retain aroma throughout the time it takes to consume a glass. The freshest vintage from a cool growing year should be your choice.

◇ **SWEET and STICKIES.** This category is California's strongest. Good examples have some degree of botrytis. White Rieslings have an "apricot and honey" nose. Gewürztraminers smell of "lichee." The wines should be served cold, as dessert. Do not match them with chocolate. They are better with simple fare like melon, strawberries, vanilla ice cream or shortbread cookies. After five years of bottle age, the wines will lose fruitiness but gain complexity. Look for good acid levels. Beware examples which become dark and start to brown after just a few years. No California examples to date have improved past their tenth birthday.

ZINFANDEL

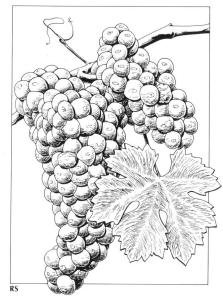

RS

There can be little debate as to which grape variety is most unique to California. Zinfandel sports one hundred years of noteworthy commercial success. Virtually every vineyard producing in the state today with vines over 50 years old is a Zinfandel vineyard. At least eight different styles of wine are made from Zinfandel grapes. Forty-year-old bottles of Zinfandel have been favorably compared to great Bordeaux and Burgundy growths. Zinfandel's origins have the surreal quality of mystery and legend wrapped up together. And finally, nobody else makes it.

California named Zinfandel, gave it a home and established its reputation. California is Zinfandel's mother. The father is unknown. Several scholarly papers have attempted to trace Zinfandel's route to prominence in California. Unfortunately they all tend to disagree with each other. It has been conclusively shown that Zinfandel and the Primitivo di Gioia from southern Italy are the same grape. Nursery records from New England, however, described "Zinfindel" and "Black Zinfardel of Hungary" in the 1830s. Anecdotal evidence indicates that Primitivo came to southern Italy after the phylloxera epidemic of the 1870s. Agoston Harazthy is often given credit for distributing Zinfandel throughout California, but that is one of the few viticultural distinctions he never claimed for himself.

Regardless of its origin, Zinfandel blossomed in the hills of California. As Chardonnay and Cabernet have increased their California acreage ten fold since 1970, red Zinfandel has paid for their popularity. To a purist, White Zinfandel is the variety's revenge. Since 1982 the price of Zinfandel grapes has risen 400%. Growers can not help but giggle when they read of wineries being investigated by the government for surreptitiously extending their White Zinfandel with juice from other varieties. In the early '80s Zinfandel vineyards were being grafted to Cabernet and Sauvignon Blanc. Today those same vineyards are being grafted back to Zinfandel.

♦ VITICULTURE

Although only a moderately vigorous vine, Zinfandel is a heavy producer. It will dependably crop 10 tons per acre in deep fertile soils. The cluster is medium to large, cylindrical, doubly winged and compact to the point of distorting berry shape. Budbreak is late and ripeness occurs unevenly from mid to late season. It is common for green berries and raisins to occur on the same cluster. Zinfandel sets a heavy second crop which ripens several weeks after the first. This uneven ripeness can surprise winemakers. They all have a story about bringing in a load of Zin, testing the sugar at 24°Brix and beginning the fermentation. Next day they return expecting the sugar to have dropped below 20°. When the hydrometer reads 26°, they don't know whether to phone their psychiatrist or turn a hose on the fermentation vat. What has happened is a release of sugar previously bound up in the raisined fruit.

Zinfandel berries are oversized, soft and thin-skinned. There is a rust colored scar at the apex opposite the stem. Large, thin-skinned, pulpy berries and a big, tightly packed cluster and late-season ripening are recipes for bunch rot. If the vine absorbs too much water from the ground after a rain, the berries will swell and some will burst. The cluster will ferment from the inside out while still on the vine. That is one reason third-generation Italian winegrowers in California swear by hillside planting for Zinfandel. Good drainage is essential for consistent quality.

Vine age also plays a much more decisive role in Zinfandel quality than it does in other varieties. Vines over 40 years old rarely produce more than 2 tons per acre. Berries are smaller. Clusters are numerous, but smaller in size and less tightly filled. Since the vines in these old vineyards are usually head pruned, the fruit is protected from sunburn by an umbrella-like canopy. Working on hillsides with head pruned vines pretty much dictates that all labor must be performed by hand. It would be prudent to cluster thin in mid summer, and then harvest the grapes on three separate occasions to get uniform ripeness. None of these points is calculated to warm the heart of a winery's banker. Growing grapes this way to make wine which sells for less than $10 a bottle ought to be considered a charitable donation. Large, corporate wineries can't do it. Remnants of old Zinfandel vineyards are a national artistic treasure. California's micro-wineries are the stewards of this resource.

◆ ENOLOGY

Red Zinfandel is generally fermented in open vats. Temperatures usually range from high 80s°F to low 90s°F. Skins which are punched down frequently will give heavier bodied wines. Fermentation rarely lasts more than 7 days. However, the fermentation tank may be covered (trapping CO_2 in the head space), allowing the skins to sink into the wine for an additional few days, or weeks. At least one small winery that makes White Zin uses the skins of those grapes to enhance their regular Zinfandel fermentation. Red Zinfandels of any style heavier than a Beaujolais-type almost always go through malo-lactic fermentation.

Choice of yeast is not a major topic among makers of Zinfandel. Although recently, a select strain isolated from the bloom on grapes in York Creek Vyd has been marketed. It is said to enhance fruitiness in the wine. Several small wineries ferment with the entire population of wild yeasts found on their grapes. This technique is generally considered to be a risk which can only be taken with limited quantities. It is also safer if the grapes come from an older vineyard with an established and relatively static microflora. Both of these criteria suit micro-wineries perfectly. The upside is increased complexity and intensity from the nose of the wine. Volatile acidity is the most pedestrian of several possible downsides.

Many of the old Zinfandel vineyards in California are promiscuously interplanted with other red varieties. This practice begat the rather punchy phrase "Dago Red." The least complimentary connotations of that generic label derive more from primitive barrel aging technique than from the quality of the Zinfandel grapes that went into the wine. Traditional Italian winegrowers, who maintained these vineyards from Prohibition until the late '60s, often employed 300 gallon oak or redwood storage vats that their "grandfather bought used." Today, most of the winemakers who vinify these old Zinfandel grapes use 52 gallon American oak cooperage.

A second variety often found in these vineyards is Petite Sirah; called "Petty Sarah" by the locals and spelled Petit Syrah by macho marketeers. Zinfandels with 5-20% Petite Sirah are darker in color, and they may acquire fruit or "pepper" nuances depending on where the grapes are grown. Paul Draper at Ridge Vineyards considers the Petite Sirah component to be an aid to longevity.

◆ STYLES

Zinfandel juice fermented only after being pressed off the skins makes the immensely popular White Zin. A little time with the skins will produce a "blush" wine. Fruity smell is the goal and acid/residual sugar balance is the most distinguishing characteristic. Trying to tell White Zins apart is sometimes like trying to determine the sex of whales from the shoreline. A nouveau wine can be made using the whole-berry fermentation technique called "maceration carbonique." Port is also made rather successfully from very ripe Zinfandel grapes. Red Zin normally falls into three styles that are not so much curiosity items.

◇ **CLARET.** More acid, lighter body and less tannin are the hallmarks of a style which has become widespread as a reaction to the ponderous Zinfandels of the '70s. The goal is a more elegant, table wine. Often the elegance comes from aging in good cooperage, and the characteristic "raspberry" aroma of the grape is de-emphasized. It is a common belief that Zinfandel grapes must get at least as ripe as 23.5°Brix to develop that smell dramatically. Some micro-wineries pick Zinfandel at three different levels of ripeness to blend crisper, more acidic juice with riper, more aromatic juice. These wines are a relatively new phenomenon. They may age quite well because of their lower pH levels. Any pleasure derived from a fresh, "berrry" aroma will be best enjoyed between ages 2 and 4. In years 5 through 7 the bouquet takes the forefront, and even expert judges have a hard time distinguishing them from Cabernets.

◇ **GUTSY.** When all the grapes are picked above 23.5°Brix, and the wine is left on the skins after the completion of fermentation, a more traditional style of Zinfandel is made. These wines are more voluptuously fruity when young, but also more tannic with higher alcohol levels. Matched to spicey cuisine, they can be a hearty restorative on cold days. Think BBQ ribs or anything Korean. The tannic bite will start to diminish when the wines are around 4 years old. Between age 4 and 6, this style of Zinfandel can be marvelous. The best ones will still have a round, berry character, but it will be enhanced by a smooth mouth-feel and "mushroom" (*Boletus edulis*) bouquet. Any of these style Zinfandels which continue to improve after age 6 are exceptional wines indeed.

◇ **LATE HARVEST.** A very unique style of Zinfandel results from grapes riper than 27°Brix. Old clone, dry farmed, ancient vines will occasionally get that ripe, or riper, while retaining at least .8% acid. If they haven't ripened slowly enough to retain good acid, raisin smells will often degrade the wine. Top examples of this style, however, may be redolent of a "bramble berry" nose into their second decade. These wines often have 16% alcohol and a few points of residual sugar left over after the yeast gave up. They can be "jammy" mouthfuls best suited to nuts, strong cheese, late night philosophizing, and even chocolate.

PINOT NOIR

RS

Few grape varieties excite as much impractical emotion as Pinot Noir. It is impossible to describe accurately. It changes in the bottle from month to month. It is a difficult vine to grow and a more difficult wine to make well. So why does everyone try to do it?

Money is one reason. French red Burgundy sells for $40 a bottle if it is even passably good quality. Great Burgundy sells for several hundred dollars a bottle. There is many times more Bordeaux wine made than Burgundy in an average vintage. Bordeaux prices respond, albeit reluctantly, to market pressure. Burgundy prices do not. If U.S. importers balk at a price increase, Belgium or Germany will be delighted (and quite capable) to pick up the slack.

If you have the cash, you can always buy a good Bordeaux with confidence. Burgundy is a much more dicey proposition. You can pay exhorbitant amounts for bottles of Burgundy only to end up wondering what all the fuss is about. A venerable English writer once said a person should consider themselves lucky if they got to taste five magnificent red Burgundies in their lifetime. He added that these people were also likely to have been in the trade.

American winemakers realize the honor and reward which will come to producers of any creditable $15 Pinot Noir. They also realize the marvelously unique role Pinot Noir can play in the panoply of wine. It has a feline grace; languid, sensuous and utterly captivating. No other red wine has Pinot Noir's ability to insinuate itself effortlessly into an embrace, much the same way cats end up on your lap. It is a challenge to make good Pinot Noir. California winemakers, lacking the roots of tradition, have a hard time resisting this quest for the Holy Grail.

The legendary stature of red Burgundy goes back centuries. However, in 1973 the O.P.E.C. oil cartel caused an overnight, worldwide jump in interest rates and inflation. It became prohibitively expensive for wineries to cellar wines very long before release. The style of Burgundy began to change. Today it is nearly impossible to find red Burgundies made in the same manner as those wines, from the middle of this century, whose memory fuels the legend so adroitly.

California Pinot Noirs have suffered a tremendous amount of bad press. That may be fairly explained by the fact that 9,500 acres of the 10,000 planted in California are located in the wrong climatic regions. The special character of Pinot Noir is lost in hot, dry growing conditions. Going back to Ambassador Zellerbach (Hanzell Winery) in the late '50s, there have always been a couple of outstanding Pinot Noir producers in California, but their success was completely overshadowed by the much larger volume of mediocre wines. During the '80s this story has begun to change. Some fifteen California wineries have received enthusiastic critical acclaim covering several vintages. It is noteworthy that most of these ascendant winemakers are using grapes from newer vineyards growing in the less frequently reviewed regions along California's coastline.

◆ VITICULTURE

Pinot Noir is a delicate vine which genetically adapts rather rapidly to its environment. A large number of clones have been identified. One of these clones is characterized by an upright growing posture, small brown pips (seeds), and a light "cherry" aroma. This clone is numbered 105 by U.C. Davis and called Gamay Beaujolais throughout California. Other clones, more closely related to the Pinot Noir which makes expensive red Burgundy, have small pips, a drooping posture and a more concentrated "blackberry" aroma. All the clones so far described here have small berries, bud early in the spring and ripen early during the harvest season. A different variety is grown in the Beaujolais region of France where it is called Gamay noir jus blanc. This grape has bigger, pulpier berries and a later ripening cycle. It is called Napa Gamay in California.

Limestone soil is considered a key to success in the thin, 40 mile long strip of hillside along Burgundy's Côte d'Or. Of course, Burgundy is 10° latitude further north than San Francisco, and likely to get summer precipitation. Have you ever noticed how many rain delays there are during the Wimbledon tennis matches? Success in Burgundy is directly related to how ripe the grapes get. Limestone is a porous soil. Good drainage speeds ripening by reducing water available to the vine for growth of wood and leaves. California has an entirely different set of water and temperature conditions. It remains to be seen what role limestone soils may play with California Pinot Noir.

Because of its early budbreak, Pinot Noir is very susceptible to spring frost. It is not a heavy producer anyway. Clusters are small, cylindrical, winged and compact. Berries are slightly oval, blue-black in color, thick-skinned and heavily covered with bloom. Cool vintages in California always result in better wines, and it is highly uncommon for rain to occur before harvest.

◆ ENOLOGY

Pinot Noir is a difficult wine to make. There are many options, which in turn lead to frequent second guessing as the wine changes dramatically over its lifespan. The task is how to marry all the components together. Pinot Noir should leave a soothing impression. The nose and aftertaste can be intense, but they should be characterized by an expansive softness rather than busy complexity. If Cabernet could be described as a witty argument, Pinot Noir would be a pillow fight.

One technique thought to enhance fruitiness is whole-berry fermentation. By not crushing the berries completely, anaerobic fermentation is said to take place in the cells, releasing color but not extracting as much tannin. Most small wineries approximate this technique by adjusting their crusher to a wide setting and thus letting some percentage of berries pass through intact.

To increase body, many wineries take a cue from Burgundian winemakers and throw some percentage of stems into the fermenting vat with the juice and berries. This idea is controversial in California. Winemakers who have participated in the crush in Burgundy point out that stems there have usually turned brown and started to lignify as growers water stress the vines to speed ripening. Pinot Noir grapes in California, at least those from irrigated vineyards, tend to have green stems with a bitter, sappy taste. Big California wineries also have a disturbing habit of chopping stems up before putting them in the fermenting vat so they can empty the tank through 2" diameter transfer lines. Either way, nobody has a technique for taking the stems back out prior to pressing the skins. Tannin forced from green stems along with the last bit of press wine is going to be rather extreme.

In order to get more color in Pinot Noir, California winemakers generally go with higher fermentation temperatures. Since the early '70s, the temperature peak of choice has risen from 75°F to well over 90°F. At 90°F fermentation proceeds quickly. Whole berries are one way to slow it down. Assmanshausen yeast is a German strain used there to ferment Spätburgunder, their name for Pinot Noir. As a notoriously slow fermenter, Assmanshausen is gaining popularity in California. Leaving Pinot Noir on the skins after the end of fermentation is another way to get color extraction.

Microbiology also plays a crucial role in Pinot Noir's development. It is no accident that France's best red Burgundy vineyards jealously guard their indigenous wild yeast strains. Small amounts of apiculate yeasts add considerable smell to any wine, but they show more clearly against the velvet backdrop of Pinot Noir fruit. Malo-lactic fermentation often proceeds slowly in Pinot Noir entraining extra amounts of its flavorful by-products in the finished wine. These components (along with lees contact) help to produce the "oriental tea," or "roasting meat," or "aged leather" descriptors so often applied to fine Pinot Noir.

Pinot Noir usually spends a year in small oak cooperage. Winemakers are more apt to underplay the oak in Pinot Noir than they would be in other red varieties. If additional complexity is desired, stirring up the lees is a more likely answer than additional time in new barrels. French oak is almost always the choice. Limousin is no more popular than Center of France oak, and four different coopers apparently split the California market.

Fining and filtration are additional points of debate around Pinot Noir. The variety is not very colorfast. It tends to throw pigment and other sediment in the bottle. This bothers fastidious, somewhat naive, Americans. Most large wineries filter their Pinot Noir into submission. Micro-vintners, who have more rapport with their clientel, cite the subtleties of Pinot Noir and express concern over what may be lost in the filtration process. These winemakers are likely to minimize rackings of the wine. They use one or two egg whites per barrel for fining and eschew extensive filtration. Large wineries call this attitude "living dangerously" because of the potential for haze in the wine or bacterial spoilage. Micro-vintners reply that they have their nose in every barrel every month, thereby planning to catch any problem before it has a chance to become serious.

◆ STYLES

Light color is a reliable way to identify Pinot Noir among a group of red wines. Pinot Noir grapes do not have all the anthocyanin pigments found in other red varieties. For that reason, depth of color is not a reliable indicator of flavor or smell intensity in Pinot Noir. Although it is true that hot growing conditions will tend to lighten the color, California winemakers who struggle for dark color often end up making needlessly awkward wines. Lightly tinted examples have been known to yield extraordinarily intense bouquet well after their tenth birthdays.

Slow maturation in cool growing conditions seems to enhance the aroma of Pinot Noir which can range from "strawberry" to "boysenberry." This key feature is an excellent quality indicator for California examples because it is so often missing from grapes grown in hot climates. The aroma has a tendency to disappear after 2 or 3 years in the bottle. At that point the wine seems to have been struck dumb. Then the bouquet starts to develop. It expands to give the wine a second, rather different, personality from age 5 to 8. This two phase life cycle is more pronounced in Pinot Noir than in other wines. Low natural acidity is a common fault in California, and the Pinot Noirs most likely to blossom after extended cellar age are those which have crisp definition when young.

A classic food to pair with Pinot Noir is duck. The meat (never mind the skin) is quite flavorful because of its fat content. White wines are generally overmatched in this comparison, but Pinot Noir shines. The easiest way to try this combination is to serve duck sausage or duck pat. Another taste treat is Pinot Noir with mushroom soup, or mushrooms in puff pastry. In both cases the richness of the food compliments the soft delicacy which distinquishes Pinot Noir from its red wine competitors.

◇ **BURGUNDIAN.** Critics who are inclined to congratulate a California Pinot Noir maker will often refer to a wine's "Burgundian" style. Then they will drop a few French vineyard names to limber up their accent and confirm their credentials. No concensus exists on what characteristics define how the phrase "Burgundian" is applied. Distinct aroma, refreshing acid levels and noticeable microbiological smells seem to be the traits most often cited as reflecting Old World charm.

In California such wines tend to come from the coolest vineyards. Grapes are on the vines for a longer period, but the sugar at harvest is rarely as high as 23.5°Brix and the pH in the finished wine stays at 3.45 or below. Fermentations may include whole berries, but stems rarely play a major role. The wine is removed from the skins at dryness. Time on the lees, or the completion of malo-lactic fermentation, may be extended for months in what Californians call "the filthy French technique." A prominent British authority on Burgundies once said, ". . .the great ones smell of shit." He was, in all likelihood, refering to the myriad smells which come from trace by-products of microbiological activity. Small amounts of H_2S generated by strains of yeast like Montrachet can make a contribution. So can limited activity on the part of Brettanomyces, a surface yeast. All these additions to bouquet are welcome at levels below an individual's recognition threshold. If their identity becomes too obvious, a wine is usually considered to be flawed.

Pinot Noirs of this Burgundian style are superbly matched to veal with almost any type of rich sauce.

◇ **CALIFORNIAN.** A second style is more aggressive, more frequently encountered, and more difficult to identify as Pinot Noir. It should not be compared to its French patronym. It should be allowed to stand on its merits as California red wine. This style is more "earthy," more darkly colored and heavier-bodied. It often has higher pH and tends to develop bouquet at a faster pace in the bottle. It often involves greater use of stems and/or longer "vatting," i.e. time on the skins after the end of fermentation.

This style does not have a pre-existing fan club. A generation of wine drinkers will have to be shown good times with these wines before a constituency arises. The Carneros Alliance, a group of Pinot Noir makers from southern Napa, may be just the group to do it too. These Pinot Noirs, however, are excellent choices with beef prime rib and pork tenderloin. These wines have all the advantages of assertive, California style, but a softer, more feminine edge than Cabernet or Zinfandel. They always remind me of Angie Dickinson acting in some police story. They may be perfectly styled for the '90s. Interestingly, the most favorably reviewed vintage in the history of Oregon Pinot Noir, 1985, was an abnormally warm and dry year there. It produced ripe, extractive, full-bodied wines which are very much in this California style. A more typical vintage in Oregon would tend toward the lighter style described above.

BORDEAUX VARIETIES

CABERNET SAUVIGNON   RS

Until the middle of the '80s, this section would have been titled Cabernet Sauvignon. The '70s were a decade when California Cabernets truly achieved status comparable to their Old World counterparts. Dilettantes now drop brand names of well publicized California Cabernets with the same aplomb they had previously reserved for famous French Châteaux. As a patriot, I would like to confer a uniquely Californian title on this section and not resort to a foreign geographical reference. Cabernet Sauvignon almost accomplishes that feat. Since the French don't use grape variety names very much, California has just about co-opted that title as its own.

My purpose, however, is not to crow about the past. This book is designed to share the excitement of the present, and to begin looking at the future. Cabernet Sauvignon has been the California wine industry's greatest artistic success. There are many winners currently being elevated to icon status. Great, but what's next? The answer is that California's most progressive vintners are looking to borrow clues from the history of Bordeaux in order to continue improving California's best wines.

John Hart, owner of the Chicago Wine Company, made a rather guileless remark in 1986 while sitting on a panel to discuss the relative aging capacity of Cabernets from around the world. John has a lot of experience with older wines because his company conducts auctions. John opined that California Cabernets rarely improve much beyond 10 or 12 years in the bottle the way Bordeaux reds do. The outrage among California advocates was predictable, immediate and vicious. It was as if John had entered a bar in Norman, Oklahoma wearing "Hook 'em, Horns" regalia. John could have side-stepped all the woofing, and made much the same point, by stating that California Cabernets are better than Bordeaux reds when both are 8 years old. John is not a salesman for the EEC versus the USA. He merely recognizes that the wines are different, and that they should be judged on separate scales.

Winemakers, as opposed to wine marketers, have recognized the same thing for fifteen years. Experimenting with adaptations of traditional Bordelais practices in California vineyards will **not** produce Bordeaux wines. But it may reveal some promising styles for California vintners to develop on their own. That is why, on Cabernet Sauvignon, California is reversing the varietal label trend it pioneered after Prohibition. California is well along the road of expanding the Cabernet Sauvignon concept to include other grapes like Merlot and Cabernet Franc. As a group this selection of varieties, popularized in Bordeaux, is very successful worldwide. It makes the best red wines of Chile and, arguably, the best of Australia. In Spain and Italy, its use is being expanded to give exciting new facets to those traditional industries.

In Bordeaux, soil and vineyard location have always been the primary consideration. Grape varieties were chosen later to match the growing conditions. Out of the 27 red varieties planted at various times in Bordeaux, Cabernet Sauvignon must have been considered quite useful for its late budbreak and its relative hardiness in wet harvest situations. Merlot would be a desireable vineyard companion to Cabernet Sauvignon because it produces larger crops, and it ripens earlier to provide fruit and alcohol in difficult years. Today the vineyard mixes around Paulliac average 75% Cabernet Sauvignon; in Graves they are 50%; in Pomerol and St. Emilion they are less than 30%.

Great Britain played an enormous role in defining the Bordeaux wine trade. The British attitude was surely influenced by their proximity to the producers. A squire in Yorkshire had to plan his purchases from Bordeaux to fit into cost-efficient loads for transportation. The historic British market needed wines which could be laid down for long periods of time. Cabernet Sauvignon is that wine. The value of Cabernet Sauvignon does not lie in its aroma. The fermented juice is barely important. Cabernet Sauvignon is fermented skins, and barrel aging. The result is usually bitter with tannin when it is young. Gradual oxidation (through the barrel and then more slowly in the bottle) is necessary to bind up the tannins and soften the wine. That is when Cabernet blooms. The wine is transformed with flavor and bouquet not present in its youth.

Winewright's membership organization bears many similarities to the historic British marketplace. Members who order the acquisition of wines through Winewrights must wait several weeks before they can take possession. If they want a bottle to drink that evening, they go to their cellar. About 40% of the wine bought through Winewrights is Cabernet Sauvignon.

◆ VITICULTURE

Cabernet Sauvignon is a vigorous vine, but a small producer. The clusters are small, conical and loosely-filled. These scraggly clusters dry out easily if they get wet. Berries are small, hard and round with large pips. The skin is thick, with lots of black pigment. Tough stems must be cut from the vine. The consistency of the stem also seems to reduce water uptake during fall rains.

Merlot is a only a moderately vigorous vine, but it is a prolific producer. If not severely pruned, it will set 8-9 tons per acre. The clusters are medium sized, conical and fairly loose. Berries are medium sized, oval, thick-skinned and heavily pigmented with a blue-black color. Merlot buds early and ripens mid-season.

Cabernet Franc is called the Breton in France's Loire Valley where it makes the perfumey, "berry" or "violet" scented red wines of Chinon and Bourgueil. It is a vigorous vine and fairly productive. Clusters are small to medium, conical and loose. Berries are small to medium, round, blue-black and juicy. Budbreak and maturity are both mid-season.

Rootstocks, access to water, pruning and virus are all ways that vine vigor can be controlled. Crop size will be a determinant of style as well as affecting the dominant aromatic character of these grapes. All three varieties tend to have "vegetive" smells when they are overcropped. Merlot seems to do best when it has access to plenty of water, but then has the crop reduced by other means. Cabernet Sauvignon can smell of Bell peppers if it doesn't ripen completely. Cabernet Franc will add a spicey component to its perfumed nose if crop size is restricted.

Various clones of Cabernet Sauvignon are identified in California. One distinguishing characteristic seems to be the range between "herbaceous" and "cassis" type aroma that they produce.

◆ ENOLOGY

Making wine from the Bordeaux family of grapes is a fairly straight forward proposition. In California, they are almost always fermented in open topped vats around 90°F and put through malo-lactic fermentation immediately. In Bordeaux, malo-lactic fermentation often concludes in the spring. In Australia, many of these wines do not go through malo-lactic. Pasteur Red is a widely used yeast in California. The micro-vintners in this book choose between several yeast strains, but rarely considering it a major factor in the final product.

Time spent on the skins is an important variable though. The Bordelais "vat" their best wines for 2-4 weeks following the end of fermentation. In California some wines are removed from the skins just before the end of fermentation. Others are left with the skins for a few days. Some winemakers only press after the cap has sunk into the wine which takes a couple of weeks after the fermentation stops. It is very unusual for a California winery to leave wine on the skins as long as 4 weeks.

Barrel aging is the heart of development for these wines. They are usually not left on the lees. The type of oak and how new it is plays a central role in the bouquet. American oak is clearly different than Nevers. Some wineries use several different woods, which they feel adds complexity. Others seek a specific type of smell. Beaulieu Vineyards has a rabid following for the dominant American oak nose in their Georges de Latour Cabernet Sauvignon. Most wineries own a range of barrels from new to 5 or more years old. They move the wine around among the barrels based on how much oakiness it seems to be acquiring. How long the wine stays in small barrels depends on how rapidly the tannins begin to soften, and the length of this period helps determine the rate at which the wine will develop in the bottle.

The winemaker plays his most conspicuous role when he assembles the final wine. Samples from individual barrels can be wildly different. In addition, he may have barrel lots made from different grape varieties, vineyards, harvest dates and press fractions. There is always a financial motivation to combine everything in the high priced spread. On one hand, blending decisions involve artistry, experience and tasting ability. On the other hand, barrels not used in the blend may require considerable marketing skill to be used profitably. Deep pockets are the only substitute for cleverness and luck in this procedure.

The last decision a winemaker must factor into his/her overall plan is the amount of time the winery can afford to hold bottles prior to release. The logical interpretation of the title "Reserve" on a label is that the wine was on the skins longer than usual, in newer barrels for a longer time, and held by the winery for an extra period. However, this phrase is governed neither by law nor logic in California. The liberties taken with it would make a political press secretary blush. Small wineries often get a break on this subject of bottle aging wine before release. Their close relationship with customers allows these wineries to make wines for aging, but to pass the inventory burden along. Mass market wines need to be fairly drinkable at the point the average consumer gets a hold of them. Therefore, big wineries must either style their wines for early consumption, or have the financial ability to cellar them 4-5 years. Jordan Winery is a very successful example of how these two strategies can be combined for maximum impact at the restaurant level.

◆ STYLES

By itself, Merlot is more opulant with round, fruity smells than Cabernet Sauvignon. It is usually not as acidic either. It matures more quickly and usually shows a distinct bouquet by age 4. Alone, Cabernet Sauvignon is a more angular wine with backbone and palpable structure. Cabernet Franc has a fine nose and obvious flavor, but it is often a little short on the palate by itself. Malbec, another of the Bordeaux grape varieties, is a doughnut. Unblended, it has smell and finish, but not much in the middle.

The amount of Cabernet Sauvignon in any blend will generally determine which side of the soft-hard spectrum it lands on. California Cabernet Sauvignon could be recognized heretofore among wines from Bordeaux by its full-bodied, powerful, vertically integrated profile. The goal of blends is to retain this intensity while adding additional smells and flavors to broaden the profile horizontally.

◇ **LIGHTER BODIED.** When these grapes are grown in deep, clay soils without a conscious effort to restrain production, their intensity is greatly diminished. The smell of the wine is often described as "green olive." They can be vinified in a lighter, less tannic style for drinking between ages 3 and 6. This style of wine is less expensive for everybody. It fulfills its natural function as an accompaniment to barbequed hamburgers.

◇ **COOL CLIMATE.** The clearest difference between Bordeaux and California is the climate. In Bordeaux grapes may be physiologically mature at 22°Brix. In Napa, most winemakers think that point is reached at 23.5°Brix. Grapes grown in cool regions along California's coastline must restrict production and leave grapes on the vine for a long time. This style usually has less tannin, but more acid. Therefore, it seems sharp and "sinewy" compared to others. The best examples are complimented by a healthy dose of French oak. These wines age extremely well. They don't begin to show their "cigar box" bouquet until age 6. As long as the bouquet stays tightly wrapped, they are said to be "closed." Once the bouquet gets itself unleashed, they continue evolving additional smells for years. They never achieve the power or intensity of the styles which follow, but they make up for it with precision. Lamb is the ideal choice to pair with this style wine.

One word of caution. When a Cabernet Sauvignon has a dominant and persistent capiscum (Bell pepper) smell at age 3, it is likely to continue down that same path forever. Don't lay those wines away if you don't like the smell.

◇ **SUPPLE, FULL BODIED.** This style of wine comes from grapes that have ripened to full maturity without undue struggle for survival. The pH is often higher than other styles, which makes the tannin seem less astringent. These wines will be "forward," i.e. maturing at a rapid pace, in the hotter vintages. Depending on clones and growing region, the early smells can range from berry-like fruit to "pipe tobacco" complexity. If the grapes were deficient in acid at harvest, the nose may cross over into a "dusty" character. "Chocolate" is a descriptor that falls somewhere in between. The "dustier" the wine, the less likely it is to age for a long time. Some wines of this style are brilliant at age 3. If so, they will likely fade after age 8. Most are too big a mouthful to really enjoy until they reach age 5. Those are best at age 10, and exceptional examples will hang on for decades.

A sauce made from morel mushrooms can be a sensory overload when served on anything and joined by a well-aged example of this wine style. Venison is a great vehicle for both the sauce and the wine, but don't overcook the meat.

◇ **MOUNTAIN GROWN.** Bordeaux varieties grown in limited top soil with good drainage tend to make concentrated, square-jawed wines which require extensive bottle age. The best ones have so much flavor the winemaker can take several steps to lighten their load of tannin without diminishing their potential for development in the bottle at all. These wines often exhibit "tar-like" bouquet, explosive flavor and lingering aftertaste.

This style rarely shows much of the complexity of which it is capable before year 8. Some examples seem dried out and empty by the time they reach age 12, but others continue to expand in the bottle through age twenty. Wines of this genre are immensely enhanced by a grilled steak. They also respond well to bleu cheese.

REGIONALITY

Soil and climate are two major factors affecting grape vines. A controversy exists over the relative importance of these factors. Europeans hold the position that soil is the dominant factor determining quality. This view is understandable given a thousand years of history during which specific plots of ground consistently produced grapes more highly valued than those on neighboring plots. Since climatic conditions vary dramatically from year to year in Europe, it is easy to infer that consistently superior quality must be a function of soil.

Most American researchers insist that no minerals are transported from soil, through vines and into berries to act as flavoring material. Depth of top soil and its permeability are thought to be the features which have the greatest affect on grapes. Both these features influence how vigorously vines grow, which in turn affects flavor intensity and the ripeness that can be achieved during a given growing season. In regions with short growing seasons and summer rain, well-drained soil is necessary to ripen grapes adequately.

European labels accentuate the impression that location is crucial to quality and to the determination of taste characteristics. These labels often seem complex to Americans because of their emphasis on geographical names. One must remember a lot of proper nouns to recognize the difference between a vineyard, a village and an entire region. The person who made the wine is usually portrayed in a role secondary to the piece of ground which grew the grapes. One shortcoming of this system is the need to legislate who has the right to use particular place names. Blood has been spilled over this issue. In fact, the phrase "Bad laws make bad citizens" sprang from a fight over labelling regulations in Sauternes. When one looks at a French label, one is either expected to know what grapes are grown in that region, or to assume that taste differences have more to do with regionality than with grape varieties.

California labels have taken a different path. Early research at the University of California determined that top quality wines are grown on a wide range of soil types, but that different grape varieties respond better to particular climates. Prohibition, ironically, caused wide planting of mediocre wine grapes in California due to Eastern demand for grapes that looked good after a three day trip in a boxcar. Consequently, after Prohibition, University spokesmen promoted varietal labelling in an effort to increase planting of premium grape varieties. At the same time, post-Prohibition distribution systems in the U.S. favored an emphasis on "brand name" labels. Today, the result is a U.S. labelling system where regional considerations play a role secondary to that of the winery and the name of the grape variety.

Big wineries are the driving force behind any distribution system. Big growers, along with big wineries, are the most persistent lobbyists when labelling regulations are being considered. "Big" generally implies the blending of grapes grown in various soils and climates to achieve a "standardized" product which consumers expect to be identical from bottle to bottle, year to year. It is much easier to market wine that is the same all the time than it is to explain differences caused by weather or switching vineyards. Choosing sources each year to achieve this standardized blend is quite an art, but there isn't much profit in trying to explain this art to the average consumer.

Micro-wineries are the only alternative to this mass distribution model in the U.S. Their products usually come from single vineyards. In fact, their volume is often small enough to come from a specific soil type within one vineyard. The results are very distinctive taste characteristics in the wines, revealing differences which are due to climate and soil conditions. It is unlikely that every person will prefer every taste characteristic thus revealed, but the educational opportunity is unparalleled. Moreover, discriminating hobbyists soon learn to predict which soil and climatic conditions will produce the results they enjoy most. Once one has discovered the intensity of unique regional characteristics, it is hard to return to the bland treadmill of factory standards.

The following sections are an overview of the major, quality-wine growing regions in California. Please note the subject is vineyard location; not winery location. All wineries can, and big wineries usually do, buy grapes anywhere and transport them many hundreds of miles.

General California Growing Conditions

Overall, California has a Mediterranean climate with two seasons. Elevations under 4,000 feet usually experience four months of wet weather with some cold each winter starting in December. Spring is mild with occasional showers in March and April, followed by four months of arid heat. October and November are mild, with intermittent cloud cover and brief periods of rain. General humidity is low, and evening temperatures drop dramatically after hot summer days.

Average **temperature** does not vary as one travels north to south in California, as most people expect. Instead, temperatures vary considerably on a west-to-east axis because of the influence of the Pacific Ocean.

Vineyards in valleys that open to the ocean are much cooler than those further inland. Edna Valley on the San Luis Obispo coast does not have temperatures like Paso Robles 30 miles away. Similarly, the Anderson Valley, which opens to the Mendocino coast, is much cooler than Ukiah on the inland side of the mountains in Mendocino County. The Edna and Anderson valleys are alike in temperature, even though one is 400 miles north of the other. The Napa Valley gets warmer as you travel north away from San Pablo Bay. The Salinas Valley gets warmer as you travel south away from Monterey Bay.

Along the California coast warm, moist, tropical air collides with cold air from the Gulf of Alaska. The result is a weather pattern found few places on earth. One main characteristic is **fog.** Redwood trees survive in this region by condensing fog in their needles and dripping water to their roots throughout the otherwise dry summer months.

During late summer, when grapes are ripening, California's inland valleys heat up. Hot air rises. As it does, it sucks cooler, fog laden air in from the ocean. Fog often stays as cloud cover until mid-morning the next day, then burns off. Vineyards on opposite sides of the coastal mountains may have identical temperatures at 2 p.m. each day and seem equivalent for ripening grapes. However, the coast-side vineyard will often get six fewer hours a day of sunlight in August, because of fog cover. Fog comes off the ocean in a layer about 500 feet high. Fog rarely rises above 1,500 feet. Thus, vineyards over that elevation will get more sunshine than lower ones which face the maritime influence.

Frost is freezing air that settles into low areas. Mountain vineyards and those on hillsides rarely get frost damage, because the cold air flows downhill past the vines in a position too low to the ground to cause trouble. Vineyards near the ocean do not have frost problems because of the moderating influence of such a large body of water. Frost damage in California's inland valleys was common before big vineyards started using expensive overhead sprinklers for irrigation and frost protection. Many small vineyards are still vulnerable, and light frost damage in the spring can trim production as much as shoot thinning would.

Aspect refers to the direction a vineyard faces. The further away from the equator, the more important aspect becomes, since the sun's rays arrive at a more oblique angle. German vineyards are almost 15° latitude further north than California vineyards. German vineyards require a southern aspect to ripen grapes. California vineyards do not. However, aspect does play a role in how rapidly California grapes ripen.

Rain usually comes to California from the northwest, in a counterclockwise motion that cuts across the northern half of the state from west to east. North of San Francisco, rain is more frequent than in the south and more likely to begin early in the fall. Hurricanes occur in the Pacific off Mexico in September each year. Occasionally, one of these storms will push rain into California from the south, but this is rare. El Nino, an uncharacteristic warming of the ocean surface in 1982 and 1983, may have contributed to early rain arriving from the south in these years, just as it brought marlin to Monterey Bay and drove the calamari and salmon further north.

Clouds are cooled as they rise over mountains (4°F for each 1,000 feet). Moisture condenses and falls on higher elevations on the western side of California's coastal range. Locations to the east are often in a rain shadow.

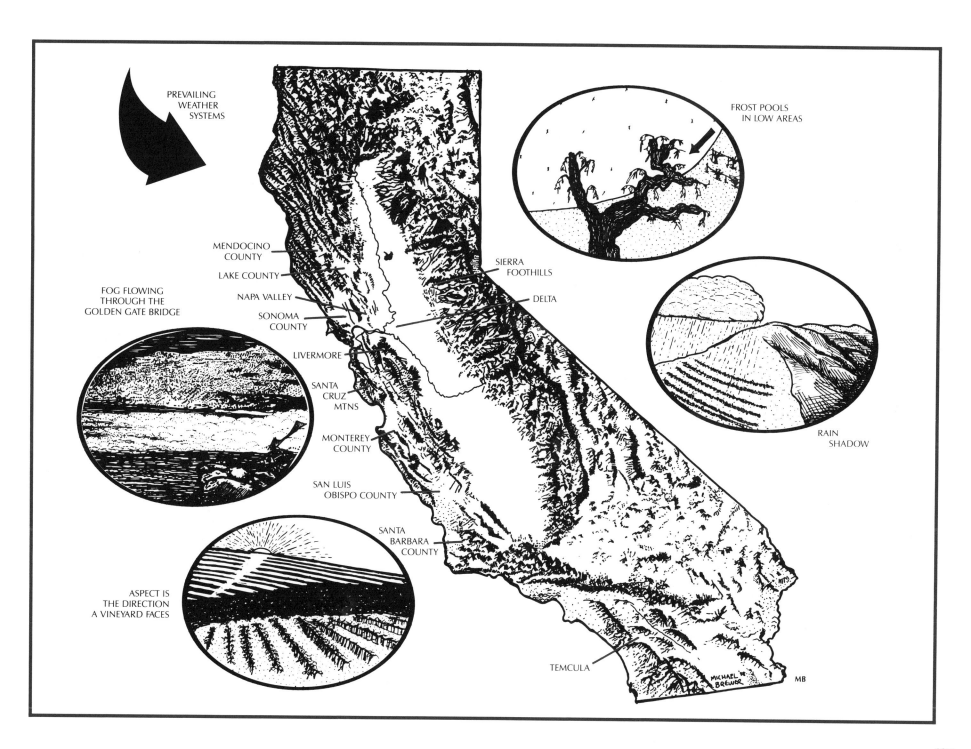

PREVAILING
WEATHER
SYSTEMS

FROST POOLS
IN LOW AREAS

FOG FLOWING
THROUGH THE
GOLDEN GATE BRIDGE

MENDOCINO
COUNTY

LAKE COUNTY

NAPA VALLEY

SONOMA
COUNTY

LIVERMORE

SANTA
CRUZ
MTNS

MONTEREY
COUNTY

SAN LUIS
OBISPO COUNTY

SANTA
BARBARA
COUNTY

SIERRA
FOOTHILLS

DELTA

RAIN
SHADOW

ASPECT IS
THE DIRECTION
A VINEYARD FACES

TEMCULA

MICHAEL
BREWER

MB

R. Wheele

MENDOCINO & LAKE COUNTIES

The social flavor of Mendocino is captured by sheepdog trials at the County Fair. An immediate impression is that it would be fun to have such a cute and competent "best friend" as one of these Border Collies. The truth is a little harsher. The dogs work because they like dominating sheep, not because they're desperate to please human beings. Mendocino is wild, and if you'll excuse the pun, woolly country. Weathered sheep fences are one of its most distinquishing features. There is a tourist trade, but no one moves to Mendocino for the thrill of catering to other people.

For a long time the lumber industry was the biggest employer in Mendocino. The Agricultural Commissioner now reports (unofficially) that high-grade Sensimilla (seedless marijuana) has replaced lumber as the most valuable crop in the County. Thousand-year-old redwood trees tower over surging ocean combers in the timeless battle of this fog shrouded shoreline. It is the primary abalone coast and a major supplier of Dungeness crab to San Francisco restaurants. A day at the beach in Mendocino implies a philosophical stroll looking for driftwood while wearing a heavy sweater. Any bikinis around will be encased in wetsuits.

As with many of California's coastal counties, Mendocino sports two rather different grape growing regions. The **Anderson Valley** is slightly west of the ridgecrest of the coastal mountains. It opens to the ocean along the Navarro River. This aspect makes it much cooler than the **Redwood** Valley which is on the inland side of the mountains near the city of Ukiah. Until recently, there were ten times as many grapes grown on the inland side of the mountains as there were in Anderson Valley. In 1983 France's Roederer Champagne house began planting hundreds of acres of grapes, which will probably double the Anderson Valley output.

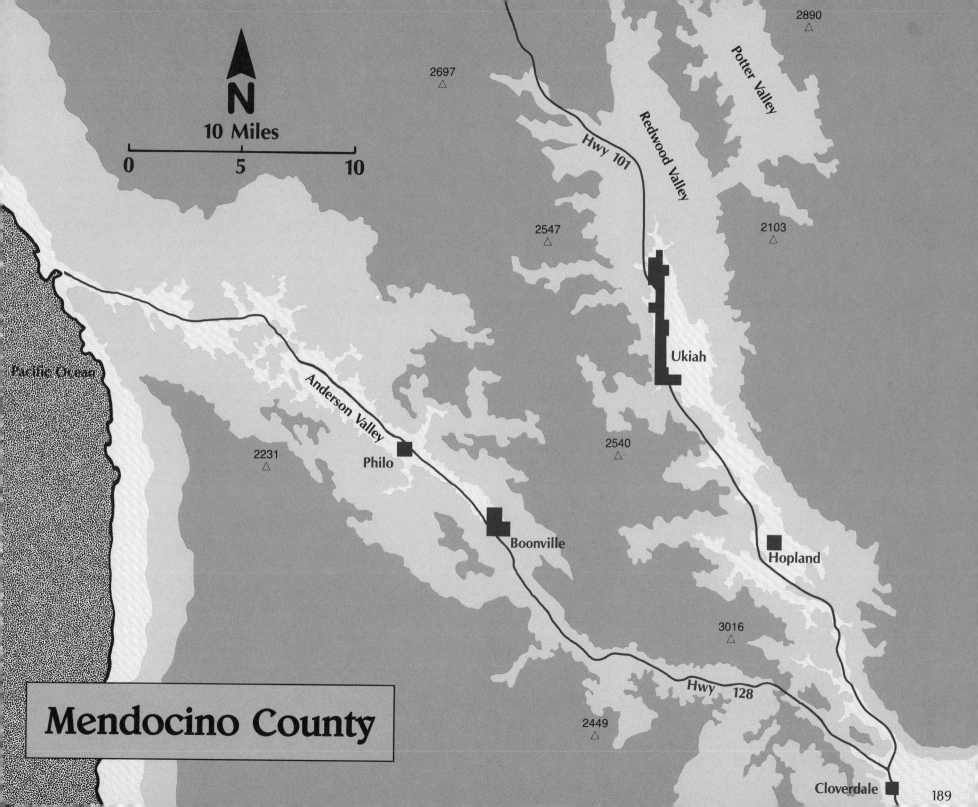

N

10 Miles

0   5   10

2890
△

Potter Valley

2697
△

Hwy 101

Redwood Valley

2547
△

2103
△

Ukiah

Pacific Ocean

Anderson Valley

2231
△

Philo

2540
△

Boonville

Hopland

3016
△

Hwy 128

2449
△

Mendocino County

Cloverdale

The towns of Philo and Boonville mark the center of the Anderson Valley as it runs northwest along Hwy 128. The southeastern edge of the valley floor is 1,300 feet above sea level while the northwestern extreme is about 800 feet. Fog comes up the Navarro River and moves into the valley several days each week during the summer. This slows ripening and benefits grapes like Pinot Noir and Gewürztraminer. White Riesling and Chardonnay grown in the valley have much more delicate aromas and much higher acid levels than their inland counterparts. Cabernet and Zinfandel are grown on hillsides above the valley where they will not be affected by the fog. Even so, cool breezes also slow the ripening process in Cab and Zin to produce much more austerely structured wines than those commonly found in California. Annual rainfall is high compared to other regions.

The inland side of the mountains is more easily accessible than the coastal side and therefore more agriculturally prominent. Hwy 101 follows the Russian River north out of Alexander Valley, through Hopland and past Ukiah. As is often the case, regional similarities overlap political boundaries. The northern halves of Alexander and Dry Creek valleys are in Sonoma County, but they generally share the climatic conditions of inland Mendocino County. The warm climate and rolling hillsides favor later ripening grapes. The Russian River has created benches of well-drained soil on which pioneer vineyards were planted to hearty red varieties before the turn of the century. The town of Asti (pop. 8), of which Pat Paulsen used to be mayor, was once the center of an immigrant community referred to as the Italian-Swiss Colony. Deposits from this community and the fishermen of San Francisco formed the backbone of a financial institution once called Bank of Italy, until it changed its name to Bank of America.

This whole region overlies a vast geothermal "reservoir." The Geysers are the world's most productive source of natural steam energy, and there are mineral hot springs all over. The A.M.A. discredited any therapeutic value from mineral baths in the 1920s in order to popularize new antibiotic drugs, but until that time 200 elegant spas flourished as destination resorts for health seekers from around the world.

Today, grape growing is an expanding industry. Urbanization in the counties bordering San Francisco Bay has driven many agricultural interests north to Mendocino and Lake Counties which are a 2-3 hour drive away.

Potter Valley is a mountain-enclosed region northeast of Ukiah in the Eel River watershed. Although mid-day temperatures can get rather warm, the elevation brings night-time temperatures down dramatically. Potter Valley is developing a noteworthy reputation for Riesling because the high water table produces a reliable environment for the formation of botrytis on the grapes at the end of the growing season. The beneficial aspects of botrytis have only been recognized in California since 1973.

Lake County sits to the east of viticultural regions which line Hwy 101 and the upper stretches of the Russian River. Temperatures may be moderated by Clear Lake, the largest body of water lying entirely within California's borders and the nation's finest bass lake, but not very much. It is a very warm climate. The social milieu is defined by power boat recreation and high stakes Indian bingo. Political sentiments and attire tend toward the cigarette-pack-rolled-at-the-shoulder end of the spectrum. Most vineyards are planted on the southwest corner of the lake, although some important ones have gone into the southern mountains which flank the road to Napa County.

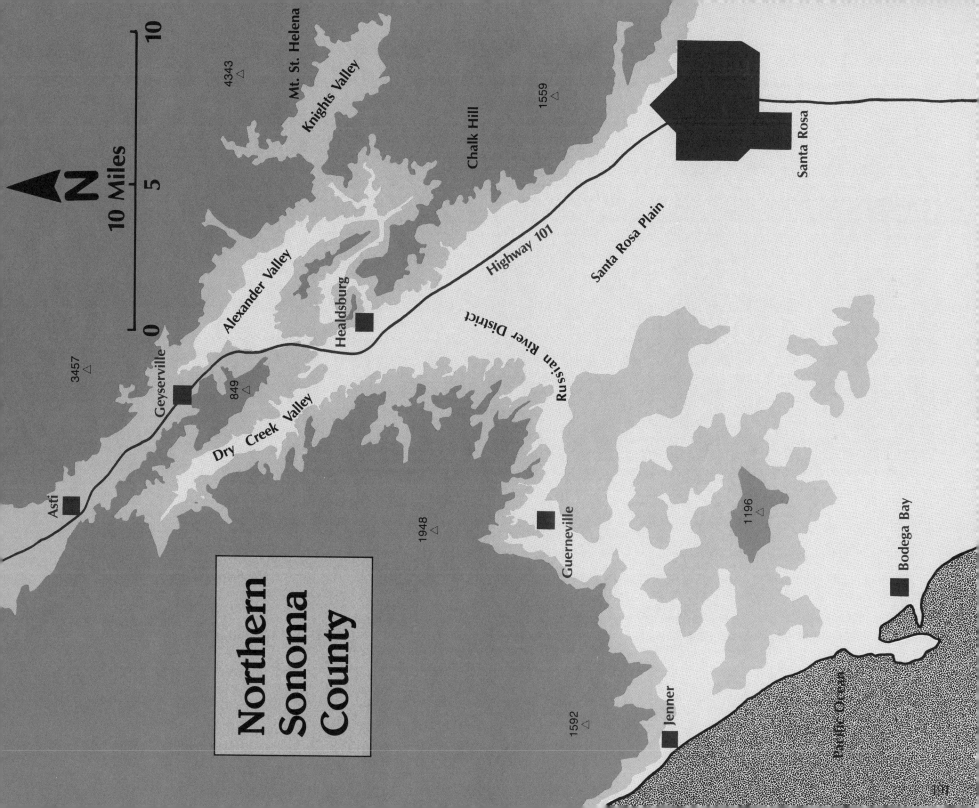

Northern Sonoma County

N

10 Miles

0   5   10

4343 △

Mt. St. Helena

Knights Valley

1559 △

Chalk Hill

Santa Rosa

Santa Rosa Plain

Highway 101

Alexander Valley

3457 △

Geyserville

Healdsburg

849 △

Dry Creek Valley

Russian River District

Asti

1948 △

Guerneville

1196 △

Bodega Bay

1592 △

Jenner

Pacific Ocean

R. Wheeler

Russian River and Jack London's Wolf House

SONOMA COUNTY

Considerable confusion results when consumers fail to draw any distinction between the town of Sonoma, Sonoma Valley and Sonoma County (listed here in descending order of precision). The town sits at the southern end of the valley, separated from San Francisco Bay by a series of pastures which were once salt marshes. The town is historically significant. It is where the U.S. stole California from Mexico just in time to reap the arguable benefits of the Gold Rush. More recently, Sonoma has been the headquarters of the Sebastiani saga. It may or may not have reflected the political mood of his constituents that Don Sebastiani was the only member of the California legislature in 1984 to vote against commending Sally Ride as the first American woman in space. "Its the principal of the thing," he said at the time.

Sonoma Valley, called Valley of the Moon by indigenous Indians, runs north in a tall triangle with its apex in the eastern suburbs of Santa Rosa, site of Luther Burbank's research. The valley is defined by the Mayacamas mountains on the east which separate it from Napa Valley, and Sonoma Mountain on the west which separates it from the rapidly urbanizing corridor along Hwy 101. Glen Ellen, where Jack London built his home, is about halfway up the valley. Low hills at Glen Ellen interrupt the cool breezes from the Bay leaving the northern half of the valley somewhat warmer than the south. Land prices in Sonoma Valley may soon preclude traditional agriculture in favor of small vineyards surrounding expensive houses. It is less than an hour commute to either San Francisco or Oakland, and the demand for weekend retreats far out-strips supply. There are many celebrity residents including the Smothers brothers and Mark Harmon.

One valuable resource of the Sonoma Valley is older vines. Several 80-year-old, dry-farmed Zinfandel vineyards struggle in the rocky, volcanic soil of the mountains. Intensely scented Cabernet is also a hallmark of these hills. Flinty Sauvignon Blanc thrives in the northern half of the valley floor, while full-bodied Chardonnay with a nose like Granny Smith apples can be found easily in the southern half.

Sonoma County encompasses all that has been mentioned above plus a whole lot more. The hub of these additional viticultural areas is the rather sleepy town of Healdsburg which lies some 15 miles north of the city of Santa Rosa. A rough grouping of these areas would include **Lower Alexander Valley** to the east of Healdsburg, **Dry Creek Valley** to the north, the traditional **Russian River District** to the west, and the so-called **Santa Rosa Plain** to the southwest. While Sonoma Valley receives most of its cooling influence from the south off San Francisco Bay, these other areas receive theirs from the Pacific Ocean to the west.

Lower Alexander Valley is the flood plain formed as the Russian River flows south past Geyserville, makes a U-turn upon confronting an amphitheater of low hills, then turns left to escape westward through a narrow gorge at Fitch Mountain. Healdsburg sits astride the river as it exits from the gorge. As you might imagine, Lower Alexander Valley features deep alluvial soil with plenty of ground water for vigorous vine growth. Botrytis can be found consistently. Cooling breezes must enter Alexander Valley through the hills that mark its southwestern boundary. Lower, or southern, Alexander Valley is cooler than Upper, or northern, Alexander Valley, but there is no clear line of demarcation. This situation is guaranteed to give promulgators of label regulations a severe headache sometime in the future.

All of Alexander Valley is warm compared to areas west of Healdsburg. If the vines do not overproduce, the wines will have a forward, ripe fruit quality that is attractive early. Sauvignon Blanc is more earthy than grassy. Chardonnay is fragrant in a peachy sort of way. Riesling is assertive in the manner that wines from the Rheingau compare to wines from the Mosel. Cabernet is particularly interesting for its chocolate overtones. Bottle aging Alexander Valley wines for an extended period of time is a dicey proposition, and totally unnecessary. Most of the vines in Lower Alexander Valley are situated on the valley floor. Planting in the area surged in the late '60s when Russ Green quit as head of Signal Oil to resurrect a historic local winery, which he renamed Simi.

The Dry Creek Valley runs south from where its namesake was dammed, producing Lake Sonoma, to a point near Healdsburg where the creek enters the Russian River. This north-south orientation results in much of the fog and cool weather from the coast blowing past the mouth of the valley without entering it. Dry Creek Valley is famous for raspberry scented Zinfandel and Graves-like Sauvignon Blanc. Soils range from steeply terraced red clay on the hillsides to sandy gravels near the creekbed. There are numerous older vineyards.

From the mouth of Dry Creek Valley at Healdsburg, the Russian River meanders westward toward the ocean 20 miles away at Jenner. Along the first several miles of this journey the river is bordered only on its north side by hills. Soon, however, these coastal hills extend 15 miles south of the river which winds its way in switchback fashion through them as it progresses steadily to the west. Fog creeps up the river from the coast all summer long and remains trapped in these S-curves several hours longer than it does in the flatter Santa Rosa Plain. This phenomenon explains the prevalence of redwood trees along the river as well as the unique characteristics of what is informally called the Russian River District. The temperatures are cool by California standards and the hours of sunshine are low. Several recent Pinot Noirs have been stunning.

Along this stretch of river it is common to find three different soil profiles in very close proximity. The bottomland will have deep soils and the coolest temperatures. The hillsides are often composed of well-drained benchlands and have more moderate temperatures. The hilltops have meager soil and the warmest temperatures. There are many older vineyards. Sauvignon Blanc is often aggressively grassy on the model of French Sancerres. Zinfandel, Petite Sirah and the Bordeaux varieties do best at the higher elevations.

The largest viticultural area in Sonoma County is loosely referred to as the Santa Rosa Plain. It runs from the hills just east of Santa Rosa across rolling dairy land to the Sonoma coast at Tomales Bay, where oysters the size of a man's fist are farmed. Historically, cows have shared this land with Gravenstein apple orchards. As the apple industry declined, and land values rose due to creeping suburbanization, many new vineyards were planted. They have subsequently capitalized on California winemakers' recent fascination with cooler climate grapes. In addition to very impressive Riesling, some of California's most acclaimed Chardonnays now come from this area. On hot summer days, the wind picks up and fog from the ocean flows over the Plain about 5 p.m. each afternoon to settle in the former swamp which was originally drained by the Petaluma River.

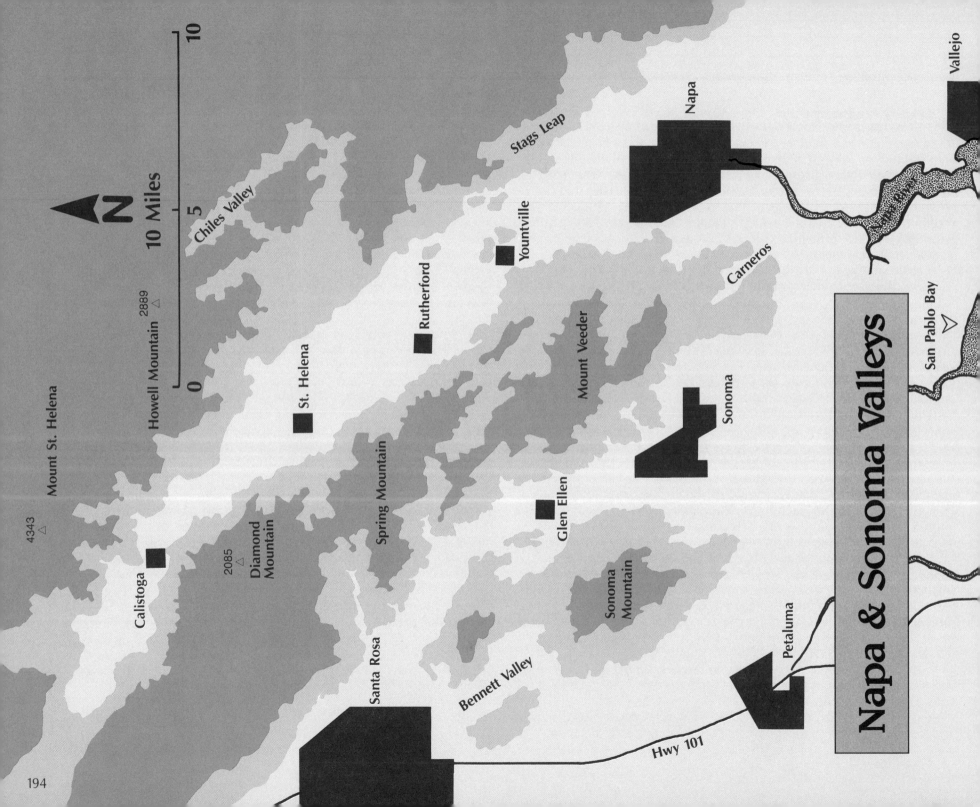

Napa & Sonoma Valleys

Vallejo

Napa

Stags Leap

Chiles Valley

Yountville

Carneros

Rutherford

Mount Veeder

St. Helena

Sonoma

Spring Mountain

Glen Ellen

Howell Mountain 2889 △

Mount St. Helena

4343 △

Calistoga

2085 △
Diamond Mountain

Sonoma Mountain

Santa Rosa

Bennett Valley

San Pablo Bay

Petaluma

Hwy 101

N

10 Miles

0   5   10

Napa County

As the number of wineries in Napa approaches 200, the marketing hype becomes further and further removed from reality. Many publicists there would have consumers believe the entirety of Napa County is a single, homogeneous growing region which just happens to be better for every grape variety than any place else in America. Of course this position is absurd. It is not ridiculous, however, for the sheer hubris of the emotion. Napa Valley is truly magic! The problem with the publicists' position is it completely misrepresents Napa's greatest virtue. Napa Valley is the Disneyland of American wine because so many *different* viticultural conditions can be found in such a small area.

If the appropriate grapes are planted in the right places, an extremely wide range of varieties and styles can be produced successfully in Napa. The corollary danger occurs when growers with more money than experience start to believe the prevailing publicity and end up planting varieties which are not appropriate for their particular piece of property.

Napa Valley is 30 miles long. It narrows from a couple of miles wide at its mouth on the Bay to half a mile wide at its apex north of Calistoga. It has a rich history and a beauty brought into focus by its concise proportions. Its proximity to the Bay Area megalopolis (fourth biggest concentration of people in the U.S.), and its plethora of public tasting rooms, makes it California's most frequently visited year-round attraction. No wine growing region of comparable prestige in the world is located as close to a major city. Napa is also the wine industry's most poignant example of changes wrought by the pressures of urbanization.

Napa Valley is almost fully planted with some 22,000 acres of grapes. To resist urbanization north of the Oakville Cross road, a County ordinance requires 40 acres of land in order for owners to get a second building permit. Land values are such that a planted vineyard costs in excess of $40,000/acre. In other words, the entry fee if you want to build a winery is a million and a half bucks . . . BEFORE you start thinking about construction costs.

This situation creates a logical distinction between people who choose to locate their wineries in Napa and people who move to places like Mendocino, Amador and Paso Robles. Tennis dresses and Mercedes SLs are standard in Napa Valley. Dirty jeans and a pick-up with a dog in the back are the uniform in Mendocino and Amador. Most Napa wineries are started by older people who have been successful in some other endeavor. They want prestige and exposure to the marketplace quickly. Napa provides it. Many of them are intent on creating a working estate while they send their children to Enology School at U.C. Davis. By contrast, younger winery owners who must support their venture out of the cash register, but who have forty years ahead of them to develop a reputation, are more likely to locate some place that land can be bought for $2,000 an acre. Debt service is one of the hardest rows to hoe for a beginning winery . . .unless one has outside income with its concomitant tax considerations. It is perhaps noteworthy that this financial situation in no way diminishes the artistic zeal of Napa winemakers. In fact, this flow of new money is a major advantage that California's wine industry enjoys over its competitors around the world.

To visualize the unique viticultural pockets in Napa County, it is helpful to start with a cross-section cut from west to east across the valley. The Mayacamas mountains between Napa and Sonoma get twice as much rain as the mountains east of Napa. This weather pattern is obvious from looking at the respective areas. If you stand in the center of the valley and look west, the hills are green and covered with trees. When you look east, the hills are brown and covered with scrub. The mountains tend to have thin top soil because the rain has washed it away. The soil that does exist is likely to be of volcanic origin. Grapes grown in the mountains are less vigorous and produce smaller berries. They ripen earlier, have very concentrated flavors and the wines often take a long time to show their bouquet at its expansive best.

As the top soil washes down the mountains toward the Napa River in the center of the valley, the largest particles drop out of the streams first and are deposited in piedmonts or alluvial fans next to the foothills. These areas are particularly noticeable along the western edge of the valley with gradual slopes running up to 200 feet of elevation. The soils are often deep with good drainage. These vineyard sites are highly prized and a great many of Napa's most expensive Cabernets grow in a narrow band called the **Rutherford Bench.** These grapes produce well, yet ripen several weeks ahead of their counterparts in the center of the valley and are capable of high degrees of maturity.

The smallest particles of top soil eroded from the mountains are carried out into the Napa River flood plain and deposited as silt. These soils are more compact and clay-like, with greater moisture retaining characteristics. They are usually quite deep. The result is that vines in the center of the valley grow vigorously. The wines are usually softer and pleasant to drink at an earlier age. Pieces of property that have had streams flowing over them with some force in the past may have stretches of gravel and sandy soil overlain with rich top soil. Caymus Vineyards is an example of this phenomenon where the high productivity of the valley floor is found in a rare combination with intense flavor.

A second important illustration of Napa Valley would be to take a trip from south to north, up the valley from the Bay in much the same manner that cool marine air travels. Napa County shares a fine viticultural area with Sonoma County called the **Carneros District.** This area forms the northern edge of the Bay south of the towns of Napa and Sonoma. It is probably Napa's coolest region. Soils in Carneros are residual, or weathered in place, and very shallow. It is hard to get more than a couple of tons per acre from vines planted here. Pinot Noir and Chardonnay from Carneros are held in justifiably high esteem by connoisseurs world wide. It is interesting, however, to compare these wines to examples made from the same varietals grown in valleys which face west onto the Pacific Ocean. The coastal wines will usually be the more extreme examples of those characteristics usually associated with cold climate such as acid, delicacy of aroma and light body. It is, therefore, not entirely surprising that grapes like Merlot and even Cabernet Sauvignon are being grown in Carneros and developing good reputations.

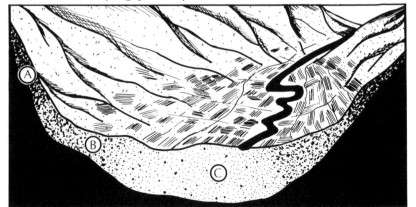

A = Thin top soil   B = Large particles, good drainage   C = Dense silt retains water

Most of the planting in Napa Valley starts just north of the town of Napa. The first distinct line of demarcation one comes to is a set of low hills dividing the valley just past **Yountville.** The vineyards between Napa and Yountville are definitely cooler than those north of these hills. It is a good area for Chardonnay, and a great area for Merlot (particularly in the clay soil where creeks have pooled coming out of the mountains). Sauvignon Blanc from this region often demonstrates the climate by being more aggressively grassy than it is in other areas of Napa Valley.

The east side of the valley this far south forms a special viticultural district named **Stag's Leap** after a sheer basalt promontory over which Indians used to drive deer. Stag's Leap is characterized by rocky soil washed down from this cliff. It is also a relatively cool area as fog laden marine air circles from the Golden Gate around the east side of the Bay and up this edge of the valley. It ends up trapped in the pocket of hills which define Stag's Leap. Two or three of Napa Valley's top ten Cabernets usually come from the Stag's Leap District every year. Often these Cabernets can be recognized by their smooth finish and a black cherry note in the aroma which separates them from their more herbaceous or tobacco scented brethren.

The mid-section of Napa Valley from the Yountville hills to the boutique town of St.Helena is classic Cabernet country. Some of the most famous wines of this area sport an ethereal, sinus clearing characteristic that might be described as whatever peppermint, wintergreen, camphor and eucalyptus have in common. This characteristic is usually called "Rutherford dust," but it probably has more to do with airborne particles than with anything in the ground. Either way, these Cabernets have been setting standards of quality for fifty years. They do it with superb structure; not with nasal tricks. The structure comes from a combination of vine age, climate and deep, well-drained soils. Those three factors unify the wines in a way that is uniquely Californian, and which overwhelms other distinguishing factors. Beaulieu Vineyards Private Reserve Cabernet is aged in American oak. Robert Mondavi often employs a significant amount of Cabernet Franc in his wine. Yet both of those wines annually reflect the region that grew them in a recognizably similar way.

"Up-valley," the northern end surrounding Calistoga, grows substantially warmer as the valley narrows and 300 foot hills pop out of the flat valley floor. The Calistoga airport is a favorite location for glider pilots because of the thermal updrafts which are caused by this topography. Cabernet gets ripe here every year before the rains arrive. These Cabs have a thick, chewy texture and a smell as complex as your grandfather's pipe. Motels in Calistoga are an inexpensive, and centrally located, place to set up

headquarters for visiting the northern California wine country. You can drive over the mountains to Healdsburg in half an hour. Treat yourself to a volcanic mudbath at one of the spas. Then get a massage (all the debutantes ask for Nick). Alex Dierkhising's Silverado Tavern probably has the world's greatest California wine list.

The mountain vineyards of Napa Valley's appellation also grow warmer as one progresses from south to north. **Mt Veeder** is directly west of the town of Napa. **Spring Mtn** is directly west of the town of St Helena. **Diamond Mtn** is directly west of the town of Calistoga and **Howell Mtn** is directly east. These mountain vineyards generally have more in common with each other than they have in common with valley floor vineyards of identical latitude, although certain unique characteristics are becoming recognized. Spring Mtn grapes, for instance, usually have higher pH than one might expect. This makes the wines drinkable earlier and reduces the value of long-term aging. Howell Mtn grapes regularly produce a spicy flavor which is most engagingly obvious in Zinfandel.

The vineyards on Howell Mtn also demonstrate an interesting consistency from year to year. It probably has something to do with being above the "inversion layer" all summer long. This situation is something of a contradiction. One would expect mountain vineyards to fluctuate dramatically in temperature from hot, sunny days to cold nights. In most places this supposition is true. However, in Napa the inversion layer traps air on the valley floor. On sunny afternoons, this still air gets hotter than the moving air on Howell Mtn. The inversion layer can also trap foggy air so that Howell Mtn warms up earlier than the valley floor on cold, overcast mornings. These variations from one microclimate to another illustrate how hard it is to generalize about growing conditions across an entire region.

Several valleys lie to the east of Napa Valley which are inside of Napa County, but not part of the Napa River watershed. From south to north these are **Wild Horse Valley, Chiles Valley** and **Pope Valley. Knights Valley** is just across the Sonoma County line northwest of Calistoga. Hearings held in the early '80s by the Federal government clearly demonstrated the political nature of regulating place names on wine labels. Growers in these eastern valleys had historically shipped all their grapes to Napa Valley wineries. Both the growers and their customers at the large wineries argued that these grapes had helped create the "franchise" implied by the name Napa Valley. After a $40,000 lobbying effort, these growers won the right to have their grapes labelled with the Napa Valley appellation. It takes the wisdom of Solomon to balance the considerable financial impact decisions like this one have against the obvious abuse they wreak on any consumer's normal use of the English language.

DELTA REGION

The majority of the water which falls on California runs to the center of the state. There it forms the Sacramento Delta before passing through the

Carquinez Straits to San Pablo Bay (true name for the northern half of San Francisco Bay) and eventually out to the ocean underneath the Golden Gate Bridge. Most people are surprised to learn that the Central Valley cities of Sacramento and Stockton are deep water ports served by ocean going vessels that pass through the Delta. Sturgeon and striped bass are game fish in the region. A popular vacation is to rent a houseboat and spend several days (usually lost, but unconcerned) trolling among the network of sloughs and islands which make up the area. Diked tracts of rich farmland produce bountiful crops here. That is, until a levee breaks, flooding several square miles with 15 feet of brackish water.

Yolo County is on the north side of the Delta. It is America's rice bowl. The flowing lines of irregularly shaped fields, and varied hues of blue and green as the rice plants mature, are very attractive especially from the air. In winter many rice growers flood their fields to attract ducks stopping over on the Pacific Flyway. **Clarksburg** is a center of northern Delta grape growing. As one might expect in an area with deep, fertile soils and seemingly unlimited sunshine, productivity is very high. Chenin Blanc and Petite Sirah are two varieties which have achieved artistic notoriety here over the last decade. In both cases the grapes' fruity aroma is unusually pronounced. Extreme bottle aging is contra-indicated.

Lodi is the small town on the south side of the Delta which Credence Clearwater Revival used to typify the experience of being stuck someplace removed from the action. It is "out in the tules" (mispronounced "two-LEES" by exasperated teenagers) which refers to the tall reeds much favored by native elk back when the region turned into a several thousand-square-mile marsh each spring. Today, the tules are commemorated only by the tule fog which rises from the ground on cold winter nights. Incidentally, tule fog is inconsequential to grape growers unless they have to drive in it. Ocean fog is a completely different matter for vineyardists in coastal valleys because it occurs during the summer growing season.

Zinfandel is the star winegrape variety around Lodi. There are many huge wineries in the area and vast acres of vineyard. Most growers can get 8-10 tons per acre and it is easy to understand when one sees the size of the vines. Trunks 40" in circumference at waist height are common. In the late '60s and early '70s Ridge Vineyards and David Bruce Winery brought some attention to the Lodi area by making massive Zinfandel wines which beat consumers about the neck and shoulders with opulent, ripe berry fruit. The wines were too alcoholic and extractive to appeal to a mass audience, but nobody who tasted one ever had any trouble recognizing Zinfandel aroma afterward. These days the white Zin boom has rekindled planting of these grapes in the Delta.

LIVERMORE VALLEY

The east side of San Francisco Bay is bounded by low hills which fall away into the Livermore Valley before rising again to support thousands of windmills generating electricity at Altamont Pass. Walnut Creek and Danville (where Eugene O'Neill spent his last years) lie at the north end of this area in the foothills of solitary Mt. Diablo. Even vestigial grape growing ceased as these towns exploded in population during the '80s. They are linked by light-rail transit with San Francisco, and they now sport headquarters office buildings to go along with their large bedroom communities. Pleasanton is a smaller town at the southern end of the area. Those who eschew the freeway can reach Pleasanton from the Bay Area by driving up picturesque Niles Canyon, where Charlie Chaplin made movies prior to the ascendency of Hollywood.

Livermore Valley starts at the line between Pleasanton and Danville, then continues to the east. It is relatively cool compared to the protected hills around Pleasanton because of the breeze flowing from San Francisco Bay toward the hot Central Valley beyond Altamont Pass. It also has extremely rocky soil. Vineyards of the Livermore Valley appear to be primarily composed of two inch pebbles. They are very hard on cultivating equipment. For twenty years the most noteworthy wines from the area have been dry whites with Sémillon and Sauvignon Blanc predominant. It is rare for these wines to have a grassy aroma, but they do have a distinctly flinty flavor and attractively angular structure. The vines are generally older than other sections of California. In fact, many new plantings in the state refer to the cuttings they use as the "Wente clone" since the origin of the vines can be traced back as far as vineyards established by Charles Wetmore in the Livermore Valley.

Throughout the '70s a large number of excellent Zinfandels were made from vineyards planted at the turn of the century near Pleasanton. Ruby Hill, the most famous of these vineyards was owned by Southern Pacific Railroad in modern times. It was sold in the early '80s to Computerland who wanted to construct a headquarters building on the property. Local residents formed a political lobbying group called Friends of the Vineyard to halt destruction of these landmark grapes. For years the debate raged in the local newspapers and town council. Computerland finally prevailed in 1983 and pulled out the Ruby Hill vineyard. Subsequent financial reversals for the Millard family that controlled Computerland resulted in plans for the headquarters building being scrapped in 1985, although it was a bit late for the Friends of the Vineyard to take much pleasure laughing up their collective sleeve. The property has since been sold to Wente and replanted to young vines for white grapes.

It is interesting to compare the last two vintages of Ruby Hill Zinfandel. The 1981 wine was made by Kalin Winery. Reflecting the warm growing season, this wine was fat and smelled of ripe plums. It was neither tannic, nor raisiny; just big-bodied and fruity. The 1982 was made by Fenestra Winery. As befits a cool growing year, the wine was light to medium-bodied and crisply acidic. However, the most distinctive character about the '82 was an obvious smell of fresh ground black pepper. Both vintages were picked at the same degree of ripeness, i.e. 23°Brix, and the wines had virtually identical amounts of alcohol. The major difference was the '82 had been picked three weeks later than the '81, and the acid at harvest was 25% higher. This startling contrast between two successive vintages, made from the same old vines, clearly demonstrates how general characteristics of regionality can only be viewed in the context of their relationship to peculiar weather patterns for an individual growing season.

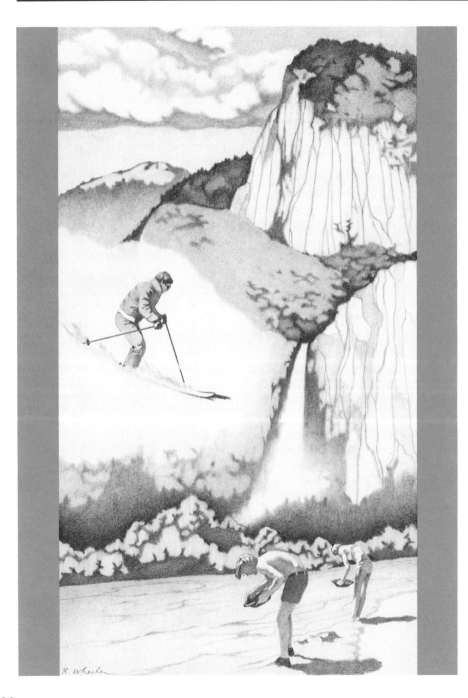

SIERRA FOOTHILLS

Amador, Calvaras and El Dorado Counties are loosely known as the Gold Country. They have a rustic air about them, and they were the scene of much frenzied activity 140 years ago in what passes for history to Californians. A drive along the aptly labelled Hwy 49 will take you through clusters of Basque restaurants, brothels turned into Victorian hotels, antique stores and saloons. All of these places have town names like Bootjack, Mormon Bar, Dogtown, Ophir, Chinese Camp and Drytown. In 1849 the Anglo population of California rose by a factor of ten as hundreds of thousands of men scrambled up into these foothills to wash away stream banks seeking golden fortunes. Bret Harte and Samuel Clemens wrote down the tales. Real money was made supplying dry goods to the miners by future robber barons like Stanford, Huntington and Crocker. It was a lively and lawless era.

Today mining activity waxes and wanes as inflation manipulates the price of gold. Cattle ranching is more likely to set the social tone in any community. Large numbers of retirees have moved to the area to enjoy the ample recreational opportunities and take advantage of real estate prices which are low by California standards. The Army Corps of Engineers and the federal Bureau of Reclamation have competed with each other for fifty years to dam every available stream coming out of the mountains. The resulting reservoirs in summer and the snow ski season around Lake Tahoe in winter create a modicum of demand for fast food franchises and automobile repair services. Life in the Sierra Foothills is not necessarily simpler than in the rest of California, but it is a touch more basic. Nature's cathedrals, like nearby Yosemite, provide the inspiration that might otherwise have to be found in cultural amenities.

Visitors wishing to sample this region might be well advised to head for the centrally located town of Jackson. Make reservations at the charmingly historic National Hotel (circa 1850), but with two caveats: (1) You will be asked if you intend to dine at the hotel, with the implication that reservations may be hard to come by if you do not. Lie, if necessary to get the reservation, but eat at Teresa's Place instead. (2) If you plan to be there on a Saturday night, under no circumstances should you accept accommodations in The Bridal Suite. That is, unless you look forward to having ALL the denizens of the Wild West piano bar downstairs bunny hopping through your bedroom at midnight in a conga line to the strains of "When The Saints Go Marching In."

Grape growing at elevations between 1,000 and 3,000 feet in these foothills goes back 120 years. It is currently undergoing a resurgence. The most important area historically is in Amador County around the towns of Plymouth and Fiddletown. It is called **Shenandoah Valley,** a coincidence guaranteed to raise Virginian blood pressure at label regulation hearings. The soil is colloquially called decomposed granite. It has very little organic matter to provide fertility. The color of the soil is a distinctive brick red due to the oxidation of its high iron content (rust). The climate is warm, but moderated by the elevation. It is not uncommon for overnight temperatures to drop fifty degrees below the mid-day high in summer. Most vineyards are planted on moderately rolling hillsides and dry farmed. At least ten separate Zinfandel vineyards date back more than 70 years. In the 1970s these grapes were made into widely acclaimed wines by wineries located outside the area. That tendency continues today, but many fine local wineries have started up in the last decade, and they are slowly making inroads on these historic vineyards.

One ironic problem is the tourist demand for white Zinfandel. It threatens to divert at least some quantity of excellent grapes from their most noble calling. A very large number of novice wine drinkers visit tasting rooms in Amador County while touring the Gold Rush towns along Hwy 49. Their palate is attuned to soda pop, they want a souvenir of the visit and $4.75 is their favorite price point. Voila! "Have I got a wine for you!" More than one Amador winery struggled to sell 3,000 cases of real wine for ten years prior to 1983. That year they made 1,000 cases of white Zin in lieu of leaving the grapes on the vine to rot in the early rain. Lo and behold, they sold all 1,000 cases in 2 months at full retail to winery visitors. These winemakers didn't start suggesting the artistic merit of white Zin to their peers, but they weren't fools either. Next year they made 2,000 cases of white Zin and sold it out even faster. Today they still struggle to sell the same 3,000 cases of real wine, but they support their families somewhat better by producing 10,000 cases a year of white Zin. Some Amador winemakers can even lecture these days on the flavor characteristics of white Zin without smiling bashfully and seeming to concentrate on their toe as it draws patterns in the dust.

The flavor of Amador red Zinfandel is unique. They have strong briary or heather smells and well developed fruit. In the mouth they leave an impression that can only be approximated by calling to mind whatever "metallic" and "salty" have in common. This flavor is actually rather attractive as a structural component of the wine, and it is apparent in other varieties, like Cabernet, grown here as well. In the past the red Zinfandels have been big-boded, extractive wines which often failed to retain their fruit over the long period of bottle age necessary to soften their tannins. More recently, however, brilliant wines have been made which retain all the virtues of the past wines in a somewhat lighter-bodied style. Another grape variety which seems ideally suited to Amador County is Sauvignon Blanc. The warm climate precludes grassy aromas and instead imparts a papaya or melon aroma which can be nicely augmented by barrel fermentation or a little oak aging. The extreme acidity of the variety is softened into a much more popular style. It is interesting to note that several rather high alcohol Sauvignon Blancs from Amador have shown remarkable bouquet development after 5-6 years of bottle aging.

A second area of the Sierra Foothills which is becoming better known all the time is located at higher elevations to the northeast in **El Dorado County.** These vineyards are newer than the historic remnants in Amador's Shenandoah Valley and cooler because of the elevation. Near Placerville at least one winery has had noteworthy success growing delicately scented J. Riesling on land which previously supported apples. Merlot from this area and fruity Petite Sirah from the one-building town of Fairplay have both developed an enviable track record of show medals.

An important consideration throughout the Sierra Foothills is to draw a distinction between those talented winemakers whose artistic products are appreciated in the larger California wine markets and their less cosmopolitan neighbors whose honest goal is to supply Gold Rush tourists with the traditional few drinks and couple of laughs.

SANTA CRUZ MTNS

The joke is that if you picked up the United States by Long Island, everything that was loose would roll into Santa Cruz. It is true that the balmy climate, tolerant attitudes and vast stretches of redwood forest within easy reach of Silicon Valley have attracted marginal personalities much the way Paris and San Francisco did before returning to the land became fashionable. The Santa Cruz mountains are populated by a disproportionate number of highly creative people whose level of motivation falls somewhat below their counterparts in New York City. The region is beautiful, vibrant with ideas and rich with winemaking history. It also has a mysterious quality heightened by a series of grisly murders perpetrated in the '70s by a string of independently deranged residents. Be sure to visit, but don't hitchhike.

The town of Santa Cruz sits on the north extremity of the Monterey Bay crescent. The University of California at Santa Cruz is a unique environment wherein students spend four years reading in 90 person colleges structured on the Oxford or Cambridge model. The student population of Santa Cruz may help to explain an occasional Socialist majority on the town council. There is a Squid Festival every year and a boardwalk (complete with roller coaster) which hosted the Miss California Pageant until recently. For the full bore experience, eat at India Joes, dance at the Catalyst, then have a nightcap at Shadowbrook on the Soquel River in Capitola. To drive back over the Santa Cruz mountains on Hwy 17 to San Jose is to experience America's narrowest freeway. Better you should stay at the beach.

Many refugees from high-tech jobs in Silicon Valley have started wineries in the Santa Cruz mountains over the last twenty years. Most of them buy grapes elsewhere because the mountains are steep and plantable acres are few. Prior to Prohibition some 2,000 acres of vines grew in these mountains. Today there are probably less than 500. Bird damage can be a serious threat because there are not many alternative crops to divert the birds attention. Starlings are quite happy to consume grapes at 15°Brix, three weeks before winemakers consider them ripe. A flock of starlings can pick very rapidly. Often the only cure is to put nets over the entire vineyard.

On the coastal side of the mountains, elevation is an important viticultural consideration. Below 1,000 feet the fog will make ripening all but the earliest varietals very difficult. Pinot Noir can be brilliant in these lower locations, but Chardonnay must be higher up to ripen. The best known vineyards are on top of ridges in the mountain range. Being above the fog, they can ripen grapes like Cabernet, and they get intense flavors from the low production found in their sparse top soils. The soil that does exist in many of these mountain vineyards tends to be rather acidic due to duff from the conifer forest.

The inland side of the mountains is substantially warmer than the ocean side, especially in the south Bay districts around Saratoga. The San Francisco peninsula is only about 10 miles wide at San Mateo and the coastal mountains are only 600-800 feet high. As one travels south, the mountains become higher and the mountain range broadens to some 40 miles across. At San Mateo the fog comes over the mountains every evening in late summer. It gets pulled up the ocean side, clinging to the hills in a dense sheet, and then flows down the inland side like a huge wave. It's indeed dramatic. As one moves south, the frequency of days on which fog makes it all the way over the mountains diminishes rapidly. At Cupertino the fog never makes it to the inland side of the mountains.

Santa Clara Valley is the inland side of the Santa Cruz mountains and the southern end of San Francisco Bay. California's connection with Mexico (past and future) are readily displayed throughout the valley in place names, architecture, advertising and school enrollments. Jitters are caused by the San Andreas Fault which runs through foothills on the west side of the valley. Before WWII this area was an extremely rich agricultural district carpeted with orchard blossoms every spring. By the end of the '50s it was the Bay Area's worst example of suburban sprawl with new asphalt displacing more of the flower ground cover each spring. By the '70s, Silicon Valley had become the name of choice and agriculture was in full retreat. As many pioneers of the California wine industry began their careers in this area as in Napa or Sonoma. Paul Masson, Almaden, Mirassou and San Martin became giants from the bounty of the Santa Clara Valley. They continue to make wine there today, but the grapes come from other places.

One remnant of the Santa Clara Valley's viticultural heritage is a district called **Hecker Pass.** It lies west of Morgan Hill and Gilroy about 20 miles south of San Jose. The Gilroy Garlic Festival harkens back to the days when immigrant Italian winemakers dominated this market, selling their wines directly to restaurateurs in 17-gallon demi-johns. Tasting rooms consisted of a plank between two barrels. Bottles with bar spouts dispensed samples into shot glasses. Vintages and varietal names were of little concern. Styles began to change when the third-generation offspring of these pioneers returned from business and enology schools. The process accelerated as land values rose. There are currently 5 or 6 old-style wineries in Hecker Pass still making generic wines from ancient vineyards of Carignane, Grenache and Alicante Bouschet. They sell all of their product direct to consumers at the cellar door. Eventually they will retire with handsome incomes when they sell their property to IBM executives whose daughters want horses.

In many ways it is sad to witness the passing of an outstanding viticultural district. Santa Clara Valley has much the same climatic conditions as Sonoma Valley, and it is much bigger. However, the situation does create artistic opportunities due to the buying power of the population now resident in the former vineyards. Talented winemakers can get a good return using high quality grapes, but they are forced to select the best locations for planting and the most impressive varieties for each location. A couple of urban emigres are trying this approach in the Hecker Pass. Restoration projects can utilize vineyards and facilities in a historical context and supply recreation to the population as well as wine. Several small wineries perform this function in the suburbanized hills above San Jose. Old vineyards, often abandoned by the Jesuits from the former Novitiate Winery where ex-governor Jerry Brown studied, are considerable prizes in the hands of the area's knowledgeable, and committed, wine craftsmen.

R. Wheeler

MONTEREY COUNTY

John Steinbeck would be pleased that the land and the people he described so poignantly have not settled down one bit since his death. Monterey County is a wonderful tapestry of rich and poor, splayed across a landscape that has truly been "touched by the hand of God." A two-mile-deep trench rises in Monterey Bay bringing nutrients to the surface where they support an unbelievable abundance of marine life. Kim Novak raises llamas in a barely accessible canyon along that stretch of Hwy 1 which film producers always choose when they want to indicate a sense of escape in their movies. The biggest, rowdiest rugby tournament in America is played each spring at a toney boys school in the middle of a private pine forest. Sand on the beaches is highly valued for glass production because its purity makes it so intensely white. The AT&T (nee Crosby) Clambake at Pebble Beach competes with United Farm Worker rallies and pesticide investigations for newspaper space. Environmentally conscious gastronomes are constantly pressured to choose between fuzzy faced sea otters (which, incidentally, can be as big as German Shepherds) and $30/lb abalone steaks. There are more mixed race couples per capita than any other county in the United States. Wild boar hunts are a frequent adventure in the mountains. The best bread comes from a Zen monastery, several companies "ranch" escargot, and you can get french fried artichokes from most fast food outlets. Dirty Harry used to be the Mayor.

Grapes have only entered this picture recently, and it is no surprise that they don't have top billing yet. There are more acres of vines in Monterey County than in Napa or Sonoma, but less than a tenth as many wineries. Most of the planting occurred in the early '70s when the big operators of the Santa Clara and Livermore Valleys recognized the graffiti of urbanization on their winery walls. The vineyards are large, primarily located on the floor of the Salinas Valley, and owned in abstentia by agricultural syndicates with professional farm managers. Most vineyards are machine harvested. The whole area is fundamentally different than the areas east of the San Andreas Fault that have been described so far. The fault marks the line where two tectonic plates come together. Monterey is on the Pacific Plate which is slowly moving north and underneath the North American Plate. Hello earthquakes. The porous soils of the **Salinas Valley** were ocean sediments at one time, and they do require irrigation. Much has been learned about Monterey County viticulture in the last decade and a half, but there is much more still to find out.

The great Valley of the Salinas stretches south from the crescent of Monterey Bay for nearly 100 miles. Through much of this length it is 20 miles across. Row crops are planted in fields that have been graded perfectly flat using laser measurements so that they can be irrigated by flooding. Water is plentiful from the Salinas River which flows out of the Santa Lucia mountains and then underground for most of the length of the valley. Soils are very sandy and mixed with a rich loam. Population is sparse, and casual conversation is greatly aided by a serviceable vocabulary in Spanish. Public schools offer year-round instructional segments to accommodate the schedules of migratory laborers' children. This is America's salad bowl, the land of the short handled hoe.

The rugged wilderness of Big Sur separates the western side of the Salinas Valley from the Pacific Ocean. All the cool marine air enters the valley from the northern end across Monterey Bay. This northern third of the valley, from Fort Ord to the maximum security prison at **Soledad,** is generally too cold to ripen grapes. Lettuce, artichokes and brussel sprouts occupy most of these fields. Cold air and fog blows into the valley on a west to east line and then bends 75 degrees south to follow the shape of the valley. There is nothing subtle about this weather. Every afternoon in late summer a wall of mist flows south accompanied by high winds. It can blow trucks off the highway. Lines of cypress windbreaks stand on the north side of all the farm houses. The cooling effect of this weather pattern diminishes gradually as one travels south, but it does not entirely dissipate until the elevation of the valley floor rises to a significant degree past **King City.** It is there that grapevines begin covering everything as far as the eye can see.

There are two anomalies to this general picture. One is Chalone Vineyard, a shrine planted in the '20s by a man who hauled water 10 miles uphill on horseback to get the grapes started. Chalone is in the mountains near Pinnacles National Monument east of Soledad. One can stand in the vineyard at Chalone basking in the warm sun while watching the cold weather front flow past in the Salinas Valley below. Because of its elevation, Chalone is much warmer than most Monterey County vineyards. The second exception is a vineyard on the west side of the valley north of Soledad. Smith & Hook Vineyard is located on a sloping bench at about 600 feet elevation. Being in the lee of the Tularcitos mountains as the cold air circles south across the valley on the eastern side, keeps Smith & Hook relatively warm. They are able to ripen Cabernet on their well-drained soils, but it takes 4-6 weeks longer than it takes in Napa. Fortunately, the winter rains rarely begin before December.

Growing red varieties in Monterey County has been a learning process. For many years these wines carried a tell-tale vegetive nose. Speculation on the etiology of this smell ranged from previous use of the soil for growing broccoli, to grape leaves in the fermentation caused by picking with mechanical harvesters. Gradually it was determined that over-irrigated vines in the cooler north end of the Salinas Valley were the primary culprits. Shifting the red grape varieties to warmer vineyards south of **Greenfield** helped. Halting irrigation earlier in the summer, so that the vines stopped growing new shoots before harvest, largely eradicated the problem. Nevertheless, Monterey County is most highly regarded for the white varieties which it can produce in prodigious quantities with excellent quality.

Chardonnay has become a big winner. In warm years like 1981, Monterey will produce half of the most highly regarded Chardonnays in the state. These wines have a distinctively exotic quality in their aroma ranging from peach to pineapple. It is particularly attractive in youth, which makes these wines ideal for sale in restaurants during the second year after harvest. The wines are notably refreshing because they have good total acid levels. One fascinating technical point though, has become apparent over the last ten years. Something about porous soil coupled with a long, slow growing season affects potassium transfer at the roots. Grapes come in with great total acid, but higher pH levels than one would normally expect. High pH seems to reduce longevity in the bottle. This characteristic has prompted several winemakers to fashion their Monterey Chardonnays in a fruitier style designed for early consumption, while seeking grapes for more austere, long aging candidates in other locations.

Arroyo Seco is a particular viticultural area west of Greenfield about two-thirds of the way south through the Salinas Valley. It is the mouth of a now dry river coming out of the mountains. More importantly, it forms a notch in the western side of the big valley which gives Arroyo Seco protection from the afternoon winds. Botrytis is fairly common throughout the Salinas Valley, but it is consistently reliable at Arroyo Seco. Luscious Gewürztraminer and J. Riesling are produced here regularly.

Another unique area can be found in the **Carmel Valley,** which is not part of the Salinas Valley at all. The Carmel River flows out of the Tularcitos watershed directly to the west, entering the ocean south of Monterey Peninsula which in turn forms the southern extreme of the Monterey Bay crescent. Pacific Ocean weather can blow straight into the Carmel Valley, but it is a steep and narrow place baffling the wind in several stages. There are not many vineyard sites that make economic sense. At least few that don't already have tennis courts on them. Those vineyards that do exist have widely varied micro-climates. Access to water is a big problem. The soils are largely sandstone and its more compact cousin, shale. Carbonate rocks derived from seashells can be found in many locations.

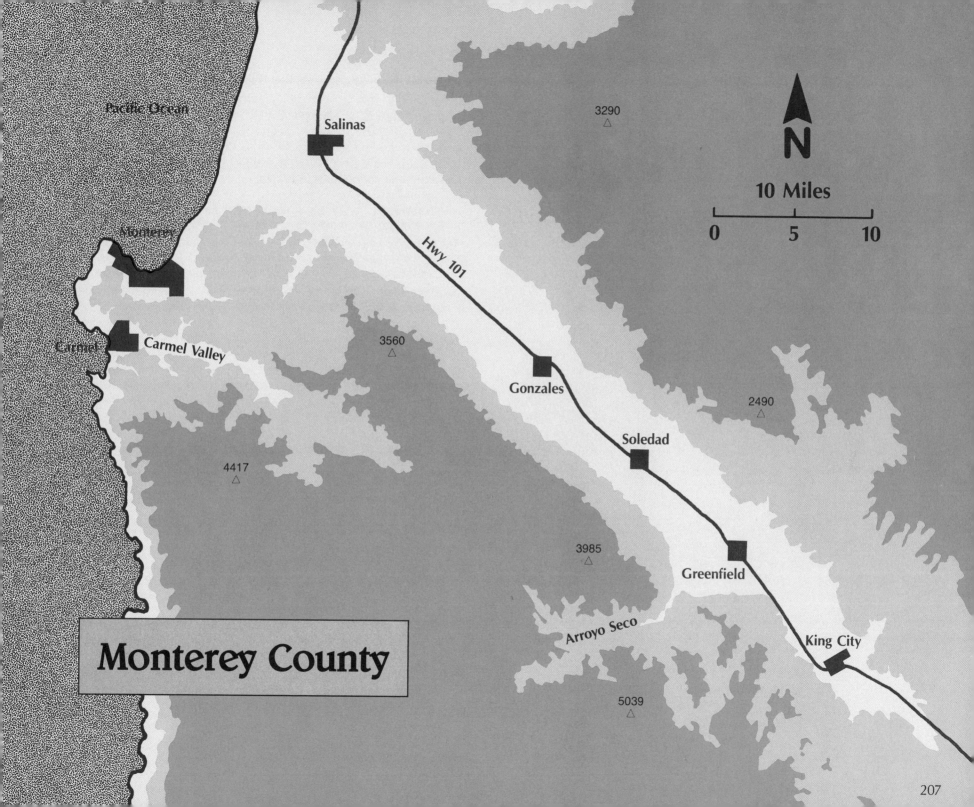

Pacific Ocean

Salinas

△ 3290

Monterey

N

10 Miles

0   5   10

Carmel

Carmel Valley

Hwy 101

△ 3560

Gonzales

△ 2490

Soledad

△ 4417

△ 3985

Greenfield

Arroyo Seco

△ 5039

King City

Monterey County

SAN LUIS OBISPO COUNTY

The U.S. Secretary of Agriculture in 1987, Richard E. Lyng, was a rancher from San Luis Obispo, a coastal county half way between San Francisco and Los Angeles. Raising cattle has been prominent here since 1772 when Father Junipero Serra chose it as the site of the second Spanish mission in Alta California. The local university produces teachers, engineers, architects and horticulturalists, but everybody still calls it "Cow Poly." Their rodeo team draws bigger crowds than their football team. Pismo clams, Hearst Castle, the men's room at the Madonna Inn, the nuclear reactor at Diablo Canyon and the state mental institution at Atascadero should be on anyone's must-visit lifetime list. Hearst Castle is probably the only one for which you'll be needing advance reservations. Stay in Cambria. Eat in Morro Bay.

Actually, San Luis Obispo is much more charming than one might think while experiencing first hand the electric-eye-controlled waterfall at the Madonna Inn. For starters, it is 200 miles from either of the state's major metropolitan areas. There is a tourist trade, but it is casual by comparison to Napa. Relative remoteness has kept many of the place's viticultural advantages out of that media generated by New York City writers in California on whirlwind tours. It is hard to get excited about an area you only see from a 30,000 foot perspective in the aisle seat of an airplane. It is also true though, that the driving distances are large by East Coast standards, so plan to visit when you have a couple of days to look around leisurely. The San Luis Obispo countryside is particularly engaging during winter and spring.

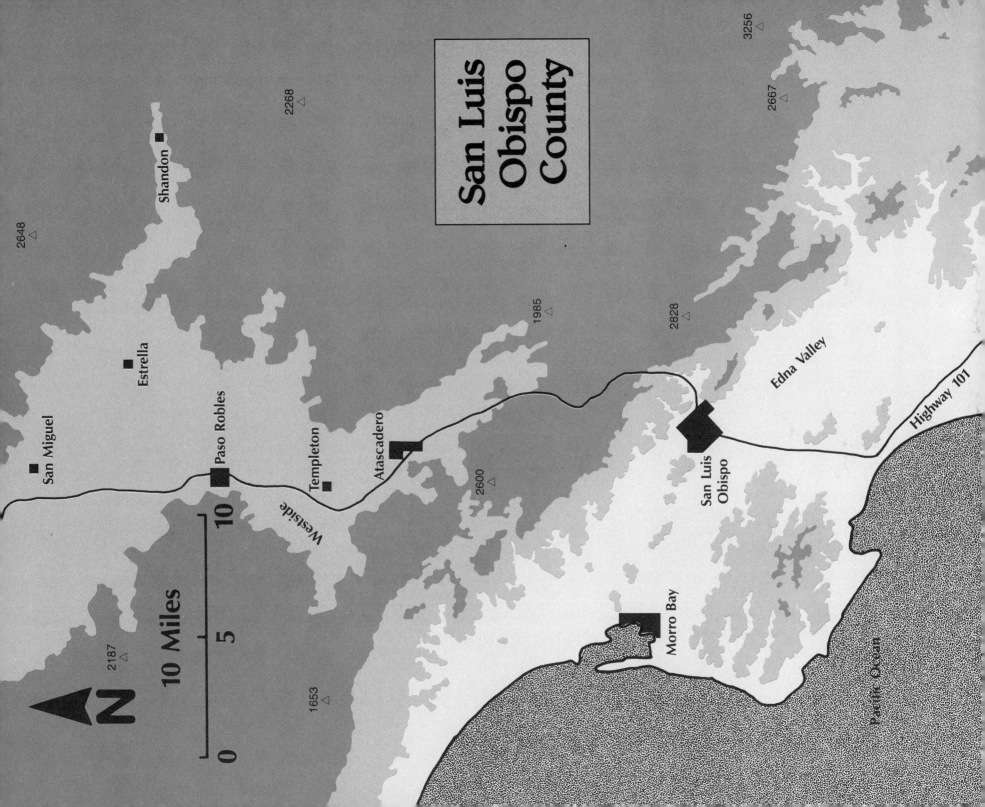

San Luis
Obispo County

N

10 Miles

10

5

0

2648
△

2187
△

1653
△

Shandon

2268
△

Estrella

San Miguel

Paso Robles

Templeton

Westside

Atascadero

2600
△

1985
△

2828
△

3256
△

2667
△

Edna Valley

Highway 101

San Luis
Obispo

Morro Bay

Pacific Ocean

Edna Valley is the grape growing district which encompasses the town of San Luis Obispo and opens to the ocean at Morro Bay. La Cuesta Grade, the road out of the valley, is the steepest section of Hwy 101 in the state. The hills climbed by the Grade surround Edna Valley and trap maritime air all summer long. It is common to drive through San Luis Obispo at 11 a.m. in the fog and then break out into bright sunshine half way up the Grade. Albeit dangerous for the driver, turning around to look toward the coast at this point will show a cotton-white blanket clearly defining, and blocking the sun out of, Edna Valley.

Cool climate and fog are conditions shared by many of California's coastal valleys. Edna Valley, however, is particularly noted for growing Chardonnay grapes which have a citral intensity to the aroma and the ability to age in the bottle for extended periods of time. Low pH is probably the reason and a denser soil structure than other Central Coast districts may be part of the explanation.

Paso Robles is a town on the inland side of the coastal mountains east of Morro Bay. Most of the San Luis Obispo County wineries are located in this area. Growing conditions are quite a bit warmer than in Edna Valley. Paso Robles is vaguely divided by Hwy 101 into a Westside district and even warmer sections to the east, with names like Shandon, San Miguel and Estrella River (pronounced ess-TRAY-ya, as in tortilla). These eastern sections have large, relatively new, plantings put in by owners who made money in the past growing alfalfa. Sauvignon Blanc, Chenin Blanc and Cabernet Sauvignon have shown some promise. Temperatures rise quickly, however, as one travels east on Hwy 46 toward the site of James Dean's demise. Water is very scarce until one crosses the County line into those Central Valley areas serviced by irrigation canals from northern California. Many have argued that the massive tracts of vineyard found there are growing tax subsidies for international corporations who first purchased the land to extract its oil.

The westside of Hwy 101 from Paso Robles to the top of the coastal mountains is much more interesting territory. It does not get fog cover and mid-day temperatures can go into the 90s. Ocean breezes blow over the ridge in the evening, however, dropping temperatures 40-50 degrees. The soils are rather alkaline and "chalk rocks" (carbonates) are quite prevalent. Almond and walnut orchards have been mainstays of the economy for a long time. Pianist Ignace Paderewski had an estate, and grew grapes here, during the first part of this century. Some interesting Pinot Noirs and Chardonnays have come out of these hills, replete with abstract references to the limestone (carbonate) component of top Burgundian vineyards. But old, dry farmed Zinfandel vineyards receive the most attention. Their pepper grinder aroma leads to lots of conjecture. One winemaker claims it comes from walnut leaves in the soil. New plantings of Merlot and Nebbiolo (the grape that makes Italian Barolos) have created considerable excitement in the last five years.

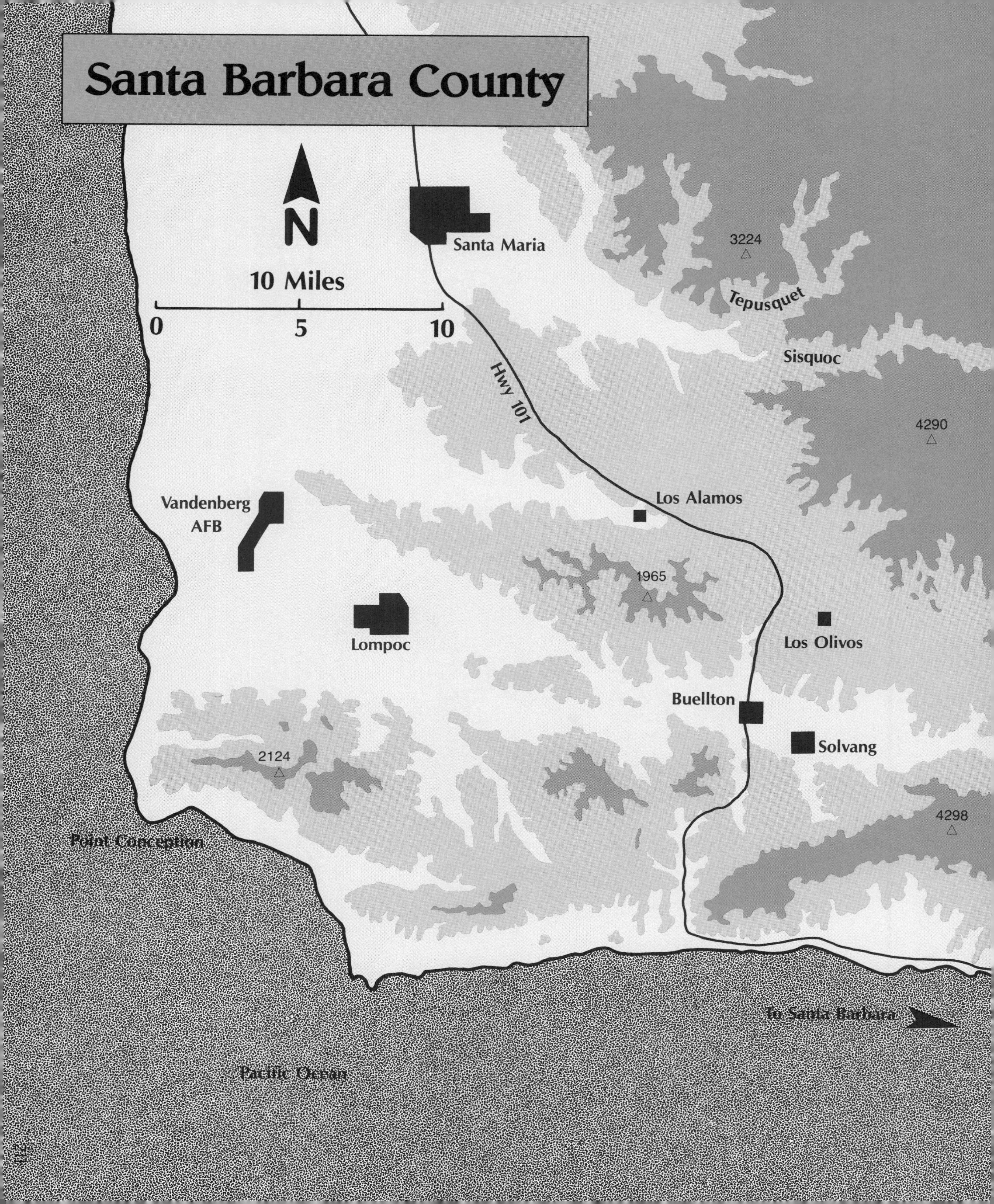

Santa Barbara County

N

10 Miles

0   5   10

Santa Maria

Hwy 101

Tepusquet

3224 △

Sisquoc

4290 △

Los Alamos

1965 △

Los Olivos

Solvang

Buellton

4298 △

Vandenberg
AFB

Lompoc

2124 △

Point Conception

Pacific Ocean

To Santa Barbara

SANTA BARBARA COUNTY

The California beach scene changes dramatically south of Point Conception. The coastline stops running north to south and begins to swing from west to east. Activities shift from dune buggies to volleyball. Nudists no longer wear ski hats, wool socks and sweaters when working on more specialized parts of an all-over tan. People actually go in the water. Citrus and avocado groves cover the hills indicating that frost is extremely rare. The city of Santa Barbara embodies this Southern California vision. It is a mistake, however, to append the city's image too rapidly on the rest of the County. Most of Santa Barbara County lies north of the mountain range that runs due east from Point Conception. The city lies south of it.

Grape growing is centered in the **Santa Ynez Valley** and the **Santa Maria Plain** on the north side of these mountains. More than one grower has been fooled by the Southern California image of Santa Barbara County into planting varieties which have trouble ripening adequately in the relatively cool climate conditions which actually pertain here. Wines like Cabernet Blanc are a pragmatic solution to this mistake more than they are a response to consumer demand.

Santa Ynez Valley may become another Napa twenty years from now. It is a convenient day trip for residents of the megalopolis that now stretches from Santa Barbara to the Mexican border. The Danish curio community of Solvang swells with 30,000 tourists eating pastry every weekend. People come up for a ride in the country and leave thinking about a home with a few acres. The population boomed for awhile during construction of space shuttle facilities at Vandenberg AFB. Ronald Reagan's ranch sits atop the mountains, and Bo Derek is one of many celebrities with equine interests on the valley floor. The fencing alone around these irrigated paddocks would support some small California counties. A license plate holder on one prominent grape grower's Corvette used to read, "Faster horses, Tepusquet wine."

The Santa Ynez River runs west from where it is impounded in Lake Cachuma to the ocean at Lompoc. Cabernet, Merlot and Sauvignon Blanc do well in the eastern sections of the valley, especially the hillsides of protected canyons there. These varieties do, however, reflect the advantages and disadvantages of grapes grown on the margins of what might be called conventional California climatic theory. They are usually styled more like European wines. In cool vintages they will show herbaceous varietal notes which can be attractive to the purist. The vintages will be more popular with the average California wine consumer.

West of Hwy 101, the region is significantly cooler. Stunning Gewürztraminers, White Rieslings, Pinot Noirs and Chardonnays have been produced from these areas. As a representative of cool climate varieties, Pinot Noir is most instructive. At least five wineries have made Pinot Noirs from these grapes which have received international attention. Compared to traditional California Pinot Noir, these wines have been lightly colored, medium-bodied and refreshingly acidic. They have also shown an abundance of cherry, boysenberry and oriental tea aroma.

North of the Santa Ynez Valley, the Santa Maria Plain runs across the San Luis Obispo County border which is marked by the Santa Maria River. There are some very large vineyards (e.g. Bien Nacido) in this district, but few wineries. The area is flat to the ocean, sandy and cool, much like the Salinas Valley. Similarly, it is a prime area for truck farming. Fragrant White Rieslings, fruity Chardonnays and cherry scented Merlots from these vineyards have become quite popular. As in the Salinas Valley, long periods of bottle age are not called for on wines from Santa Maria Plain grapes.

East of the Plain, a couple of canyons run back into the mountains. They get a little bit of protection from the wind and feature benches above the river bottoms on which to plant grapes. **Tepusquet Vineyards** (pronounced teh-poos-KAY) was a pioneer in this area. Many interesting wines have been made from their grapes in the last ten years by wineries all over the state. In general, delicacy of aroma gives way to more intense varietal smells as one progresses further up the canyons and away from the Plain. Production per acre is substantial, but acid levels remain very high by comparison to the inland regions of California.

TEMECULA

It is hard to escape the impression that Temecula is more of a giant real estate speculation than it is a viticultural district. Miles of sandy moonscape line Hwy 15, an inland freeway from San Diego to Riverside. The natural scrub vegetation is sparse, and it apparently evolved to spend long periods without water. As recently as 1975, there was not much here. Today there are hundreds of new housing tracts. Golf courses seem to be the major form of employment. Avocados and citrus have expanded out of gently rolling groves and up onto the most improbably steep, rocky cliffs. Why are these people here, and what do they do to earn a living? A northern California cynic might be tempted to conclude that some political cabal is warehousing voters who draw income from outside the area in the form of pensions. It wouldn't be the first attempt to engage that spiral of pork barrel legislation which pumps increasing amounts of water onto the desert until the population growth achieves a momentum of its own. Promoters then take huge profits on real estate. It's the history of the arid West. To paraphrase Mark Twain, "Wine's for drinkin', water's for fightin' over."

The irony is that the same residential growth which begat a fine viticultural district ten years ago, now threatens to destroy it. Housing tracts with imported water, and power for air-conditioning, could be placed anywhere in this hundred mile stretch of desert. And they are. Grapes are not that flexible. **Temecula** (pronounced teh-MEHK-you-lah) is a very special location climatically. There is an opening in the coastal mountains behind Camp Pendleton Marine Base called Rainbow Gap. As the Mojave Desert to the east heats up during the day, it pulls cool air from the ocean through this channel and directly across Temecula in a narrow stream. As a result, the temperature in the vineyards rarely goes over 80°F. The grapes receive a unique combination of high sunshine (candlepower for photosynthesis) and low to moderate air temperature. A few miles to the north or south of Temecula, afternoon temperatures may be 20°F hotter. Artistic experimentation with these grapes is still embryonic, but there have been some excellent examples already.

Sauvignon Blanc from this district is nicely structured with an earthy, flinty backbone and a floral component to the nose. Petite Sirah is expansively fruity, like a Beaujolais with good weight. Botrytized Chenin Blanc has been brilliant on occasion. Cabernet, from a high elevation district in the coastal mountains called La Cresta, is very impressive with medium body and a violets or cherry note to compliment the wood. These Cabernet Sauvignon grapes from La Cresta, blended with new Merlot plantings from Temecula, will bear watching in the future.

Temecula was a sleepy little desert village with a couple of primitive wineries and a few vineyards until a large insurance company started to build an instant community there called Rancho California. Eli Callaway, former head of Burlington Industries, moved in to plant grapes and make wine in a big way. The proximity to San Diego, and the novelty of a prestigious local wine business, attracted many visitors. Several small, amateur winemakers decided to devote themselves to this growing opportunity and set up shop. New vineyards were planted. Sales promotions by this burgeoning group of vintners made Temecula even more popular as a destination for day trippers from Los Angeles and San Diego. Meanwhile, the bedroom community of Rancho California enjoyed (at the very least) a public relations advantage over its tract home competitors to the north and south. It grew like the Blob.

Today, the latest developments of single family stucco homes on quarter acres sit cheek-to-jowl with the original vineyards. It doesn't take an urban planner to recognize the confrontation that must inevitably ensue. Home owners want to increase their land values. Agriculture, even premium grapes, can not return enough money to justify the land usage in a situation of rapidly increasing land values, sewer bonds and municipal taxes. The special climatic conditions of Temecula limit the amount of land that is suitable for viticulture. When that land is covered with houses, the goose will be dead and any debate over the value of the eggs will be moot.

VINTAGES

They say a little knowledge is dangerous. That is especially true when discussing California wine vintages. A cool year with heavy rains in mid-September might be a disaster for Zinfandel, but could be great for Gewürztraminer. A vintage that produces great Chardonnay in Monterey might not be "the year of the century" for Chardonnay in Napa. Grapes in California range over a 700-mile stretch from north to south, and at least 150 miles from east to west. There are many differences among microclimates in a given year.

ANNUAL CYCLE FOR GRAPE VINES

The end of the growing year for grape vines occurs each winter when the average temperature (figured by averaging the coldest temperature at night with the warmest temperature during the day) drops below 50°F. At that point sap stops flowing in the vine, carbohydrates withdraw from the leaves into the trunk and leaves fall off. This dormant condition is necessary for the production of top wines. Grapes grown in mild climates, or years when winter temperatures are not cold enough to force dormancy, tend to be bland and undistinguished. Mild temperatures also allow grape pests to overwinter in sufficient numbers to cause significant crop damage during the subsequent spring and summer.

Traditional wine grapes (*Vitus vinifera*) can tolerate winter temperatures down to 5° or 10°F. Places like New York and Washington State occasionally experience "winter kill" when lower temperatures damage portions of vines which are exposed to the air. A particularly traumatic experience for New York vines occurred in 1980 when temperatures dropped from 60°F to 10°F in one December day. Sap froze in vines and exploded their heads and trunks. Luckily this phenomenon is rare. It seriously reduces production for several years. The highest elevation at which grapes are planted in California is 3,000 feet in the foothills of the Sierra Nevada mountains. At elevations below 4,000 feet in California, extremely cold temperatures never occur, and it is rare for snow to remain in any vineyards for more than a week.

Most vineyardists prune their grape vines during January, February and into March. The care taken in the pruning process, as well as decisions about the number and location of buds left on the vine, will be important determinants of vine productivity and grape quality during the subsequent growing season. Severe rain storms during this winter season sometimes flood sections of vineyards, even covering the vines on occasion. Flood waters recede quickly, however, and permanent damage only occurs if vines or trellises are ripped out of the ground by the force of the flood current.

The amount of rainfall during January and February (when California gets 80% of its precipitation) is not as important as the amount during March and April when vines are beginning to grow. Drought during winter, as happened in 1976 and 1977, can have serious repercussions because it reduces the amount of water available for spring irrigation as well as the amount of water retained in the ground. However, rainfall in the spring will normally have more effect on plant growth than rainfall during the winter.

As average daily temperature rises above 50°F, sap starts to flow once again in the vines and growing shoots "push" from buds. Early ripening varieties like Pinot Noir and Chardonnay push buds first, often starting in early March. Late ripening varieties like Cabernet Sauvignon will begin pushing buds three or four weeks afterward. Frost is an issue during this period because it will freeze growing tips, killing them and reducing production. Frost danger usually passes in California by mid-April although in 1980 there was a frost in Napa Valley on May 10th, and in 1970 there were 20 nights of frost in April.

RB

Grape vines in California will produce most of their annual growth during April and May. Therefore, spring rains which increase the amount of water available to the vines will have a noticeable effect on the vigor of the vines and the amount of crop that is set. Ideal conditions are cool temperatures with rain in March progressing gradually into mild temperatures with sunshine in April and May. Too much rain in April and May can cause fungus problems which weaken vines.

"Cluster set" usually occurs the first week of June in California. That is when a tiny flower forms at each location which will eventually be occupied by a berry. The "clusters" at this point look like furry little baubles. Each flower must be pollinated for the berry (containing the seeds, or "pips") to form. Rain during cluster set can be a disaster because it tears flower petals away and keeps many grapes from getting pollinated. However, rain during the first week of June is extremely rare in California. It is much more common in Europe. A more likely problem in California is extreme heat. Temperatures over 95°F will cause most vines to shut down growth processes in order to conserve moisture. In these conditions flower petals can drop off or "shatter," and some percentage of berries will not get pollinated. The result is "shot" berries which never ripen, remaining small and green within the cluster.

Each bud puts out a main shoot and is capable of putting out a secondary shoot if the main one is damaged or the vine is extremely vigorous. Quality conscious growers may remove these secondary shoots to limit production. A similar technique, called cluster thinning, involves cutting off portions of clusters when vines set more clusters than the grower feels are consistent with top quality. Both of these methods are rare because they are very labor intensive, and thus expensive. Secondary shoots will also set small secondary clusters which ripen several weeks behind the primary clusters. Whether or not these "seconds" get harvested along with the primary clusters has an effect on the sugar/acid balance of the fermenting juice.

Bud break in ancient Zinfandel vineyard

Most vineyardists will disc weeds between their vine rows underneath the soil in May or June. This maneuver not only reduces the vines' competition for nutrients but it also increases air flow through the vine which holds down fungal problems. Cultivation also starts to dry soil out. By July growers of top quality grapes would like their vines to cease production of leaves and wood in order to focus energy on ripening the berries. Withholding water until the vines are slightly stressed is an effective way to accomplish this goal.

Traditionally, the ripening of grapes is thought to require 100 days of sunshine after cluster set. This ripening period is very important to the characteristics of the vintage that the wine will show. A preponderance of cloudy, overcast days in July and August will produce different results than a series of hot spells. "Veraison" is the French word for the point at which green berries change color to show the distinctive pigmentation of grape varieties. This point of maturation is generally reached at mid-August.

By the end of August/early September wineries are usually starting to harvest grapes in California. Harvest is the most anxious part of the year in the wine industry because it is the time when the grapes are most vulnerable to bad weather conditions. There is a tremendous amount of work to be done which often requires precise scheduling. It is the only time of year when a change of seasons seems obvious in California. The question is always: When will the Eastern Pacific high pressure ridge start to dissipate, thus allowing the jet stream to bring Pacific storms into the vineyards? If California winemakers want to marry science to religion, late September is the time to consummate that union.

The first grapes to be harvested every year are those used for sparkling wine. Next come Pinot Noir and white varieties like Gewürztraminer, Chardonnay, White Riesling and Sauvignon Blanc. Petite Sirah is in the middle followed by Merlot and Zinfandel, then Cabernet Sauvignon. Warm, inland valleys and dry farmed hillsides will ripen more quickly than cool coastal valleys or irrigated vineyards on clay-like soils.

In the average year, California starts getting rainstorms north of San Francisco in mid-October. Most of the white varieties and half the reds will have been picked by then. South of San Francisco rain is much less likely to arrive until December.

Rainstorms have several bad effects. Vineyards get muddy which keeps equipment out of them and disrupts the orderly pace at which large wineries would like to bring in fruit. When the sun is not shining, ripening is halted. Worse, grapes absorb water out of the ground which dilutes both

sugar and acid in the juice. A rain storm of short duration followed by a couple sunny days with breezes will not cause serious problems. That phenomenon would not be very different from normal use of overhead irrigation equipment. However, a rainstorm of several days followed by overcast, humid conditions can cause extensive damage. Grapes swell with water, and in thin-skinned varieties, berries burst causing rot inside the clusters. During damp years, some growers spray their vines with wetable sulphur to retard growth of mildew. Sulphur on grapes at harvest can cause a rotten egg (H_2S) smell in the wine.

The opposite side of the weather coin occurs when harvest is attended by heat waves. In extremely hot

Shot Berries   RG

weather, grapes ripen so quickly that large wineries can not pick them, nor process them through their equipment, fast enough. Inevitably some grapes will be left on the vine until they are over-ripe. Small wineries are less likely to have this problem because the volume of grapes they process allows more flexibility.

The best conditions for ripening and harvesting grapes in California are temperatures between 70° and 90°F with dry weather into November.

It is perhaps ironic that most people want to visit California's wine regions during August and September in order to observe crush. Not only are winery personnel extremely busy at that time of year, but the weather is usually quite hot. Furthermore, the countryside is all dried out and brown from months without water. December through April are much more attractive months in California. Hills are green. Yellow mustard grows between statuesquely pruned vines and temperatures are very comfortable. Rainstorms are usually brief, followed by crisp, clear days with magnificent views. Finally, winery people have time to be at their hospitable best.

Discriminating Between Vintages

Let us define terms.

Vintage refers to the year in which the grapes are grown and the wine fermented. Vintages can be good, and they can be bad. Use of the word "vintage" as an adjective with positive connotations (e.g. "vintage year") is a throwback to an era in Europe when no wine could be made in years which had poor weather. Using this antiquated European model, a warm and dry growing season would be considered "ideal for the vintage" where vintage indicated the actual processing of the grapes at harvest.

It is no wonder that California's Wine Institute seized upon this peculiar connotation in their public relations campaign to extrapolate: "Every year is a vintage year in California." It certainly is true that every summer in California is relatively warm and dry. So what? The same thing can be said about Libya.

Warm and dry are *not* universally ideal. They just happen to be the end of the spectrum that suits European vineyards best, primarily because they are uncommon there. Claiming ideal European conditions for California vineyards is a little like venerating mammary glands on a bull.

There are two major characteristics which can be generalized about any vintage in California. One is average temperature during the summer. Number two is when rainstorms began to arrive in the vineyards.

♦ WARM YEARS

Very hot years will favor red wines like Zinfandel and Cabernet. They will also favor the coolest growing regions, i.e. coastal valleys. Hot conditions tend to produce wines which are described as "forward." That means grapes get completely ripe. The wines are usually quite fragrant with fresh fruit aromas early in their life. However, the lifespan of the wine will probably be somewhat shorter than a comparable wine grown in cool conditions.

Chardonnay can be very impressive from areas along California's coast in warm years. Those vineyards usually ripen a full month behind Napa Valley. In warm years, coastal Chardonnay loses its extreme citrus quality and gains a perfume which might be described as "peach or pineapple." When these wines are released at age one, they win all sorts of awards and sell very well in restaurants. After five years they begin to show the diminishing effects of such an ebullient youth.

1981 is a premier example of a warm vintage in California. In fact, it was one of the shortest and hottest growing seasons of the century. It firmly established the Central Coast in general, and the Salinas Valley in particular, among California's best areas for Chardonnay. It even changed many people's minds about the advisability of growing Cabernet in places like the Santa Ynez Valley. '81 Cabernets from all over the state began receiving rave reviews at competitive tastings in 1984 and 1985. These wines were opulent, and very mature, even before their fourth birthday.

♦ COOL YEARS

The vast majority of California's grapes are planted in warm inland valleys. These grapes will receive adequate sunshine to ripen properly in almost any vintage. Rather than the European problem of unripe grapes, the most common fault in California wines is over-ripe grapes. Raisin smells, and flabby structure caused by lack of acid, are hallmarks of California's inexpensive wines. For this reason, cool vintages are often best for a majority of California's wines. Pinot Noir, White Riesling, Gewürztraminer and inland valley Chardonnay all seem to benefit from cooler weather.

1980 was an example of a cool vintage. It was one of the longest growing seasons, and latest harvests, in California history. In general, California wines from 1980 have very high acid levels and low pH levels. The irony about 1980 was the summer's most pronounced hot spell occurred during the last week of September/first week of October. Temperatures went to 110°F. Grapes, which had been maturing slowly, all finished ripening at once. Harried pickers passed out in the vineyards. Big wineries couldn't process the grapes fast enough, which caused many of them to leave some of their grapes on the vine too long. 1980 is not remembered with affection by most winery workers because of its difficulties. The wines are often anomalies of big body, ripe smells and high acid. Micro-wineries don't have as much difficulty scheduling their harvest, and were thus able to produce some superb, well balanced, red wines in 1980 which have the potential to age well beyond normal expectations.

◆ WET YEARS

The benefit, and the caveat, about cool weather is it lengthens the growing season. Dry weather through harvest is a tremendous advantage to almost any wine. Rains usually begin north of San Francisco in mid-October. Chardonnay and Sauvignon Blanc are usually harvested there in September. If the growing season is lengthened by two weeks, and the first three-day storm of the season arrives in mid-September. . . Well, let's just say that some (undetermined) percentage of the grape clusters are going to have some (undetermined) degree of bunch rot. Hand pickers can leave as many of the rotten clusters as they notice in the vineyard. Machine harvested fruit is another matter. Winemakers who produce very limited quantities can also hand-sort clusters on a board before they go into the crusher. Factory wineries must forego this pleasure.

Either way, vines will have absorbed a lot of water which dilutes flavors, acid and sugar in the berries. The eventual retail price of this wine may not reflect its dismal origins either. Some percentage of the crop gets left on the floor. If the winery and/or grower needs a set amount of income for the year, each bottle must cost correspondingly more to make up for volume not realized. This sort of economic pressure (often incarnate as a banker) explains some of the distorted publicity one hears about wines from particular vintages. It also explains why public relations professionals can demand high salaries.

1982 and 1983 were wet vintages in California. '82 was a cool year and '83 was a warm one, but they both received extended rainstorms in mid-September. More unusual was the fact the rain came from the south, affecting the Central Coast as well as the North Coast.

◆ RECENT YEARS

1984 and 1985 were fine vintages for red wines in California because there was no rain until late in the fall. Both years are significant improvements over '82 and '83.

1984 was hot. It produced fragrant Chardonnays in coastal valleys and middle-of-the-road whites elsewhere. Cabernets and Zins are excellent for replenishing cellars with wines to drink from 1988 to 1990. Cabs and Merlots from cool areas like Santa Ynez will be particularly good examples for collections from those regions.

1985 was a very cool growing season. It favors Pinot Noir overall, Chardonnay from mountain regions, and Cabs or Zins destined for extensive bottle age. Napa and Sonoma reds from '85 have great structure as well as deep, concentrated fruit smells. They will provide a superb foundation around which to base a cellar for consumption between 1990 and 2000.

In future evaluations, '84 will probably develop along the lines of '74, while '85 develops along the lines of '73. The weakness in this comparison is that '74 was highly publicized as Vintage of the Decade, and '85 is going to receive that treatment this time around. It is instructive to note how perceptions of quality have changed. '74 was warmer than '73, just as '84 was warmer than '85. The warmer vintage will develop in the bottle faster and show ripe aroma from an early age. Those characteristics win County Fair judgings and please the wineries' banker. When interest rates were high during the '70s, it was particularly difficult for wineries to wait on wines developing in the cellar. '73 produced hard red wines which seemed more tannic than the '74s. Today, most of the '74s are fading, but the bouquet of the '73s continues to blossom most impressively.

Winemakers now look to acid level and pH, instead of harvest sugar, when predicting how their wines will develop. Wineries have begun altering their position on what constitutes top quality. They are currently suggesting that cool years without rain may be California's best in traditional inland areas like Napa. Coastal areas, newly planted since the early '70s, may find the converse to be true. Throughout California both '84 and '85 represent impressive quality. The '85s have better structure, but when bottles are consumed should depend on grape variety and location of the vineyard. Comparisons between the two vintages should provide excellent illustration well into the 1990s.

1986 was a long, cool vintage. It began early and did not delay the harvest. It was also a fairly dry vintage. It will be truly memorable for a great many wines. The mole on the face of this beauty was a two-day rain storm beginning September 7th. After the rain in the north of the state, and several days of overcast weather, no rain fell until mid-November.

In places like Napa, Pinot Noir and most of the white varieties were harvested before the rain. It is a fabulous year for those wines. Cabernet and Zinfandel will also produce great wines, but perhaps not as highly regarded as the '85 vintage. The second of two superlative vintages always seems to suffer a little bit in collectors' memory.

The early rain barely reached California's Central Coast areas where vineyards are much cooler, and later ripening, than in Napa. The harvest in the Central Coast was impeccable and many people made spectacular, long lived wines. Chardonnays have not been as fragrant early on as they would be in a warmer year, but they are developing elegantly. The "numbers" on Central Coast Chardonnay were the best in ten years. Late ripening reds from the cool coastal valleys may have found benefit in more summer sun, but they will surprise people after 6-8 years.

The winter of 1986-7 was cold and dry. Snow fell on the mountains between Napa and Sonoma in mid-November, and then again at the end of March. There was virtually no precipitation in between, which ruined California skiers' season and began discussion of water rationing. Adequate spring rain, very few nights of frost and an extremely warm end of April/beginning of May launched the '87 vintage quite early. Grapes, which would normally have flowered the first week of June, began flowering the first week of May. Heat during flowering also caused a certain degree of "shatter," reducing the size of the crop.

Although the summer was relatively cool, harvest began two weeks ahead of normal, in mid-August. Hundreds of forest fires throughout California blanketed the state with smoke for two weeks in early September. This event had little effect on the vines other than to reduce sunlight and slow the rate of maturation. Winemakers, who had rushed to prepare for the early harvest, found themselves sitting around chewing on their fingernails while the grapes maintained a holding pattern slightly below optimum ripeness. No rain had fallen by mid-October when an early October heat wave finished ripening the few grapes still left on the vines.

Crop levels for 1987 were significantly below average. Predictions of great quality follow announcements of a short crop as night follows day. In fact, predictions of great quality follow announcements of any harvest with vexing regularity. It is the euphoria of the season. Production people start running around wineries frantic with the excitement of hard work, and publicists don't want to be left out. So they phone up a couple of business editors. Publicists do not get paid to tell editors, "The grapes started arriving here at Ch. Beauzeaux this morning, and boy do they look awful." Usually a story written by formula appears, i.e. weather report + harvest date last year + crop size = excellent quality + generic statement by winery president. It is called "harvest fever," and it only means there are less than 120 shopping days 'til Christmas.

One clue to the quality of the '87 vintage lies buried in the next to last paragraph of any article on the harvest. Publicity agencies for big wineries report, "the crop is small, but it should be excellent because sugars are up and acid levels are down." This documentation is an example of getting the facts straight, then blowing the interpretation. Good sugar and reduced acid are ideal in France. The exact opposite applies to California.

The '87 vintage in California required most winemakers to add tartaric acid at the fermenter. High sugars may result in elevated alcohols and extractive wines. 1987 is beginning to resemble 1976 and '77, the last years of pronounced drought. The wines of '76 and '77 had concentrated flavor, but were awkward in youth and no more graceful after eight years of bottle age. In '77 the extended drought severely reduced crop levels, which induced several prestigious wineries to raise their prices dramatically. Their winemakers went all over the country announcing that the quality of the wines justified the price. This rearview report is not intended to accuse said winemakers of consciously misrepresenting the truth. Rather, it seems that a small aesthetic dog was being vigorously wagged by its large financial tail.

It will be 1990 before solid judgements on long-term development of the '87 red wines can be reached. Early reports indicate overall quality significantly below the '85 and '86 vintages. '84 appears to be much more attractively priced and styled for short-term consumption.

1988 VINTAGE REPORT

The last section explained differences between warm and cool growing seasons in California along with the difference between wet and dry harvest periods. These general vintage characteristics are, by far, the most important ones. They need to be applied to specific grape varieties and specific regions, though, to be useful. Pinot Noir and the white varieties are picked six weeks earlier than Cabernet and Zinfandel. A harvest that is ideal for Chardonnay can be completely ruined for Cabernet by a week of rain at the end of September. Likewise, cool coastal vineyards are often picked 4-6 weeks later than warm inland vineyards. Thus, a cool year which results in magnificent Chardonnay from Napa might delay the Chardonnay harvest in Santa Barbara until after the rain begins.

A number of secondary characteristics also play a role in defining each vintage, although they will be much less significant than the two characteristics I've just mentioned. These secondary factors include:

♦ Drought and its effect on production volume
♦ Frost during bud break or rain during flowering
♦ Winter temperature
♦ Spikes of summer heat

Before continuing with this point about California vintages, let's look at some background. Deserts girdle our planet in two bands of high-pressure air called the horse latitudes (20°-35° north and south). The tropics lie between these bands along the equator. As the Earth spins, the surface at the equator moves with greater velocity than the surface nearer the poles. For rather complicated reasons, this differential produces a consistent trend of rising air over the tropics. Rising air cools, and drops its moisture in the tropical rainforests. Then, the now-dry air tumbles from high in the atmosphere out into the horse latitudes. As it comes down it is compressed into warm, dry, high-pressure air systems. San Francisco lies just below 38°N latitude. California's wine growing regions are right on the margin of these arid horse latitudes. By contrast, all of France lies north of the 40th parallel and some German wine producing districts lie north of the 50th parallel.

Hence, drought is not a very common consideration in the traditional view of vintage quality. Drought simply does not occur in those European vineyards which have been the focus of wine study for several hundred years. The most obvious effect of reduced water to grape vines is a diminution of the crop size. Europe generally equates reduced production to quality. Regions like Burgundy have even gone so far as to codify limits on production in their labelling laws. (Of course the gap between passing a law and enforcing it sometimes needs a Carl Sagan description to do it justice.) It is a tempting leap of analysis to say: (a) drought reduces crop size; (b) reduced crop size in "top vineyards" (read France) means improved quality; therefore (c) drought means improved quality.

This argument is specious; it appears plausible while failing to account for critical exceptions. California is not France. You may have heard that statement before. You will certainly hear it again if you stay tuned to Winewrights. In Europe, reduced crop size is necessary to achieve ripeness. California rarely has trouble getting grapes ripe. In fact, over-ripeness is a much more likely problem here. In periods of high temperature (over 100°F) or inadaquate moisture, the stomata (tiny surface pores) of grape leaves close to prevent evaporation. The vine just shuts down. What do French wines know from high temperatures or inadaquate moisture? Drought reduces crop size, but extreme drought does not improve quality. If it did, Frenchmen would be queued up around the block to join the Foreign Legion in Algiers.

The 1987 vintage from California is likely to be given a public relations treatment called "spin" in politics. There is no question that crop size was down dramatically. Marketing professionals from the wine industry know instinctively what that means. Prices will be going up. Already, consumers are being told through compliant members of the press that quality is exceptional. I doubt that will prove to be the case. The word drought doesn't come up very often in these wine articles, but it is headline news elsewhere.

Compare the 1976 & 1977 vintages to what we know about the 1987 & 1988 vintages. Forget the 11 year cycle of sunspots that is thought to effect these matters. 11 years is an average. This could be a coincidence. During the winters preceding 1976 and 1987 there was less rainfall than normal. Spring was also dry, which induced early bud break. Grapes began flowering the first week of May in '87, a full month ahead of expectations. In both these years, harvest began several weeks before the wineries anticipated it. Water was available for irrigation, so nobody thought vines would be affected very much. Red wines from 1976 had strong flavors and heavy body. So what if they did need a little acid adjustment? In theory these wines appeared to be blockbusters.

The winters of '76/'77 and '87/'88 were drier still than the ones immediately before. By spring, water rationing plans were going into effect. Consumers were being told to only flush their toilets once a day. Never mind that 85% of the water in California is delivered to corporate farms in the Central Valley for 1/10th of its actual transportation cost. Ignore the fact that these mega-farms produce crops already in surplus, thus driving small family farmers out of business. Is showering with friends such hardship that it justifies anybody rocking the boat? Neither winter was particularly warm — the acacia trees didn't bloom until mid-February — but spring passed virtually without rain. Hot spells alternated with frost in March. Grape vines began leafing out early once more. There was scattered frost damage which combined with low ground water to reduce vine vigor and canopy cover.

In spring '88 some vineyards reported flowering before the end of April. Conscientious winery owners began rescheduling their August vacation plans. The last week of May was extremely hot. Then a very strange thing happened. Several inches of rain fell throughout the state during the first week of June. The results of this heat/rain whipsaw were readily observable by mid-July. In some varieties shot-berries outnumbered normal ones 3 to 1 on many of the clusters. Predicted crop size was off 25-50%. Poor canopy development threatened Chardonnay with sunburn in many places. The harvest began in early August.

The relationship between '87 and '88 has a familiar look to it. The '76/'77 drought was more severe, but the pattern is similar. Those earlier drought years produced wines of formidable structure. One might expect as much from the seriously reduced crop sizes. Unfortunately, the wines had little charm in the short-term and mediocre aging qualities over the last ten years. Do vines fail to produce certain smell components during periods when they are subjected to extra stress? Does lack of naturally occurring acid play a role, or is it merely an indicator?

Answers are hard to come by, and it is too early to condemn 1987 or 1988 to the trash heap. We should merely recognize that, contrary to popular belief, California does not receive a steady diet of identical years climatologically. California sits squarely between the heavy rainfall of the Pacific Northwest and the arid deserts of the Southwest. "Normal" California weather is an average. It only occurs 3 or 4 years out of 10. The rest of the time is split between heavy rain and no rain. The odds are very much in favor of a couple of drought years every now and then. '87 and '88 look like logical choices. Early rains came in '71 and '72. They returned again in '82 and '83. Obvious coincidence. This 11-year-cycle stuff is just too pat. However, evidence seems to indicate the decade of the '80s has already had its share of warm years, cool years and wet years. It would not be overly superstitious to label '87 and '88 as strong candidates to represent the decade's dry years.

Which brings us to a cheap trick much beloved by authors of wine books. The VINTAGE CHART. Only this one will be different. This one is a "forced ranking" of years within each decade. No PR hype here, and no expense account lunches. Playing by these rules, some year *has* to finish at the bottom. It's brutal. Winewrights will be hearing from wineries about this one. Probably won't be an exchange of pleasantries either. Nevertheless, it does make a point. The best year of a decade for Cabernet will NOT be the best year of a decade for Chardonnay. There WILL be differences between years and within each decade a full range of conditions are likely to show up. Hobbyist consumers should enjoy this exercise. It isn't simple nor completely accurate, but it's not impossible or entirely wrong. The point is merely to indicate the repetitive nature of certain weather conditions, and thus encourage you to keep an eye on the big picture.

INLAND VALLEY CABERNET/ZINFANDEL

1970	10	1980	9-
1971	4	1981	5
1972	1	1982	3
1973	8+	1983	1
1974	9-	1984	6
1975	2	1985	10
1976	5	1986	8
1977	3	1987	4
1978	7+	1988	
1979	6-	1989	

Key: 10 is the best; + and - signs are used to massage the grades, as in B+.

◆ EXCEPTIONS

When attempting a vintage chart for California, one must make two distinctions. One is which grape varieties to address, and the other is which growing regions. Note the choices made in the chart's title. They were chosen as the most popular grape varieties for extended aging and the most widely recognized growing regions.

Certain departures from the chart above can be predicted. For instance, '81 and '84 were very warm years. Those conditions produce fine Cabernets from inland valleys, but they mature early and lack long-term aging potential. Cabernet from cooler, coastal valleys is another matter. It can be elevated to superstar status by a vintage which is just too hot for optimum results in Napa Valley.

Likewise, Pinot Noir ripens early and does best in cool years. Pinot Noir was brilliant in '75 and '82 because it was harvested before the rain which subsequently hurt Cabernet and Zinfandel. 1979 was the best vintage of the '70s for Chardonnay although a late rain made Cabernet rather variable. '81 and '86 were extraordinary years for Chardonnay from the Central Coast. The heat in '81 and a two day mid-September rain north of San Francisco in '86 may have compromised other regions somewhat.

View this report as what it is — one man's opinion. If your knee-jerk reaction is to disagree strongly, do yourself a favor. Either ignore me, or examine the motivation you may have for holding the position you do. Often one's allegiance to a particular vintage is directly proportional to the volume of that vintage in one's cellar. It may be a chicken and egg argument. Or, you may have acquired certain vintages because your interest and your disposable income peaked when those years were on the market. Perhaps you knew a rather glib merchant who had taken a large position in a particular vintage. Financial advantage only comes from speculating on the quality of a vintage **before** the marketplace passes judgement. Sometimes this judgement doesn't go the way the retailer speculated. He still owns the wines and has to resell them. Winewrights acts like a stockbroker to procure wines for members. Winewrights does not take title to the goods nor own an inventory of wine. The opinions expressed here may or may not be accurate (that's what makes the wine game a horserace), but they are objective.

CELLAR MANAGEMENT

MARKET FORECAST

The California wine market began a dramatic shift in 1987. The changes will take several years to work their way through the system, but people who recognize what is occurring will have a definite advantage. It is not a new phenomenon. In fact, the history of the California industry is larded with these boom-bust cycles.

Part of the reason these fits and starts are so common is the fact that newly planted grapes require 3-4 years before they produce a crop. The wine then takes a year or more to come into the marketplace. When demand and prices are at a peak, growers plant more grapes. During the five years they have to wait for their product to become saleable, the market usually changes. More often than not, new acreage begins bearing fruit just as demand is leveling off. Big supply and mediocre demand result in low prices. Vineyardists go broke. Eventually, low prices encourage demand to rise again and the whole process starts over. In the past, this cycle has averaged about ten years to come full circle.

Today the currency exchange rate is also an important contributor to the California wine industry's boom-bust cycle. European wine consumption (per capita) has dropped about 25% from its peak in the early '60s. When the U.S. dollar is strong, the resulting lake of French, Italian and Spanish wine floods U.S. markets at ridiculously low prices. By way of illustration, you should realize that it costs nearly a dollar to put anything in a wine bottle with a cork and appropriate finishing touches. The distribution system marks that figure up at least two, and more often, three times. If you see a 750 ml bottle of wine on the supermarket shelf for $2.39, you know somebody is taking a beating. At any given time you can look to see which countries are producing the bargain specials. France subsidizes its wine industry the same way the U.S. subsidizes many agricultural products. In France there is no political alternative. Something like 15% of the French population draws at least a portion of its income from the production or sale of wine. When the U.S. dollar was worth 10 francs in 1984, the French government offered to reimburse their wine producers for 70% of the costs they might incur while marketing in the U.S. French bankers then were giving 120 day terms on invoices for wine sold in the U.S.

Inevitably, the worm turned. By 1987 the U.S. dollar bought only 5-6 francs. Good European wines cost 2-3 times what they did just a couple of years before. The result was a slow dawning awareness on the part of U.S. consumers that California wines represented pretty good value. Retailers had to sell their existing inventories before they began emphasizing this fact to their customers, but at the end of 1988 everyone is saying that California wines are bargains. Europeans are selling their wines to each other and to the Japanese, while importing California wines.

Of course, by the time everyone realizes what has happened, they will be wrong again. California wines started to be relative bargains in 1986. By late 1988, demand had increased and prices had risen sharply. French wines were quite expensive and that created room for California wines to move up. In fact, proud California winemakers feel it is their patriotic duty to get a comparable price. Moreover, they had not had any price increases during the middle of the '80s. By 1988 they had three superb vintages ready to appear in the marketplace, and prices started to go up fast.

Many business activities document this historical scenerio. In 1985 huge Central Coast vineyards were renting tanks at large processing facilities to crush grapes for their own account because they couldn't sell them. They were also offering deals to small wineries whereby payment for the grapes could be delayed until the wine was sold. Talk about opportunity. 1985 was the best quality vintage of the '80s, but small winery and vineyard owners were going around dropping comments as to how they would "entertain an offer" to sell their properties. Nobody wanted to help them. Nationally, distributors were dropping small California brands right and left. Consolidation was rampant among traditional sales channels. That same period saw the beginning of "fighting varietals," cork finished wines priced between $5 and $7. Kendall-Jackson and Glen Ellen wineries grew 3,000% from 1984 to 1988 by exploiting that particular market niche.

By late 1988 the shoe had moved to the other foot. Vineyards that grafted their Zinfandel vines over to white varieties in 1984 were grafting them back as prices for Central Valley Zinfandel grapes moved from $175/ton in '84 to $525 in '87. Growers stopped returning winery phone calls. Wineries stopped returning distributor phone calls. Half the marketing executives in the trade quit their employers to "launch my own business." Bulk wineries like Franzia paid top dollar to acquire huge premium vineyards. The Santa Rosa *Press-Democrat* ran weekly interviews with dairy farmers who complained about their milk price subsidies and acknowledged their intention to plant 50 acres of wine grapes. Producing vineyards tripled in price. Hiram Walker bought Clos du Bois. Britain's biggest discount wine store bought California's (Liquor Barn) with its huge "in-place" inventory. Japanese companies bought Ridge Vineyards and Chateau St. Jean. Kendall-Jackson and Glen Ellen raised prices 25-40%, somewhat relaxing the combative posture of their varietals, and introduced $20 "collector" bottlings. *Wine Spectator* cited the following price examples in July 1988:

WINE	VINTAGE	PRICE	VINTAGE	PRICE
Ridge Montebello Cabernet	1982	$18	1984	$40
Phelps Eisele Cabernet	1983	$25	1984	$35
Diamond Creek Cabernet	1984	$25	1985	$30
Cakebread Cabernet	1984	$16	1985	$20
DeLoach Chardonnay	1985	$18	1986	$20
Clos du Bois				
Flintwood Chardonnay	1985	$15	1986	$19.50
Grgich-Hills Chardonnay	1984	$18	1985	$22

The boom was first seen at the production level. There was a frenzy of activity for grape contracts in California during the spring of '87. Micro-wineries in *The Winewright's Register* were also good indicators of demand building up in the marketplace. Those that took 9 months to sell out in '86 only had inventory for a few months in '87. Many of them increased their capacity and outgrew Winewright's arbitrary 10,000 case production ceiling. Winewright's bi-monthly *Report* clearly called this change in May 1987 and woefully predicted price increases of 20-30% by Christmas 1988.

This prediction proved accurate. It demonstrated that public perception lags 18 months behind reality. The reason is the way information is tied to product in the traditional three tiered distribution system and its press support mechanism. When situations change, it takes 18 months to clear "old" product out of the pipeline. By Christmas 1988, 2 years after the upward "boom" curve began to occur, retailers and the press are starting to come alive with reports on how HOT California wines are getting to be. This boom will accelerate and likely reach full stride by Christmas 1989.

If U.S. interest rates rise 50% from their 1988 levels, foreign currency exchange rates will quickly reverse the trend which started this latest wine "boom." Otherwise the process will be much more gradual. Expenses at California wineries will continue to rise. French oak barrels cost $185 in 1984. In 1988 they cost $425. Urbanization continues unabated in major viticultural districts. Grapes planted today in response to rising prices won't bear fruit for a minimum of 3 years. If interest rates do rise, so will winery expenses. This last point will be especially true when the current crop of financial gunslingers try to leverage their acquisition of winery properties at purchase prices which would be considered high by historical standards. An increased number of distribution and sales-type middlemen will also contribute to ultimate consumer cost. It is not unreasonable to predict the price of California's best wines will increase another 50% between 1988 and 1991. The best vintages of the '80s will be worth considerable more money in the early '90s and then significantly more again when a new boom begins in time for the turn of the century. The optimum time to buy vineyard property will occur between these two boom periods, i.e. the middle '90s. Plan ahead.

MARKET STRATEGY

The "boom/bust" cycles of the wine industry are an object lesson in why it is valuable for a consumer to have a wine cellar. It is also a clear illustration of why "followers" will always have to pay more for good wine than those who arrive at their buying decisions independent of the crowd.

Great wine is never produced in a continuous, steady flow. There are differences between vintages in California, and even more pronounced differences between vintages in Europe. Equally important, winemakers switch jobs with startling frequency in California, and changing financial situations at individual wineries can have a profound effect on quality. There will be periods when the market is full of tremendous Chardonnays, followed by periods of relative mediocrity. This moving picture will be overlaid by the boom-bust cycle of prices.

Having a wine cellar allows a consumer to take the long-term view on prices and quality. You can buy substantial quantities during those "windows of opportunity" when low prices and high quality occur simultaneously. Then, you can drink out of your cellar (and grin like the Cheshire Cat) when the situation changes and your less adroit friends are stuck with a choice between high prices or mediocre wines. It is axiomatic that adroit buyers will have to recognize a "window of opportunity" for a particular grape variety from a particular region BEFORE it is widely written up in the wine press. Publicity, of course, closes a window by raising demand.

An extreme example of this phenomenon is the Cabernet made by Randy Dunn. The 1980 vintage was spectacular. The 1981 vintage was also great and had the added advantage of earlier drinkability. Both wines sold for $12.50. Nobody jumped off of any buildings trying to get the stuff. In the summer prior to release of the 1982 vintage, Randy was written up in *Newsweek* magazine. Randy's '82 and '83 Cabernets are good wines to be sure, but it is unlikely that either year will go down in history as Vintage of the Century. Demand, on the other hand, increased to the point of tears. As the excellent '84 and '85 vintages came out, prices had doubled and tripled. Now, one is only allowed to purchase bottles from a kneeling position. Is any wine worth such abuse? Perhaps the experience is akin to being hazed as an initiation to the fraternity of wine. The phenomenon is tunnel vision on the part of consumers and a modern day version of the Labors of Hercules for wine merchants. Everybody in this dance is using the Dunn Howell Mountain Cabernet as a test of their relationship to the other players. Questions of value have been forgotten as big buyers long to feel the blood flowing through their purchasing muscle.

So much for hindsight. Randy Dunn himself is a marvelously unassuming personality who would never have initiated such madness. The market did it. And Randy's mother "didn't raise no fools." The question to ask is which wineries are in the same position Randy Dunn was in when he brought out his '80 and '81 Cabs? Instead of negotiating what humiliations are necessary to get Dunn Cabernet, we should all be researching unknown wineries who are currently releasing superb '84, '85 and '86 wines.

A prudent buyer needs a wine cellar and a 5-10 year budget based on their consumption of fine wines. If you have proper facilities, a wise suggestion would be to take a substantial position on '84, '85 and '86 California reds and '86 California Chardonnay by the end of 1989. If you also know your ten year consumption budget, you would not get hurt by purchasing six years worth of reds and three years worth of Chardonnay. This position requires you to spend 40-50% of your ten year budget in a brief period of time. Obviously, some research would make sense if you are going to commit a lot of funds, and then stand aloof from the market for a couple of years.

In the May 1987 *Report*, Winewrights stated that '84 and '85 were both good, although different, vintages. It's true. The '84s are excellent wines; much superior to '82 and '83. The '84 Cabernets from cool coastal areas may be the best wines ever to come from those vineyards. Moreover, the '84s are forward, early maturing wines ideal for consumption between 1988 and 1992. They are a perfect way to get a wine cellar started.

What Winewrights didn't do in 1987 was GO COMPLETELY NUTS over the '85s. That shortcoming will be rectified right here, right now. **The 1985 Cabernets and Zinfandels are definitely the vintage of the decade, and they may well be the Vintage of the Century.**

Winewrights has an opportunity to taste a great many wines blind in vertical comparisons. In *every* case the '85 wines mop the floor with the competition. It doesn't seem to matter very much who made them. An '85 Cab or Zin from a mediocre winery will consistently outscore an '82 or '83 from any winery, irrespective of price. This is not a particularly radical observation. In poor vintages, only the best winemakers turn out good wine, and they are easily distinquishable. In great vintages, everybody makes good wine, and the pack is much closer upon the heels of the best winemakers.

The most fascinating characteristic about '85 Cabernets is a deep berry-like smell. The wines have plenty of body, color and extract, but even in the barrel the tannin was not harsh or astringent. They truly are pleasant enough to drink at age 3 or 4 with meat or cheese. At the same time, '85 was a very cool growing season. The wines have excellent acid. They will age well through the turn of the century. "Drink now, but great for aging" is a horrible marketing cliche. It is almost never accurate, but the '85s are an exception. Which is not to say you should buy '85s for current consumption. You should get '84s for that. Buy '85s for drinking from 1992–2000. But you ought to taste a bottle of each '85 as you put them in your cellar just for the experience.

So there you have it. Let no one say that Winewrights equivocated on the 1985 California Cabs and Zins. Some of them were released and completely sold in early 1988. Certainly the "deals" were largely gone by then, but mark these words. If you shudder at the price '85 California Cabernet commands at Christmas 1988, you will be absolutely dumbstruck in 1990 through 1992. By the turn of the century, 1985 California Cabernets will cost 3-10 times what they do in 1989.

In the midst of this hoopla, the '86 vintage for California Cabernet and Zinfandel WILL be overlooked. Early tastings indicate very good quality. It was another cool vintage and the "numbers" were excellent. The vintage's problem is going to be how to get media attention while everyone is in a dither about the '85s. There will also be the issue of price. If '86 is seen as clearly second string because '85 is All-World, it may be a good buy. Like Nebraska's second string, it can probably whip any third vintage on the market. Individual wines will be better in '86 than in '85. 1986 will definitely be a better vintage than '82 and '83, and it will be a much longer lived vintage than '81 and '84. The true worth of the '86 vintage may not be fully known in the marketplace until the mediocrity of the '87, and perhaps the '88, vintages becomes obvious to consumers. Therefore, it is likely to present a "window of opportunity."

CELLAR STRATEGY

I taught wine appreciation classes on the Stanford campus three nights a week for fifteen years. Among other things, this activity allowed me to exercise my cellar more vigorously than most private collectors. I learned a lot about acquiring wines from this ability to cull the cellar on a regular basis.

I came to the conclusion that 2 vintages out of 10 in California were decidedly poor, 3 vintages out of 10 were adaquate, 3 out of 10 were fine, and 2 out of 10 were spectacular. The problem is how to rank a vintage during the period when it is available for purchase. It is, of course, much easier to evaluate a vintage after all the critical press reports are published, but by then the wines will have disappeared, or gone up precipitously in cost. That axiom is rather central to the gamesmanship aspects of this hobby. One's purchasing decisions must also be overlain with a pragmatic recognition of market conditions like price to value ratio.

I'll use Cabernet Sauvignon and my personal consumption of 36 bottles/year as an example. The following targets represent my purchasing strategy:

Vintage Quality	Years Out of Ten	Different Wines to Acquire	Bottles of Each Wine	% of Cabernet Inventory
POOR	2	6/yr	1	5%
ADEQUATE	3	8/yr	2	15%
FINE	3	12/yr	3	30%
STUPENDOUS	2	24/yr	4	50%

As you can see, I am seriously hung up on diversification. That is my personal peccadillo, not my recommendation. I'm a naturally curious sort who much prefers small amounts of many things to a surfeit of the same thing, no matter how great the quality of that one item may be. We are, of course, speaking about wine. The advantages of this preference are particularly clear when one considers how inexact human perception of smell and taste can be. It is not just that wines CAN change. The wines WILL change, and so will your preferences. However, you may choose to concentrate on a few wines in multiple case lots. Be my guest. That is surely an area where reasonable people may disagree.

The numbers on my strategy chart are averages. I am prone to increase the number of bottles of an individual wine above the target figure if it is a moderately priced discovery, and decrease them if it is a widely recognized item priced like heirloom jewelry. But then my financial station in life is not entirely consistent with an acquisitive personality.

Combining my vintage chart (see Vintages chapter) with my cellar strategy above, you can see clear tactical goals. My inventory contains a few tasting examples from each vintage and region to service my academic interest. I have large amounts of 1980's that are now coming ready. I am currently purchasing '84s to replace my '81s for short-term consumption. I am now making a major move on '85s which will eventually surpass the move I made on '80s. I will make a significant play on the '86s, but I'll select carefully because the market conditions then won't be as favorable as they have been on the '84s and '85s. I'm not likely to bet the ranch on '87s or '88s, but I suspect the odds will warrant a close examination of the '89s.

CELLAR CONSTRUCTION

This section will tackle the planning process you need for a cellar. It will also give you a special design for arranging bottles conveniently. To demonstrate sincere concern for your well being, let's start with some long-range warnings. It may be a good idea to calm your unconscious fear that wine collectors are all slaves to their hobby.

The fun of a good wine cellar is in its active management. Thoughtless, or frantic, acquisition is a kick for awhile, but then you have to drink the stuff. A cellar should impress people not with its size, but rather with the number of difficult decisions it took to assemble it. No one gets every decision right. The wines change over time and so will your taste preferences. All wine cellars need to be "culled" on a regular basis. A wine cellar should be viewed as a living, changing organism; not a stone ediface.

The first thing you should do is analyze your consumption pattern. The goal here is to determine an appropriate size for the cellar. Most collectors go on a purchasing binge early, then regret it five years later. In the beginning they shy away from choosing between wines because they lack the perspective that comes with actually using the cellar. Next, they go into a hoarding period where the wines in their cellar take on sentimental value, like heirloom jewelry. Finally, the idea takes root that buying must cease because inventory is starting to surpass the owners' life expectancy. Planning won't eradicate these tendencies, but it may moderate the most virulent attacks. Start by writing down how you plan to *consume* the cellar.

For me, 15 cases/year would be a generous supply of fine wine. That is a bottle, which deserves extra attention, every other day. Bear in mind that I drink much more wine than your average Joe, but a lot of it is consumed in business settings which don't require my wallet to rear its tiny head. No one will call you a lightweight if you think 8 cases/year would be plenty for you (2 fine bottles per week). Nor are you an alcoholic if you and your spouse need 50-60 cases/year (2 fine bottles per day). Maybe you entertain a lot.

The next step is to realize that half your consumption of fine wine each year is *not* going to come from your aging stocks. 40-50% of the good wine you drink each year is likely to have been purchased within 18 months of the time you drink it. You will want space to store this wine, but you will only need space for a one year supply.

Now comes the fun part: Allocating cellar space appropriate for the volumes you will want in specific categories. Let me list the categories I use. You will note that I have a distinctly patriotic bias. You can translate these categories into a broader picture for yourself.

Grape Variety	Age From Vintage Date (Years)	Total Btls Consumed Per Year	Btls Taken from Storage Annually	Storage Space Needed
Zinfandel	2-4	12	0	24
"	4-6	12	12	48
Pinot Noir	2-4	12	0	24
" "	4-6	8	8	36
" "	6-10	4	4	48
Cabernet, et al	4-6	12	12	24
" " "	6-10	12	12	48
" " "	10-15	12	12	108
Chardonnay	1-3	12	0	24
"	3-5	12	12	48
"	6-10	12	12	48
Sparkling	na	12	0	24
Sauv Blanc	1-2	12	0	24
" "	3-5	12	12	36
Dry Riesling & Gew	1-2	12	0	24
Sweets	1-2	6	0	12
"	3-5	3	3	12
"	6-10	3	3	24
		15 cases	8.5 cases	53 cases

Once you fill in your own consumption pattern, it is easy to estimate the total space you will want. Notice that my space estimation includes the bottles which I buy for current drinking. A 60 case cellar will accomodate my most indulgent moods. It will also visually compell me to manage inflow and out-flow with some degree of structure.

THE SECRET. Arrange bottles on three different levels. One is for long-term storage. A second is for near-term consumption. The third is for display.

From the floor to a waist-high shelf I use six vertical bins. These column shaped areas are approximately 18"' wide by 18"' deep by 36"' high. They are divided by a board in the middle to give twelve compartments. Each compartment is labelled with a year in the future when its contents are expected to enter the game. At present I have two 1990 (claret versus Burgundy bottles), two 1991 and two 1992 bins. I have one each for 1993, 1994, 1995 and 1996. I have one labelled 1997-9 and another labelled 2000+. As purchases are made, bottles are removed them from their cases and stacked in these columns. If I buy six bottles of XYZ 1985 Cabernet, I

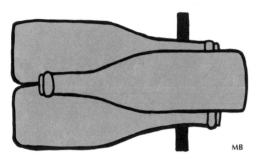

MB

put one bottle each in the stacks labelled 1993 through 1996, one bottle in the stack labelled 1997-9 and one in the 2000+ section.

It is a good idea to use a "french stack" which is actually two columns facing each other. The advantage of the french stack is 50% more wine in the same volume of space, and a better thermal mass to maintain temperature. The labor involved in getting a bottle from the bottom of the stack also tends to reduce drunken pillaging of one's best inventory.

Above the column-like stacks are diagonal bins. This is your current drinking supply. Wines bought for current consumption go directly into these diamond bins. The bins are labelled with the names of grape varieties and styles. Once a year you empty the column stacks which have reached maturity (i.e. this year I moved the ones labelled 1989) into the appropriate diamond-shaped bins. You then re-arrange your two out-year stacks. It takes me about half an hour. Next year you move the two 1990 stacks into the diamond bins. One of the two empty columns will become your second 1993 column. The other will become your 1997 column. Your out-year columns will be re-labelled 1998-2000 and 2001+ (refer to diagram). The diamond bins are only one bottle deep, i.e. 12". This arrangement leaves a 6" lip on top of the columns to act as a handy table when you're jus' foolin' aroun' in the cellar.

Above the diagonal bins, an overhead reach, place a single row of scallop-shaped racks. These hold bottles you are prone to show off. Some wines have much more value as collectors' items than they do aesthetically for consumption. This section is easy to "lock down" if your circumstances warrant extra safeguards.

My whole storage facility measures 9' wide by 7' high by 18" deep. It holds 24 cases on top and 36 below. The beauty of the arrangement is that it provides visual cues. The wines are presented to you when they are ready, instead of being forgotten in a pile of boxes at the back of the closet. You don't over-buy wines which all mature at the same time because that column becomes full. You also notice if your actual consumption pattern differs markedly from your prediction because the diamond bins for certain types become empty. In short, the system prompts you to manage it correctly.

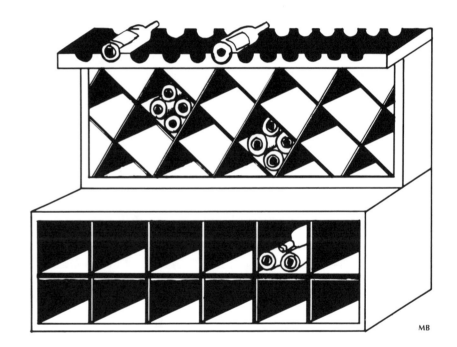

MB

NOTES ON A TASTING GROUP

The very best way to increase your confidence and sophistication around a bottle of wine is with comparison tasting experience. It takes the same amount of time and costs about as much as going to the movies. And, given the state of cinematic art, it is a lot more entertaining. First you will discover there are not any right or wrong answers. As they said 2,000 years ago "De gustibus non disputatum" (about taste there can be no argument). Wine conversation is a parlor game. It is ideal for people who think that Scrabble fails to afford enough opportunities for cheating. Second, you will discover that preferences and opinions can be quite fervently held and colorfully stated. Therein lies the fun. Teaching yourself to be aware of smells may seem a little "New Age" at first, but it quickly becomes a powerful source of pleasure. Don't worry, you can always pretend to be thinking about baseball scores.

The following are suggestions from the bimonthly Winewright's Report:

◆ LOCATION

An organizer needs a place to hold tastings. That can be a difficult issue. Therefore, it often makes sense to hold tastings in the same location each month once a good one is found. The best locations allow participants to sit with room for six to eight glasses in front of them. Some homes accommodate tastings well, but most need to restrict the number of participants rather severely in order to provide comfort. Moving the tasting to a new home each month may seem democratic, but it is a burden for participants to find a different location each time, and the inaugural event in any place will always be more trouble than repeat performances.

◆ GROUP SIZE & NUMBER OF WINES

The social proclivities of the group weighed against their desire to experiment will determine these points, assuming that the location hasn't already dictated the answers. Close friends who prefer to focus their attention on conversation will want larger amounts of fewer wines. Dedicated wine hobbyists who demand clinical attention for tasting will want a greater number of wines. There are 24 ounces in a bottle. Social groups usually have 8-12 people tasting 6-8 wines. The number of bottles actually opened can be adjusted to fit the number of people who actually show up. The goal is to have available something between 10 and 18 ounces/person. Remember, you do not have to finish each bottle. The ideal group size for more clinical interests is 16 tasters doing 12 wines in two flights of 6 each. Two flights allows a white and a red to be tasted each evening. 16 tasters yields 1.5 ounces/person/bottle which is plenty for evaluation purposes.

◆ MONEY

Another difficult issue is that 20-40% of the expected participants will often fail to show up. Entreaties to commitment and responsibility will do no good. Wine tasting is fun, but it is not central to a normal adult's self image. Rather than suffer ulcers from the deleterious effect no-shows have on financial planning, it is best to accommodate the situation with pre-established policy and a little flexibility.

A social group should have 15 people on the roster, a clinical group 20. Price at a social group should be the cost of the wines and the food divided by 8. Price at a clinical group should be (wines+food)/12. This way a per person dollar figure can be established ahead of time. Any person on the roster who fails to communicate their regrets at least 24 hours before the event should be charged half price if they fail to show up. It is easy to employ excess money that builds up from persistently good turnouts. Emergencies make the 24-hour rule seem harsh on occasion, but the average dollar penalty rarely reaches two figures.

◆ GLASSES, FOOD & ACCESSORIES

Washing glasses for the whole group is a tremendous burden. It doesn't have any of the psychic rewards found in procuring the food or wine. A good suggestion is to find glasses in 6 or 8-pak cardboard cartons which participants can bring with them. More importantly, they can take them home from each meeting and wash them. It is prudent to have a few extra boxes around for people who forget theirs, but the potential to share glasses usually alleviates any big problems in this regard. Don't forget to bring a corkscrew! Have a decanter of water available for rinsing mouths and glasses. Dump buckets are always a good idea.

Food can be quite elaborate if the group is social and wants a meal. Bread and cheese are fine though. It is important to have something for people to put in their stomachs while they are drinking wine, particularly if they have just come from work without eating.

♦ SCHEDULE, WINE & NOTICES

To ease communication it is convenient to have a regular schedule, i.e. first Tuesday of each month. The general category of wines should be determined at the meeting one month ahead and the responsibility for getting the wines assigned at that time. Give Winewrights a call.

Communication can be accomplished easily by xeroxing the group's roster with addresses onto sheets of self-adhesive mailing labels. The monthly message can then be xeroxed onto normal sized sheets of paper which are folded in thirds, stapled and stamped. It takes about ten minutes, start to finish, once you get set up.

♦ TASTING FORMAT & SCORING

Social groups can be quite successful with a walk-around format and show-of-hands scoring. Any format which you can pull off with regularity should be encouraged. It is always a hoot, however, to compile group scores in order to spur conversation. To that end, you should give "blind" tasting a try. Have one person wrap the bottles in newspaper secured with tape to hide the brand names. Remove the capsules and the corks. Replace corks loosely in different bottles. Have a second person label the bottles in an alphabetic sequence. Don't unwrap the bottles until scores have been turned in.

In lieu of a lengthy, and rather dull, treatise on scoring systems, let me suggest one used successfully by the Winewrights staff. It is a forced ranking hierarchy using a hedonic scale. At least I think it is. Actually I'm not sure I know what any of those phrases mean.

The idea is to rank the wines in order of preference, then array them over an expanded hierarchy so that spaces can be inserted wherever you perceive significant differences in quality. We use a 25-unit hierarchy with the number one position indicating the best (or first place). It should be viewed as a bell shaped curve. Thus, 50% of the world's wines would end up between 10 and 15. Real good wines (20) would fall between 5 and 10, while slightly flawed wines (20) would fall between 15 and 20. Any wine falling in the 1 to 5 range should be absolutely extraordinary (5), and any falling in the 20 to 25 range (5) should have been dumped out at the winery.

For example, let's say you are tasting six wines (A-F). You decide that you like them in the following order: C, E, F, A, D, B. You think C may be one of the best examples of the grape variety you have ever tasted. You think B would strip paint. E and F are distinctly more pleasant to you than A and D. The following scores might reflect your feelings in the 25-unit hierarchy Winewrights uses:

C	 2	A	 14
E	 8	D	 15
F	 11	B	 22

This expanded hierarchy allows you to show groups of preferences with enough distance from each other that they effect the compiled results. The hierarchy is anchored around the 10-15 range to get everyone to employ it the same way. Add up everyone's numbers for each wine thusly:

	You	Lance	Miyako	Chelsea	Alphonse	Patience	**Total**
Wine A	14	12	23	8	18	10	**85**
Wine B	22	20	13	23	25	16	**119**
Wine C	2	8	15	10	9	14	**58**
Wine D	15	13	14	11	14	12	**79**
Wine E	8	16	10	14	15	15	**78**
Wine F	11	14	12	15	20	9	**86**

The lowest total is the group favorite. Clearly it is wine C in this example. Wines D and E are functionally tied for second place. As are wines A and F for fourth place. The group has solidly confirmed your opinion of wine B.

Numbers won't tell anyone what the wine tastes like. They do provide a modicum of cover behind which to hide when taking cheap, but extraordinarily witty, shots at your friends conversationally. Since you are the bright one, of course, you have little to fear by way of return fire. In any case, should the heat get too intense, just fall back with those old chestnuts, "my nose has been a little stuffy this week" or "it is hard to smell anything while sitting next to this cedar door" (you sly dog).

SERVICE ESSAYS

In Greek mythology, Dionysus was the god of joy, hospitality and wine. Sired by Zeus, Dionysus was the only god said to have a mortal parent, his mother Semele. Our word "symposium" is derived from the Greek name for meetings where learned people gathered to drink wine and talk. Wine has been synonymous with human interaction for millenia.

In writing about wine and reaching for clear, unequivocal statements, one is tempted to disregard the importance of the surroundings in which the wine will be consumed and the expectations that each consumer will bring. Make no mistake. The way wine is served and the attitudes of the people participating will govern the perception of quality.

This chapter attempts to move in a slightly different direction from recitations of ritual and etiquette covered in other books. The purpose is to broaden readers' awareness of the human beings holding the glasses and how their attitudes take form. Wine industry personnel confront these points each day they engage the marketplace. As with the other controversies on which this book focuses, reasonable men and women disagree over these poorly understood issues. Winery people talk about them all the time though. An attempt is made here to present an "insider's view" with pragmatic advice for hobbyist consumers.

Professional winery spokesmen rarely address topics like teenage drinking, or the role of music in persuading people that a wine is "good," or why water should be available in every tasting room. At least they don't do it candidly in public. Perhaps the reason is that only big wineries have spokesmen. Big wineries can manipulate their product, but they are several steps removed from the circumstances in which it will be consumed. This situation leads them to promulgate the philosophy that a wine or worse, a brand, will be exactly the same each time it is encountered. Bushwah. That is like saying a mirror will look exactly the same no matter who stands in front of it. Small wineries are less likely to fall into this trap. Small wineries have a more direct, more immediate relationship with the consumers of their wine. To big wineries, the "surface" of the product is everything. To small wineries, the "service" of the product is everything.

A famous Zen koan inquires whether there is any sound when a tree falls in the forest if no one is there to hear it. Wine has the same relativist nature to human beings. Do smell and taste pleasure exist if no people are there to perceive them, and talk about them? Does joy exist without people to share it? There is ample reason the consciousness of antiquity could not conceive Dionysus without the aid of a mortal. Wine is not just a drink. It is an event, a memory, a community.

PSYCHOLOGY

Many Americans free-associate the word "wine" with the concept of pretension. The stereotype of an American wine drinker is a man seeking to put on airs. Progressive industry spokesmen are constantly trying to downplay this image in order to broaden the market. They tell beginners to ignore conventions of phraseology or ritual and instead "drink what you like." This effort has merit. Few southern European populations bother to critique a glass of wine. They merely consume it — lots of it.

I suspect, however, that this image of the American wine snob has more to do with America than it has to do with wine. The pleasures of wine drinking involve very powerful stimuli which are derived from human psychology; not from the bottled liquid. This cultural envelope surrounding fine wine can be a barrier, but it is also quite valuable. I don't blame alcohol for alcohol abuse any more than I blame matches for arson. The alcohol in wine is not significantly better or worse for you than the alcohol in beer or vodka. But the cultural ritual is! Wine has a 4,000 year history during which many human beings have learned to exploit its advantages and minimize its problems. Americans are usually introduced to this cultural envelope well into their adult years. It is no wonder that a lot of dogs will favor tricks from their youth. Consider, however, the respective cultural envelopes surrounding wine versus tequila. Is it accurate to call one pretentious and the other fun? Which one do you think would be better for your body over a twenty year period?

Rather than attempting to eliminate pretension, I suggest harnessing it. In most cases it is an example of psychological need grabbing the cultural envelope and running amok. "Snobbery" is a pejorative name we use to categorize behavior wherein individuals attempt to differentiate themselves (slightly) from a group. These folks don't want to be alone. They just want to be recognizable. America can accomodate that need and enjoy drinking wine too. We do it with jewelry, clothes, homes and cars all the time. If you understand the physiological and psychological factors comprising smell and taste pleasure, you will become much more tolerant of supercilious individuals you encounter, and much more confident of your own impressions.

Secret Number One lies in learning to separate stimuli which originate in the glass from everything else that might alter one's perception. Most people blur this distinction because they fail to admit the influence of, and carry little respect for, the category I've labeled "everything else." It is an extremely important set of stimuli. Neither category is intrinsically more valuable than the other one. Nevertheless, prevailing opinion seems to hold that stimuli from the glass are "true" and everything else is hocum. Don't let yourself make this mistake. Expectations, group interactions and serving manipulations all contribute rich enhancements to the wine drinking experience. They *are* the cultural envelope. They *do* alter your perception. And the perception is the experience; the stimulus is not. Without this "everything else" category, you only get half of what you pay for in a bottle of wine.

Secret Number Two is separating the "recognition" effort from the "preference" function. It is one thing to register the existence of certain smells, and quite another thing to decide whether or not you like them. Your "preferences" will change over time, as well as in various social situations. That is expected. But the goal in the "recognition" function is to train yourself to be consistent. Professional wine judges have lively debates merely trying to ascertain the quantitative differences between two wines. Variations in how the samples are handled along with diverse body chemistries and sensitivities will result in disparity among the receptors being activated for each individual. A concensus descriptive vocabulary is equally hard to come by. The difficulty of this "recognition" task is enormous, but results can be verified by sophisticated quantitative instruments. There *are* right and wrong answers. "Preference," or qualitative distinctions, are entirely another matter. Conventionally accepted standards exist and certain characteristics indicate expense, rarity, mishandling, or predict future development. However, there are *no* right and wrong answers about what an individual should dislike, or enjoy.

This freedom in the area of "preference" provides a convenient screen with which to disguise a justified lack of confidence in our "recognition" abilities. I accept the utility of this behavior. All one has to do is blend a little "recognition" into a lot of "preference." Compound this technique with a one hand/other hand statement, and you will be completely unassailable. A good idea when surrounded by wily strangers. "This wine has nice fruit, but the finish is harsh." You have implied personal experience while simultaneously covering exposure to your rear. Detractors may take issue with your choice of "nice" or "harsh," but these are value judgements to which your are entitled as surely as you would be to a preference for blondes or brunettes. This conversational technique works well. It is common, and you should employ it in lieu of an apology about your wine acumen. However, you should also understand that you are engaged in a cultural interaction. You are servicing a psychological stimulus. Actual recognition of stimuli from the glass of wine is not essential to performance of this role.

Secrets #1 and #2 clearly augment each other. Purely objective analysis

of wine involves focusing on the liquid in the glass to the exclusion of all other stimuli. The wine is "worked" to make it reveal certain characteristics. Samples are compared side-by-side without clues to their identity. Each wine is described as thoroughly as possible without the distraction of trying to "value" component characteristics. Notes are taken at several points in the process. This clinical approach improves anyone's "recognition" ability tenfold. Its not what average citizens call great fun, but it makes distinction between wines extremely obvious. Expert wine tasters would never bet on their own ability without bringing these techniques of concentration and protracted examination to bear. Likewise, buyers or their professsional representatives would be well advised to have results from this type of clinical examination available before they apply subjective, "preference" considerations to their purchasing decisions.

Selling a particular wine, or serving it to guests, changes the situation 180°. "Preference" is largely determined by the "everything else," or cultural envelope, category in Secret #1. Instead of avoiding psychological influences, one wants to employ them to enhance the enjoyment of the experience. Humans, from expert wine judges to novice consumers, are prone to attribute enjoyment levels to organoleptic (smell and taste) stimuli from the glass. The truth, however, is those stimuli are easily overpowered by visual and auditory stimuli from the environment. Smell and taste are primitive senses more closely linked with our hormonal system than with the cognitive centers of our brain. We have evolved as visual and auditory animals. We react very quickly to those stimuli, even when they are delivered at subliminal intensity. Visual and auditory cues are much more likely to come from people than from a glass of wine. We say a "bad" wine ruined the evening when, in fact, the poor social consequences of the evening have altered our perception of the wine. Some people wonder why they can't recognize flaws in a certain wine, when actually they have only experienced a vocal advocate influencing group preference. There is no reason to decry these manipulations. They can be rather confusing until you get your bearings, but they also add significant opportunities to the social milieu that is a basic ingredient of wine appreciation.

♦ **EXPECTATION.** Having your sensory perception influenced by a preconceived notion is not some kind of mental laziness. It is due to the fundamental biochemistry of the brain. Neural pathways are established by repeated use. Thus, interpretation of sensory data is a function of matching the most recent input to patterns from one's experience. If you've never smelled garlic, you won't be able to identify it the way a Sicilian would. Likewise the sensory search pattern in your brain can easily be driven by suggestions with which you are familiar. If your nose is plugged up and you bite into an onion with your eyes closed while someone asks you what type of apple it is, your mind will match the sensory data to a neural search pattern for apples. It is not that your sensory receptors have been fooled. It is the cognitive portion of your brain logically investigating the most dominant sensory cue — in this case, the auditory word "apple." The incompatible data runs into neural cul de sacs, while the matching nerve impulses move easily along well-used pathways.

If you want to gauge how important expectations are to the wine tasting experience, notice the increased tension in the room when normal cues about the wine are removed. Blind tastings, where the wine labels are hidden, are but one example. Refusing to tell tasters what grape variety is involved will crank the anxiety up another notch. Hiding prices will have a similar effect. Care to guess what your friends would think of a $30 wine you served after first decanting it into a screw-top bottle? Professional wine judges usually give better scores to wines in an awards round than they did when the same wines were scored in an elimination round. Everybody wants cues to help narrow the search pattern in their brain.

Expectation is such an important influence that it is almost impossible to eliminate when evaluating a glass of wine. Manipulating it is the subject of much marketing philosophy. As a host, you should realize the most important factor affecting your guests enjoyment of a wine occurs when you introduce the wine just before pouring it. A remark can make or break a wine. A clever story can guarantee the outcome you desire.

In the wine appreciation classes I taught on the Stanford University campus for 15 years, I was often asked if "it is worth paying an extra $10 or $15 for some more expensive brand on a special occasion in a restaurant." I pointed out that the answer would probably be no if the wine were going to be clinically and objectively evaluated by the guests. But, of course, it isn't consumed in that manner. The role of the wine choice in a celebratory situation is usually to cue expectations. "Now we're having fun." The price is one of the clearest messages that can be sent at that point. An increase of 10% on the dinner check seems like a prudent investment to guarantee positive expectations for the whole meal, I would say as my Scottish grandmother twirled in her grave.

♦ **DISTRACTION and EXHAUSTION.** An ability to concentrate on the wine in your glass is nearly as important to objectivity as the suppression of expectations. This ability can be developed. Most experts have idiosyncratic behaviors they use to focus their attention. They appear to swirl the wine absent mindedly when actually they are performing a preparatory

ritual. Some twitch their nose, others loosen their jaw or breathe deeply. In all cases they are attempting to shut down peripheral awareness, primarily from visual and auditory sensations. Distractions could be intrusive chatter or music, visually stimulating people or activities or displays, and competing smells from food or flowers or perfume. In carefully controlled tastings, judges usually face a wall, and the room sounds like the 18th green at the Masters while Jack Nicklaus putts for the championship. That is, a Masters where half the gallery are cleaning their teeth and spitting into washbasins.

After about eight wines, all but the most rigorous tastings begin to loosen up. I conduct classes for 70 people at a time using 12 different wines. I'm rarely given a microphone. I have learned to say anything which may be of importance to the whole group before serving the eighth or ninth wine. My ability to command attention drops precipitously at that point. It is tempting to conclude that the effects of the alcohol are responsible. However, the same phenomenon occurs when untrained tasters are spitting the wines out. I suspect exhaustion is the culprit. It is hard work to focus one's attention on bringing elusive smell and taste sensations from the recesses of our primitive brain up to the level of cognitive awareness and discussion. After an hour most people are pooped. I get the same experience from looking at abstract paintings.

In order to extend their concentration resources, professional judges learn to focus, then relax, alternately. This technique has the added benefit of allowing their taste buds and smell receptors to recover between sensations. They focus their attention on a wine for about 5 seconds while they sniff it and roll it around in their mouth. Then they relax for 30-45 seconds while they compose some written notes. Every 15 minutes or so they get up or look around the room to unleash this tight perspective. Then they return again to the task at hand.

You can use a similar technique to heighten your guests' perception of smell and taste in wines you serve at a dinner or party. In that situation, there will likely be conversation, music, food and other stimuli diffusing people's attention. Focus everyone on the wine for a brief period by stopping the music and introducing the wines between food courses. This sensory interlude will augment the party. Your guests will think the wines are unusually good. The truth will be that you delivered a unique social massage by concentrating the energy of a group in such a way as to make each person unusually sensitive for a small window of time. The contrast between their lack of sensitivity when distracted and their improved sensitivity when the whole group is thinking about one thing, will remain a strong memory for them. They won't realize that you, rather than the wines, caused it.

Hugh Johnson tells a story which illustrates another way distraction can be put to work for a wine's benefit. He was visiting a small winery in northern Italy. The winemaker gave him a tour of the place and then excused himself to keep another appointment. The winemaker's demure, but extremely attractive, 20 year old daughter joined Mr. Johnson for a simple meal on the veranda and a tasting of the winery's product. Three hours later, Johnson had concluded that the wine was spectacular. He returned to England with several bottles and glowing reports of this moderately priced, but astonishingly high quality discovery. The worth of the wine grew each time he retailed the story. To his surprise (and a credit to his humility), upon arrival in London each bottle he opened seemed bland, bordering on insipid. Hint: It isn't the wine that doesn't travel.

♦ **HALO EFFECT.** In any group, some people will be more sure of what they are doing than others. Those with the lowest confidence levels will watch people they think are competent to get behavioral cues. If several people begin acting in a similar way, group or peer pressure will induce others to unconsciously adopt the same behavior. A few people will thus create spheres of influence on certain subjects which radiate throughout the entire group. This phenomenon is true everywhere, from second grade classrooms to cocktail parties and from corporate offices to trial juries. It is well documented.

To objectively evaluate a wine, you must shield yourself from the halo cast by others. It can be subtle. If you look up at a blind tasting and see one of the speakers on the dais grimace after putting wine C in his mouth, you *have* been influenced no matter how much you may try to compensate. Another form of this problem was called the "error of leniency" by Maynard Amerine when he chaired the Enology Department at U.C. Davis. I resolutely agree that it's impossible to evaluate a wine objectively while making eye contact with the winemaker.

To manipulate subjective opinion, you should be one of the halos. Being the person who chooses and pays for a bottle of wine is usually credential enough to cast a fair sized halo. Gossip, or a few adroitly chosen facts, will serve equally well if they can be delivered with panache. The key is to indicate that you know something about this wine, winery, winemaker or vineyard that is not common knowledge. Once your halo is in operation, however, you must take caution with what you say. People will be sifting through your remarks looking for hints they can enlarge upon in their own conversations. They may miss your point and seize upon some line you meant to throw away.

♦ **PROXIMITY.** One pronounced characteristic of a wine will influence tasters' opinion about the wine's other characteristics. For instance, an alluring nose will favorably color one's perception of the wine's acid balance. It is therefore possible to draw attention to a singularly strong feature with a finely worded description and effectively hide a wine's weak points. This marvel of generalized attributes extends further than you might think. Elaborating on a label's artistic beauty, or a vineyard's pedigree, or a winemaker's congenial nature, or a bottle's rarity will all confer positive stature on the wine's taste and smell. So will expensive glassware. The reverse is equally true and much more likely to be a factor. For some reason American wit is more highly tuned on the negative side of most equations. One sharply worded zinger, launched early, can sink a wine. If you secretly wish to champion that wine's cause, you must rejoin quickly to cancel the harmful remark. Be careful though. Prefacing a retort with exclamations like, "Yo' mama!" may prematurely reveal your lack of objectivity. If you have several wines in the field, you'll need to pick your spots prudently based on the halo value of individual detractors.

♦ **FIRST WINE FAVORITISM and CONTRAST.** These two psychological influences are called "Time-Order" errors in organoleptic evaluation. Professional wine judges mitigate both by tasting through any set of wines in various random orders. "First Wine Favoritism" means that the first wine tasted will tend to be prefered if all other factors are equal. Dr. Amerine speculates that "in making a quality judgement on the first sample one has no immediate frame of reference for purposes of comparison." Lesson: Don't serve your best wine first at a dinner party.

"Contrast" refers to the way a difference between two wines is perceived as exaggerated in the second wine. That is, a medium-bodied wine will seem light-bodied when tasted right after a heavy-bodied one. If you want particular wines to show well, serve them in conjunction with lesser quality examples.

WINERY VISIT PROTOCOL

Vacation visits and day trips to a wine growing region are among the top three tourist attractions in California. Millions of people do it annually. The opportunity to escape city pressures for a period of leisurely country driving is always a treat. Meals become gastronomic adventure whether they are return-to-nature picnics or haute cuisine served in elegant restaurants. Wineries offer a romantic entre to California because they reflect seasonal change, the rhthym of the vineyards. They provide depth to anyone's experience of an area through their interest in history, climate, geology, economics, scientific sophistication and artistic endeavor. Grape growing and winemaking can be hard manual labor, but the dollars involved lend an air of worthwhile gentlemanly pursuit to even the most primitive operations. Although one may encounter haughty pretension and bored indifference on occasion, the majority of winery personnel exude folksy charm and hospitality while they dispense education. Very few people come away from a winery visit without an increased sense of personal relationship to the product. A glimpse of the vintners' lifestyle *will* enhance your ability to enjoy a bottle of wine at home with friends.

There are some basic differences between wineries however. Big wineries have facilities and a staff specifically designated to service visitors. Robert Mondavi, for instance, has 40 people engaged in hospitality at the winery. Several large wineries feature top quality multi-media presentations. Souverain and Domaine Chandon have excellent restaurants on their premises. A visit to Christain Brothers includes a view of the world's largest corkscrew collection. Numerous winery tasting rooms double as art galleries. Many are furnished with antiques or built in dramatic architectural styles. Appointments are not necessary in these places. They are generally located along major routes of travel, and thus easy to find with the help of guidebooks available throughout the region.

Micro-wineries are another story. In most cases one or two people do all the work. Entertaining visitors is time subtracted either from vineyard and winery chores or else from their family obligations. It is a tribute to the conviviality of the product that these wineries agree to host visitors at all. Making an appointment is more than a mere courtesy. The odds on finding someone home without an appointment are long. Many micro-wineries are very hard to locate, and some are virtually inaccessible to standard automobiles without special instructions. Do not be offended if these wineries decline to see you at your convenience. Some have restrictions on their Use Permits which make it legally unwise. The staff at Winewrights does research at tiny wineries all the time. If we call 10 micro-wineries for appointments the next day, we are likely to only reach 5 on the phone and then find 2 available to meet us for business. The plus side of this situation is that one eventually gets to visit with an owner/winemaker instead of a professional public relations agent. The difference in knowledge and candor can be extraordinary. It justifies some preparation on the part of the visitor.

When attempting to make an appointment to visit a micro-winery keep the vintner's interests in mind. Their wine is not going to be one of the choices presented to you in the average liquor store or restaurant. Hence, they have little incentive to compete for your attention by pouring hefty doses of alcohol and approximating a party atmosphere the way larger wineries sometimes do. Beer drinkers who drop in off the highway for a few quick pops before dinner are not a market little wineries hope to penetrate. Micro-vintners want to focus their promotional time on that narrow segment of the population who seek out and appreciate rare, limited edition wines. So pre-qualify yourself over the phone. Mention that you entertain at home a lot or belong to a tasting group. Say that you are looking to discover wines for your cellar which can't be found in every neighborhood store. Remark that you gained your curiousity about the winery while taking a wine appreciation class. Membership in Winewrights serves as a credential precisely because participating wineries know members pay an annual fee and have the ability to order limited distribution wines.

At the same time, you should not treat small wineries like notches on the gun butt of life by overscheduling yourself. Leave the door open for serendipity. Nothing is more frustrating than having a winemaker take a shine to you and offer to open a bottle of his special sold-out award winner when you are already half an hour late for your next appointment. And that is exactly what will happen. First you will underestimate the driving distance between wineries. California is bigger than many people realize. Then you will get lost. It happens to me every day, and I've been doing this for a living nearly 20 years. If you spend the entire day falling further and further behind schedule, you will **not** have fun and you will insult the principals of the wineries that have taken time off to see you. Wineries are more likely to give you an appointment if you imply the entire trip is being undertaken for the express purpose of seeing them. They're not naive, but everyone enjoys a little flattery. At most, you should seek one small winery appointment in the morning and one in the afternoon. It will be easy to fill in around these with stops that do not require appointments.

Word of caution #1. Touring wineries can be exhausting. Going to more than three in a day, or doing it for more than a couple days in a row, is work, not play. Members of your party will lose their sense of excitement after several ounces of wine and a few hours in the hot sun. You will enjoy yourself more, and stave off friendly revolution, if you gear the tour toward the least interested members of the group. Leave yourself the chance to stumble upon social and sporting events, or craft displays, or points of historical interest, or wildlife and nature areas. A visit to wine country should be an exercise in relaxation. Do not apply the stamina that makes you a success in the business world to a subject which is essentially a hobby. Wine has wonderful connections to many other fields. Develop your capacity for curiosity and self-entertainment by exploring some of these tangents.

Word of caution #2. Think about your body ahead of time. It is possible to consume 30 ounces of wine at three wineries. One shudders to consider the condition of people who hit eight wineries, and then drive two hours to eat at an expensive restaurant in San Francisco. Lethargy barely describes the symptoms experienced by most people around 3 p.m. when they fail to take precautions during a day full of winetasting. If you want to be worth a damn at the end of your trip, you should plan on utilizing at least some of the following techniques:

◊ **Spit** the wines out. You heard me. You will get the same organoleptic pleasure whether the wine exits your mouth through the front or the back. Most wineries are constructed with drains in the floor so they can be hosed down. Winemakers taste all day long by spitting wines out. Most of them will gain respect for your sophistication if you do the same. They will recognize your interest in taste over intoxication. Moreover, the ability to expectorate wine adroitly is impressive to anyone in the industry. It's like a secret fraternity grip. The idea is to maintain a tight pattern on the target. You can practice in the shower. The key is loose lips. While developing your expertise, you should probably plan on close proximity to the receptacle. In elegantly furnished tasting rooms, it may be wise to step outside and annoint some of the landscaping. Tell the gardener you are driving.

◊ Drink lots of **water.** After every wine sample, rinse your glass if water is available and consume the rinse water. Force yourself to drink a big glass of water in the morning. Do it again before going to bed. This technique will require you to locate restrooms more frequently than normal, but few winemakers equate bladder size with connoisseurship. Wineries are elaborately engineered pieces of plumbing to start with. They all have a loo. The alternative to this technique is a low-grade hangover and a mouth that feels like cotton candy by mid-afternoon. If you can supply your party with cold bottles of mineral water instead of sweet soda pop around 3 p.m., you will be the most popular person in the car.

◊ Eat **food.** Have breakfast even if you normally don't. Carry some bread and cheese to help remove the tannin from red wines which would otherwise build up in your mouth. Producing cold celery or apples at 3 p.m. will make you a hero.

◊ Get some **exercise.** Find a place to swim, or play tennis, or take a vigorous half hour walk. Concentrating on smell/taste sensations for long periods of time will make you feel tired, but your muscles will probably have been more quiescent than usual all day long. Doing something to get your blood moving will help metabolize alcohol out of your system. Unless your are extremely strong willed, it is prudent to make exercise plans ahead of time which will be hard to back out of. You will feel great after exercising, but you may be a little slow getting started.

◊ Take a short **nap** and a shower before dinner. When people realize they don't have to change into more formal clothes to eat in one of the fine local restaurants, they sometimes forego this break in the action. You should plan on taking it. The combination of sun, travel, meeting people, and attention to smell/taste sensations will take more out of you than you realize. Chances are good that dinner will present marvelous new sensations. Too many wine country visitors end up semi-conscious at precisely the point they spend the most money. You should call a recess from conviviality in the late afternoon to let everyone's mind sort through all the new input it has been receiving. Refreshed, you will enjoy the evening more and wake up the next day without that sneaking suspicion that some bulldozer has been working overtime in your hotel room.

Another difference between large wineries and small ones involves the way you should behave once you arrive. The professional hospitality staff at big wineries plans on directing the action. They have a prepared format and can not handle large numbers of people if they deviate from it very broadly. In short, your role is largely passive. At micro-wineries, the number of visitors is much smaller, and your host may only perform this function a couple of times per week. S/he is likely to spend most of the working day doing other winery jobs. Tour guides at big wineries deliver their presentation several times per hour, and their winery information has usually come from someone else. At micro-wineries you are expected to play a more active role than at big wineries, and you get more rewards for doing so.

Sometimes this distinction in roles is subtle, but it is accurate nonetheless. Too many tourists think that a winery is a winery, and therefore all winery representatives will adopt the same position in a group interaction. These tourists should content themselves with visiting big wineries who present a show in exchange for the right to deliver a commercial massage. The roles there are analogous to those when you stroll into an automobile showroom. A visit to a micro-winery, however, is more analogous to someone granting you an interview in their home. They have not agreed to provide cake and cookies. They do expect you to have a nodding acquaintance with the subject, and they assume you will want to direct the conversation toward your specific areas of interest. Many of them won't even bother with the canned pitch of generalities if you indicate your background knowledge and areas of interest right away. Do this with a probing question. Don't fall into the trap of monopolizing the conversation with longwinded recitations of well known wines you've tasted and wineries you've visited. Mention one or two wines you particularly like (as opposed to expensive brands you think you should like) and a winery that is doing something unique you find interesting.

Here are three lines of inquiry which can help get you started:

◇ Is there a particular style the winemaker shoots for (choose a grape variety they produce)? When and where do they pick grapes to accomplish it? Any special viticultural techniques? What winemaking methods enhance that style? Have they changed styles over the years?

◇ Do they have a significant track record with this particular wine or grape variety? How does this wine change in the bottle? What have they noticed as differences from vintage to vintage?

◇ How did they (as an individual) come to be doing what they're doing?

Most micro-vintners will employ an impressive depth of technical understanding and considerable personal flair to provide wonderful insights if you merely indicate a sincere interest. One way to do that is to take notes, and perhaps some pictures. If you are invited to taste wine, it is almost incumbent upon you to take some written notes. Failure to do so implies that you are not putting as much into the event as your host is. You are not necessarily expected to buy wine. Micro-vintners realize that their wine is not going to benefit from several days cruising around in your trunk at

150°F. However, you should do your host the courtesy of inquiring about how wines can be purchased in the future.

Self-sufficiency is the key to good times when visiting small wineries. A minimal amount of equipment will give you the imprimatur of experience, will avoid placing annoying pressure on others and will open up many opportunities for spontaneity which you might otherwise turn down.

◇ SHOES. Not only should they be comfortable, but they should be able to withstand walking in dusty vineyards and on wet winery floors. Save the fashion statement for dinner in the evening.

◇ SWEATER, HAT. From May through September, California can get extremely hot on the inland side of the coastal mountains. Having a hat available will make you more comfortable when you get a chance to do something where shade is hard to come by. At the same time, winery interiors are often kept below 60°F by insulation and jacketed fermenting tanks. Carry a sweater or light windbreaker which you can put on and take off without commotion so you don't have to leave every cellar after fifteen minutes. Your sweater may also come into play unexpectedly if you drive to the coast or when evening falls. Visitors are always surprised by these 40°F temperature shifts.

Don't worry about the formality of your attire. People generally dress up for dinner in San Francisco. In the wine country, however, men wearing ties in even the most elegant restaurants are usually the minority.

◇ WINE GLASSES. Since it is a virtual necessity to have a car, why not stick a couple of small wine glasses into the trunk. You can bring them from your hotel room wrapped in a towel if you fly in empty handed. All these do is give you the ability to drink fine wine when and where you want without having to resort to plastic tumblers. At home you always drink wine in locations where glasses are available, or where tasting it is not necessarily the idea. The wine country is going to present opportunities you don't encounter at home.

◇ CORKSCREW. See wine glasses above.

◇ KNIFE. It doesn't have to be a weapon. A paring knife will do. The idea is to be able to cut bread, cheese and salami without having to rediscover stone age technology. Putting it in the glove compartment will make group compromises on the subject of what constitutes an acceptable picnic much more possible.

◊   PEN. If you carry it, you will take notes. If you have to look for it when you want it, you won't.

◊   MAP. Phone booths are sometimes hard to come by when you are lost in rural country. Cross roads may be ten miles apart. It is also much easier to follow directions over the phone if you are looking at a map. Buy a regional road map for 75 cents in any mini-grocery or service station. Tourist wine guides can give you addresses, phone numbers and relative locations, but their maps are often artists' renditions which ignore scale and important roads. Having a regional road map will alert you to many points of curiosity the wine guides miss.

Being invited to taste wine at a micro-winery is also different than at a large winery. You want to minimize the glassware that has to be brought into play. Consider ways in which you can compare two wines side-by-side by selecting a healthy partner and sharing glasses. If invited to taste wines from the barrel, be prepared to step forward quickly as the wine is taken out of the barrel. Wine thieves are difficult to manipulate between the barrel and your glass because they drip, and that can attract fruit flies if not wiped up.

Wines in barrel are not meant to be compared to bottled wines. Many vintners hesitate to show wines out of the barrel to novices for this reason. Reds will usually be fairly tannic. So take your time and swirl them around vigorously to introduce lots of air. The nose of these wines will seem subdued. Concentrate more on their aftertaste for an indication of how they will develop in the bottle.

Always hold your glass by the stem or base. Look at the color of the wine. Swirl it around and smell it. Notice how it changes in the glass over a ten minute period. Make some comments using descriptive similes, i.e. smells like "cedar" or tastes like "cherries." Winemakers are interested in your reaction. They want to know that you are concentrating your attention on the wine for a few minutes. Pick out the characteristic which you find most noticeable and remark on it. You need not say that you like it, and you probably shouldn't announce that you don't like it. But you want to demonstrate how it fits in with your experience. Mention wines that you think are similar, especially if they are highly regarded or more expensive. Comment on whether you could enjoy the wine now with a certain dish, or would rather keep it in your cellar for future development. Remark on the relationship between two of the wines that you are tasting by saying, "#1 seems softer" or "#2 seems fruitier."

Finally, realize that it is your role to conclude the proceedings in a timely and gracious fashion. Give winemakers plenty of opportunity to accept your departure without having to initiate the subject themselves. Pretend that you are a guest in their home. Feel free to accept any and all hospitality that is offered, but don't stand around waiting for the big finale that usually comes at the end of a large winery hospitality tour (right before the invitation to visit the gift shop on your way out). Remember, at micro-wineries you are the active party. Failure to recognize a polite conclusion may imply that you expect something which has not been freely offered. Having given generously of their time, the principals at tiny wineries might understandably resent such an implication.

The bottom line is that large wineries give some of their corporate attention to anybody just about any time. Micro-vintners give all of their attention to a few people on special occasions. You should understand and appreciate the difference. It is definitely worthwhile experiencing it. The time a micro-vintner spends with you is much more valuable than the profit they might make on selling you a couple bottles of wine. If you are sincerely interested, however, most micro-vintners will take great pleasure in showing you around. It doesn't make financial sense for them to do so, but artistic wine is their passion first, and only a business secondarily.

WINE & HEALTH ISSUES

The following essay is excerpt from the January 1988 issue of WINE-WRIGHTS REPORT, a bi-monthly membership newsletter available from the publisher of this book.

Health issues have dogged the U.S. beverage alcohol industry for centuries. As an example, Maine has passed and repealed Prohibition four separate times. Someday I'd like to write a book on the subject. It would be a self-help, talk-show special making a religion out of moderation, satisfaction and balance. I think those are skills that can be taught to 90% of the population, and fine wine is an excellent medium for demonstrating them. Those principles apply to sex, food and gambling as well as to drugs and alcohol. *Everybody* grapples with these issues at one time or another.

My parents didn't drink, although they had liquor in the house for guests. At college, I was a fraternity social chairman. I paid a lot of dues discharging that office, and I developed some troublesome tendencies later. I was also quite lucky in several nasty situations. Many kids pay extreme penalties going through the same learning curve I did. Americans should not make their children chart that path blindly over and over again. I took a BA in Psychology at Stanford, and later got a credential in Substance Abuse Prevention from U.C. Santa Cruz. From 1975-78 I was President of a non-profit group funded by the California Department of Education to investigate and implement primary prevention curriculae in 7th and 10th grades. I also taught wine classes three nights a week for 15 years.

During the '70s I worked hard to construct an alliance between the wine industry, the Department of Education and moderates within the "alcoholism constituency." Our theme was individual responsibility. We lobbied for primary prevention programs, which embrace the entire population before a problem occurs, instead of relying solely on early intervention and treatment. We promoted smell and taste pleasure as alternatives to intoxication. We had eye opening success in the classroom, but could never construct a political concensus. Wine industry leaders distrusted anyone active in the health field, lumping all those souls together under the titles "neo-prohibitionists" and "label fascists." As in most political issues, the most strident voices got the most attention. Abstentionist philosophy dominated government agencies. I was equally vilified as a "pusher" by one side and a closet Carrie Nation by the other. Everyone seemed more interested in tossing rocks at the opposition than in finding techniques to actually reduce alcohol-related health problems. School prevention money dried up after California passed Proposition 13 (property tax reduction) in 1978.

Ten years later, politicians have become absolutely spastic trying to occupy the high ground on substance abuse issues. I'm delighted to see activity in the field, but moral mendacity turns my stomach. Worse, the hypocrisy of the positions being touted dooms them to failure. Kids are more perceptive than we think. They respond better to role models than to persuasion or logic. Substance abuse is a complex subject. Experimentation is not abuse. Abuse is when you keep doing something after it hurts you. Abuse is a symptom more than a cause. Legislated, "magic bullet" cures are a sham. If we truly want to reduce this large problem, we must be prepared to do more than dabble. It will take generations, and it will cost lots of money. Applying small amounts of money for limited periods of time merely wastes resources. Our society idolizes thrill seeking and conspicuous consumption in hundreds of ways every day. Then we sentence our kids to learn about substance use from their most precocious peers. I find it amazing the majority of people *do not* develop problems. Can anyone seriously consider warning labels on $10 bottles of Chardonnay as anything more than a diversion from the real issue?

The problem is not apathy. Some adults refuse to admit kids have a legitimate curiosity about grown-up pleasures and a natural desire for status among their peers. Other adults are reluctant to expose insecurities which may have developed unconsciously during their own youth. Abstention is an easy suggestion for these adults to make. It's not a bad idea; it's just unrealistic. It ignores everything we know about adolescent psychology, and it fails to distinquish between symptoms and causes. Let me cite two illustrations:

◇ I addressed nearly 50 school Boards in 1976 in order to set up the research design for our primary prevention project. In every meeting someone stood up to say, "But Mr. Cass, we don't want our kids *taught* how to drink." I had to dance around the issue or lose the school. It really sapped my energy because I wanted to rejoin, "Would you rather they learned from me in the classroom, or from a 16 year old in the back seat of a car?" Alcohol education, along with sex education, had been mandated by law for schools in California in 1971. In practice, classroom sex education consisted of the standard plumbing diagram with vocabulary test. Graduates of that program are struggling to support teenagers of their own today. Half the schools had never heard of alcohol education. The other half figured it must be a film.

◊ Nancy Reagan created a lot of publicity for an abstentionist philosophy with her "Just Say No" campaign and related public service broadcast spots. Yet Mrs. Reagan spent 6 years doing daily business with Michael Deaver, who then tried to use alcoholism as an excuse in court for illegal behavior.

I submit that drugs are a straw man. The problem goes deeper. It goes to the level of personal responsibility. We have to stop giving kids the impression that it is a teacher's responsibility that they learn, or a policeman's responsibility to keep them out of trouble, or a doctor's responsibility to keep them well. We can't legislate safe substance use any more than we can legislate honesty. We have to educate individuals to become internally resistant because it is in their own best interest. Moderation does that, but abstention often times does not. Scare tactics are consistently contradicted by any child's daily observations. Normal, healthy people behave in ways that work for them. They stop doing something when it hurts them. If they don't, the problem is more deeply rooted than the availability of a substance. Until we discover how to confer self-esteem while removing anxiety and boredom, there are going to be substance abuse casualties. Legislation can change the symptoms, but it can't cure the problem. I doubt laws alone can even reduce the problem.

On the other hand, I think fine wine can. It is surrounded by behaviors and attitudes which are new to most Americans. Learning to take smell and taste pleasure is a positive, seductive technique. It is not a form of discipline. Recognizing quality in wine requires one to realize the value of balance. That concept alone is central to moderation. It subliminally redefines one's notion of satisfaction. If two drinks are fun, four drinks are not automatically more fun. A little tannin in red wine is good, but a lot is rarely better. The same can be said about chocolate eclairs, lottery tickets and number of sexual partners. Moreover, fine wine comes with thousands of years of protective cultural ritual. It provides entertainment and a trigger to conversation which eliminate the value of drunken antics. Wine consuming cultures like southern Europe have a very low incidence of alcohol related health problems. Regions of the U.S. that publically treat drinking as a sin can not make the same claim. People who appreciate fine wine make excellent role models. America needs more of them.

♦ WINE INDUSTRY ISSUES:

◊ **FETAL ALCOHOL SYNDROME.** Twenty years ago researchers named a group of problems found in some children born to practicing female alcoholics. Besides low birth weight, these babies had a particular set of facial abnormalities and a slow rate of development. It was determined that most of the damage occurred during the first three months of pregnancy.

No responsible industry spokesmen today would deny the existence of FAS. It is hard to isolate the cause because most babies showing the symptoms are born to women who smoke heavily and lack proper nutrition, in addition to ingesting large amounts of alcohol. Debate has centered around two points: What level of alcohol consumption can be considered safe for pregnant women; and what can be done to stop pregnant women from drinking too much? Detailed investigation has failed to show any risk from moderate consumption (two 4 oz. glasses of wine with a meal). But common sense, and every physician in America, will tell women to refrain from all drugs as much as possible during pregnancy. The problem does not occur among conscientious women who pre-think their pregnancy. It occurs when alcoholic and binge drinking women fail to realize they are pregnant during the first tri-mester.

Warning labels, similar to the ones found on cigarette packages for a quarter century, are continually proposed as a way to fight this problem. Warning labels don't cost much. They don't have much effect either. Experience indicates that their greatest impact is to make the alcohol beverage industry defensive. An alternative would be to do 20 hours of preventative, sex and drug education in 7th grade classrooms all over the country. School-based education is expensive and difficult to perform well. It is also a political football of extraordinary proportions. I see a potential trade-off here, but neither FAS nor warning labels are big enough issues to command overt co-operation between industry and government. Instead, the industry feels it must put money into electoral politics to keep these proposals bottled up in legislative committees.

◊ **SCHMIDT-DeLINT THEORY.** This name neatly summarizes several issues. Schmidt and deLint were two statisticians who claimed per capita consumption to be directly proportional to alcohol related health problems. They proposed general measures which they claimed could be shown to reduce per capita consumption. The quality of their research has been debated extensively, if not conclusively. Nevertheless, the goal of reducing per capita consumption has been widely adopted by government

health agencies. Examples of Schmidt-deLint proposals are:
(a) Increased taxation.
(b) Restrictions on advertising.
(c) Fewer hours and locations of sale.
(d) Raised age for legal consumption.
Obviously, lowering per capita consumption is not a goal shared by alcohol producers. A compromise may be occuring naturally. Dollars spent per capita on alcohol continue to rise, while volume consumed per capita has dropped over the last few years. We are buying smaller amounts of better stuff.

A comparison of the consumption curves in the U.S. and Italy also tends to refute Schmidt-deLint theory. Italians drink double the absolute alcohol per capita that Americans do, yet Italians have fewer alcohol related health problems. The key is that *everyone* in Italy drinks relatively moderate amounts on a regular basis. The Italian consumption curve is flat. In the U.S. 15% of the population drinks 50% of the absolute alcohol; 35% of the U.S. population doesn't drink at all. Abstention must be a choice arrived at through experimentation because studies have consistently shown 80% of our high school seniors reporting at least one drunken episode during the previous year. Drinking in America is not done with wine at meals on a regular basis. The majority of it is done with hard liquor and beer at irregular intervals. The U.S. consumption curve shows less absolute alcohol per capita than Italy's, but exaggerated occasional spikes. An unbiased observer might be tempted to conclude that those spikes are the feature that causes the increased level of problems in the U.S.

Taxation is a prominent issue in an era of budget deficits. Distillates are taxed at a much higher rate than wine or beer. Distillates are also much cheaper to produce and therefore much more profitable. The wine industry has had a long and uneasy alliance with distillers because of the financial clout distillers have brought to the political arena since Prohibition. In the mid '80s Seagrams threatened to upset that arrangement with their "Equivalency" campaign. Seagrams is the second largest wine producer in the U.S. They spent $5 million advertising the fact that a shot of hard liquor has the same amount of alcohol as a 5 oz. glass of wine or a 12 oz. can of beer. The rest of the wine industry saw this campaign as a preliminary lobbying effort for equivalent taxation. Seagram's claims of social responsibility were fairly humorous when juxtaposed with their simultaneous billboard ads for gin. Those ads featured torso photographs of young women in underwear, sitting on the laps of middle aged men who were dressed in the remnants of tuxedos, with a caption that implied drinking Seagrams Gin would create such opportunities.

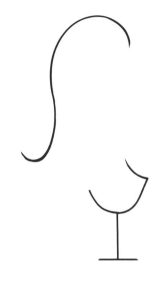

You probably recognize that advertising genre. Sexual fantasies are a common theme. They may be germane to perfume and jeans, but they mislead when applied to alcohol. The Porter's soliloquy in *MacBeth* states the case accurately when it points out that alcohol raises interest while ruining performance. Of course, Shakespeare can't be found on prime time television. Without years of real life experience, a TV watcher might conclude that the right six-pak causes everyone to lose 20 pounds and shed their foundation garments. "Light up the night." Somehow I don't get the feeling Michelob was promoting taste pleasure as an alternative to intoxication. What is it about Spuds McKenzie that makes 20-year-old models raise both elbows over their head and smile knowingly as the camera cuts past them? That's not my reaction when faced with a pit bull wearing dark glasses. "The fun starts here." Does that mean Seagrams wine cooler is a necessary antecedent to a good time? I mean I've consumed *all* those products, and I've never met *any* of those women. In fact, I used to need an extra can or two of the product to dull my feelings of inadaquacy. Is this the way America wants to teach social skills to adolescents?

Wine Institute, the industry's lobbying and PR organization, has a voluntary advertising code for its members. It's an admirable document. Most wineries portray their product with food. As a practical matter few wineries advertise on TV because of the expense. More consolidated industries, like the big 5 brewers, use TV all the time. The messages in the paragraph above were delivered several times an hour for months. I don't support censorship, but if neo-prohibitionists want to play hardball, tinkering with the business tax deduction for irresponsible ads would have a lot more effect than warning labels.

◇ **DRUNK DRIVING SANCTIONS and DRINKING AGE.** Most everyone agrees that carnage on the highway is a tragedy. There are about 50,000

U.S. traffic fatalities a year, half of which are listed as alcohol related. For perspective, I'll just point out that handguns in the U.S. kill 22,000 people per year. A majority of highway accidents, with or without alcohol involvement, are caused by males under age 25. The wine industry has supported legislative action to raise the legal drinking age to 21 nationwide and to apply strict penalties for drunk driving. No one knows how to keep unlicensed, repeat offenders from driving cars without incarcerating them.

These topics are pointed examples of an attempt to treat symptoms legislatively. Lowering speed limits has had more effect on highway fatalities than changing the drinking age. Perhaps the wine industry went along with increasing the drinking age because there wasn't much money involved. Beer has traditionally been the beverage of choice for teenagers. Were it not for wine coolers, I bet the wine industry would happily trade a 30-year-old drinking age for the opportunity to sell wine in grocery stores nationwide. But I personally doubt that raising the drinking age to 21 creates the desired effect. Daily wine with meals in a family setting seems to work much better in southern Europe. My own empirical evidence suggests several results contradictory to the legislative intent:

◇ A 21-year-old drinking age turns alcohol into a rite-of-passage. The allure of drinking, and the perceived value of the substance, are enhanced by the risk, cost and creativity required to obtain it (cf. the attractiveness of expensive cocaine over low cost amphetamines or legal caffeine). These obstacles are not, however, so great as to screen out individuals with the slightest motivation. In fact, peer status is derived from surmounting these same obstacles. Such status provides more motivation than any attachment to the substance does. Some kids experiment with alcohol simply because "prudish" adults say they shouldn't. Isn't rebellion almost synonymous with adolescence? What do you think rock-and-roll is all about?

◇ Infrequent opportunity reduces any motivation to employ moderation techniques. It fosters a binge attitude. Total volume consumed may go down, but I suspect the number of individual episodes reaching a danger threshold actually increases. Alcohol as a cue, and an excuse, for atypical behavior becomes so ingrained that many people emerge from youth unable to perform certain social functions without preheating themselves. If you doubt that familiarity has a moderating influence, you should look up some research on how co-ed housing reduces overt sexual behavior among college students. When was the last panty raid you heard about?

◇ A 21-year-old drinking age segregates the population at greatest risk away from their more moderate peers, as well as from adult guidance. Positive role models are nowhere to be found. In effect, society guarantees that some number of people will acquire their formative attitudes about drinking in extralegal situations. Great individual amounts of danger will be concentrated on a limited number of people in the at-risk population, in order to avoid spreading small individual amounts over a much larger group of moderate, responsible teenagers. We are putting our most powerful players on the bench during the most crucial part of the game.

Learning to drink safely takes time. It is not enough to know intellectually what you should do. Positive techniques have to be ingrained subconsciously as habits and attitudes. The same is true about learning to drive safely. A similar statement can be made about learning to interact on a social/sexual level. It is always hard to make a transition from external cues for behavior (parents setting limits) to internal cues for behavior (you decide for yourself when to leave the party). Simultaneous acquisition of these talents is what makes the age from 15-25 so difficult, and so dangerous. Practice and experimentation are important parts of the process. No one gets the necessary skills for their birthday. The trick for society is to learn how to provide practice time without maiming anyone.

I happen to think cars are the most dangerous part of the equation. Turning a 16-year-old loose in a car is anologous to throwing a non-swimmer into a pool. Americans grow up wedded to automobiles in a way that makes *not* driving, when drunk, a particular hardship. Witness the number of wealthy politicians who get arrested for it every year. Well-intentioned people simply fail to see any alternative. It is one thing to convince Americans they shouldn't drive drunk, and another thing to teach them ways to avoid doing so.

I have an idea. It would make enforcement easier, which is an important component of expectations about, and respect for, the law. It would teach valuable skills for later life. It would lower insurance rates for everyone. Most controversially, it would thrust adults into scenes they presently ignore. It would bring practical considerations to the forefront and reduce the notion that substance abuse may be some kind of moral issue. My humble proposal is to lower the drinking age to 16 and raise the driving age to 21. It won't happen, but Americans would learn something from discussing it.